Groundwater C[illegible] in the United States

Veronica I. Pye

Ruth Patrick

John Quarles

Groundwater Contamination in the United States

University of Pennsylvania Press Philadelphia 1983

Design by Tracy Baldwin

Library of Congress Cataloging in Publication Data

Pye, Veronica I.
Groundwater contamination in the United States.

Bibliography: p.
1. Water, Underground—Pollution—United States.
I. Patrick, Ruth. II. Quarles, John. III. Title.
TD223.P93 1983 363.7'394 83-6695
ISBN 0-8122-1152-9
ISBN 0-8122-7896-8 (pbk.)

Printed in the United States of America

Contents

Tables

(All tables have been reproduced as they appeared in the original sources.)

Tables

Figures

Figures

Following page 188

Acknowledgments

Work began on this project in the fall of 1981. The authors wish to thank the members of the Environmental Assessment Council of the Academy of Natural Sciences, Philadelphia, and its Advisory Committee and their colleagues as well for their guidance and reviews. In addition we are indebted to the state and federal personnel, too numerous to mention individually, who willingly made available information on groundwater quality which formed the basis for this assessment. Drafts of the report were reviewed by persons familiar with one or more of the topics covered. For review and comment we are grateful to John Aitcheson, Neil E. Armstrong, Stan Back, John Bredehoeft, Phillip L. Buckingham, David Burmaster, Larry W. Canter, Edwin H. Clark, George Comstock, Brian E. Doll, Nancy Dwyer, A. Blakeman Early, Harold F. Elkin, James J. Geraghty, Khristine Hall, James C. Hildrew, Kazuyoshi Kawata, Jack Keeley, Gerald Kotas, Jay H. Lehr, Paula Magnuson, Marian Mlay, Gloria Rowe, Robert Tucker, Jacolyn A. Simmons, and Donald W. Smith. The chapter on State and Local Measures for the Protection of Groundwater Quality was prepared by a consultant to the Council, Frank Goodman, and his research assistant Imogene Hughes.

We wish to thank Robert G. Dunlop for his advice and guidance during the preparation of this book. We also wish to thank Jocelyn Kelley and Steven Roberts for their technical assistance, Jo-An Breidling and Diane West for typing the manuscript, and Su-Ing Yong for her art work.

The financial support for this project was provided by a grant from the Glenmede Trust, Philadelphia, and by a gift from Mr. Laurance S. Rockefeller. We are deeply grateful for this support.

Acknowledgments

Although a relatively high degree of consensus was achieved among all those concerned with this study, the responsibility for the content of the report is exclusively that of the authors.

Veronica I. Pye, Research Director
Ruth Patrick, Chairperson
John Quarles, Chairperson of the Advisory Committee

Environmental Asessment Council of the Academy of Natural Sciences, Philadelphia, March 1983

Preface

The purpose of this book is to define groundwater and describe the natural and anthropogenic factors that can alter its quality. The known effects of groundwater contamination on human health and the environment are discussed and possible methods for mitigating contamination are examined. Federal and state laws and regulations pertaining to groundwater are described.

The work has been sponsored by the Environmental Assessment Council of the Academy of Natural Sciences, Philadelphia. The purpose of the Council is to identify environmental problems before they become environmental issues, and to gather scientific and other data which relate to the problem. The Council also seeks to bring together the laws and regulations related to the problem. Once a high degree of consensus as to the facts has been obtained from the Council and the Council's Advisory Commitee, the information is distributed through various media to legislative bodies and agencies and the public.

The members of the Council are Robert G. Dunlop, Caryl Haskins, Richard E. Heckert, Lane Kirkland, George Lamb, Charles F. Luce, Ruth Patrick (Chairperson), Glenn Paulson, William Reilly, Laurance F. Rockefeller, Abel Wolman, and George Wills (Secretary). Dr. Veronica I. Pye is Research Director of the groundwater project.

The Advisory Committee members are Robert R. Bonczek, David Kilkeary, Abraham Lilienfeld, Thomas E. Lovejoy III, J. Michael McCloskey, Joseph E. Penick, John Quarles (Chairperson), Sheldon Samuels, Jack Sheehan, Carroll Williams, and M. Gordon Wolman.

Overview

Groundwater is the source of about 50% of the drinking water in the United States and is used in large quantities for irrigation and for industrial purposes. It varies greatly in quantity and quality throughout the United States. Groundwater occurs at different depths in aquifers, which may or may not be confined and which have variable potentials for recharge.

The contamination of groundwater results from the addition of organisms and chemicals and varies greatly in the severity of its effects on man and the environment. The contaminants derive from every aspect of man's life in society: our homes, agriculture, utilities, industry, and transportation. The impact of these sources of contamination on groundwater varies from one part of the country to another. Once the contaminants are in an aquifer, they move much more slowly than they do in surface water and undergo relatively little change or dilution.

Although no federal laws and few state laws have groundwater contamination as their major focus, there are many federal and state statutes that can control or mitigate groundwater contamination. The mitigation of groundwater contamination can be accomplished by reducing products or wastes which produce non-degradable chemicals, by regional planning that protects aquifer recharge areas, by technology which improves the management of waste-treatment facilities, by well-devised monitoring systems which will detect the presence of a contaminant before it causes a severe problem and, by rehabilitation.

One

Groundwater Contamination in the United States: An Executive Summary of the Technical Report

This study of groundwater contamination in the United States is undertaken to identify what is known about the severity, extent, and sources of the problem, to determine what legal and regulatory framework is presently available to protect and manage groundwater and, finally, to provide some options, together with their consequences, for dealing effectively with both present and future problems rather than providing recommendations for action. It also points out gaps in that knowledge.

Contamination has occurred in most regions of the country and will probably continue to occur. Once contamination is detected there is a choice as to whether to take action and, if so, what form that action should take. The type of actions vary with the type of contamination and its hydrogeologic and geographic setting. There are regulatory agencies at the federal, state, and local levels which have requirements that may prevent or correct many types of groundwater contamination. For future causes of groundwater pollution the question is whether or not to take action that would completely or partially prevent such contamination.

The Importance of the Groundwater Resource

Between 40 and 50% of the population depends upon groundwater as its primary source of drinking water. Approximately 75% of American cities derive their supplies, in total or in part, from groundwater. The states vary in their dependence upon groundwater. Those in the arid West, where there are few permanent rivers, lakes, or streams, are much more reliant on groundwater than the states of the more humid East. In 1980, 88.5 billion gallons of groundwater were used in the United States per day, and 68% of this total was used for irrigation. The total use in 1950 was 34 billion gallons per day (bgd), and in 1970, 68 bgd.

What Is Groundwater?

Groundwater, as considered here, is water that occurs in permeable saturated strata of rock, sand, or gravel called aquifers. Groundwater comprises approximately 4% of the water contained in the hydrologic cycle, which consists of the movement of water between oceans and other bodies of surface water, the atmosphere, and the land. Groundwater is recharged by precipitation.

Types of Aquifers

The two main types of aquifers are unconfined and confined. An unconfined aquifer is not overlain by impermeable material, and precipitation may percolate down to the water table. Water in the aquifer is at atmospheric pressure. The amount of water in storage is dependent on seasonal cycles of natural recharge. A perched aquifer may occur where there is a limited layer, or lens, of impermeable material above the water table, forming a zone of saturation above it.

The second major category of aquifer is the confined aquifers, which are sometimes referred to as artesian aquifers. They are bounded, top and bottom, by layers of relatively impermeable geologic formations termed aquitards. The natural aquifer is completely saturated with water that is under greater than atmospheric pressure. Some have discrete and variable recharge areas where the geologic material of the aquifer forms an outcrop at the surface. A few aquifers have no recharge areas.

The area of aquifers may be regional or local, and some, such as the Ogallala in the Midwest, may extend across several states. This fact is important when one comes to consider the institutional organization for the management and protection of groundwater.

Most aquifers occur at variable depths within 2,500 feet of the land surface. Estimates of water in storage within 2,500 feet of the land surface within the conterminous United States range from 33 quadrillion gallons to 100 quadrillion gallons which varies in quality. It would be possible to drill a well with a yield sufficient for domestic use in almost every region of the country.

Factors Affecting the Natural Quality of Water

The natural quality of groundwater is affected by the geological characteristics and climatic conditions—in particular, the temperature and rainfall—of the region. When evaporation and transpiration exceed precipitation, as in the arid Southwest, the recharge of groundwater takes place only in "wet," or multicycle years. Some aquifers, such as the Ogallala, have little, if any, recharge. In the East, where precipitation usually exceeds evaporation, unconfined aquifers are easily recharged. The natural chemical content of groundwater is influenced by the type and depth of soils and by the subsurface geologic formations through which the groundwater passes. The leaching of the soil and rocks is influenced by the pH of the precipitation and by the metabolic products of organisms. In the aquifer the water reacts with the geologic material, usually increasing its content of total dissolved solids (TDS). Naturally occurring radionuclides may render the water radioactive. The hardness of water reflects its calcium and magnesium content and may render the water unfit for domestic or industrial use. U.S. Public Health Service drinking-water standards consider 500 parts per million (ppm) TDS the maximum permissible, although the Safe Drinking Water Act regulations considers water with up to 10,000 ppm TDS as potentially potable. Water from some aquifers is unusable due to its high salinity or to the presence of naturally occurring toxic substances such as arsenic and radionuclides. Natural groundwater may be unfit for certain uses or be of the highest quality that can be used for drinking water with no pretreatment.

Relationships Among Groundwater Quality and Quantity, Surface Water, and Land Use

In the arid areas, where evaporation and transpiration can greatly exceed precipitation, the mineralization of groundwater due to leaching is a significant cause of saline groundwater, and evapotranspiration further concentrates the salts. Pumping at greater than recharge rates can increase the degradation of groundwater. If pumping lowers the water level in the vicinity of coal mines, the exposed sulfur-bearing rocks may be subject to oxidation. Should the water levels increase, the oxidized sulfur-compounds would dissolve and increase the acidity of the water. In coastal areas, where there has been an increase in demand for water, increased groundwater pumping may cause saltwater intrusion into potable aquifers.

Most of the low flow of streams is supplied by groundwater. If the aquifers are overpumped and recharge does not occur, the stream flow may cease during periods of drought. The contamination of groundwater by contaminated streams may occur if a negative pressure develops in the aquifer from the use of groundwater.

The recharge of aquifers may be greatly reduced by paving the land surface in recharge zones and by altering the vegetation cover so that precipitation may run off instead of infiltrating. Siting of contaminating activities in recharge areas without careful consideration of practices which could eliminate or reduce contamination will cause a threat to the quality of groundwater and hence its usability.

Thus, the relation between groundwater quantity and quality, between groundwater and surface water, and between groundwater and land-use patterns must be taken into consideration in any protection and management strategy.

Sources of Groundwater Contamination

There are three main mechanisms by which the chemical composition of groundwater may be changed: by natural processes, by man's waste-disposal practices such as those for sanitary wastes, liquid industrial wastes, solid wastes, and radioactive wastes, and by spills, leaks, and agricultural activities and other sources unrelated to disposal.

The Movement of Contaminants

A contaminant usually enters groundwater from the surface of the land, percolating down through the aerated soil and the non-saturated zone. Reductive and oxidative biological processes in the root zone may degrade or biologically change some of the contaminants. Plant uptake can, in some instances, remove certain heavy metals.

Once a contaminant reaches the aquifer, its movement is determined to some extent by its solubility in water. If a compound is not very soluble in water it would be expected to be less mobile in groundwater. The density of a contaminant also affects the rate of its movement. Low-density fluids will tend to float on top of the water table, while higher-density contaminants will sink. Once in the aquifer a contaminant will generally move with the groundwater and at a similar speed, which varies between a fraction of an inch to a few feet per day. Under idealized conditions such transport would form an elliptical plume of contamination with well-defined boundaries. Flowing groundwater naturally undergoes little mixing due to the fact that movement usually occurs under laminar flow. Some dilution occurs by dispersion. The result of these phenomena is that the contamination remains relatively localized over long periods and becomes less diluted than would be the case in surface water.

Types of Groundwater Contamination

The types of chemicals which emanate from anthropogenic sources are extremely varied. They range from simple inorganic ions such as the nitrate from septic tanks, feedlot wastes, and the use of fertilizer, chloride from highway deicing-salts, saltwater intrusion, and certain industrial processes, and heavy-metal ions, for example, the chromium from plating works, to complex synthetic organic compounds resulting from industrial and manufacturing processes, some of which are found in household cleaning fluids, e.g., trichloroethylene. Compounds of low solubility may yield solutions that are toxic or offensive. The chemical composition of wastes deposited in landfills or surface impoundments is often known; nevertheless, when the constituents of such wastes interact, new compounds may be formed. Many industrial waste-disposal practices now incude the stabilization of wastes, thereby rendering them less active chemically. It is still possible, however, that leachate production may transform some of the constituents.

Risks Posed by Different Types of Contaminants

The degree of risk posed by contaminants varies according to many factors. These include the volume and toxicity of the contaminant, its concentration in the aquifer, its persistence in the environment, and the degree of human and environmental exposure to the contaminant. In addition, the number of persons affected, or likely to be affected, over time and the percentage of available groundwater both locally and regionally should be taken into consideration. If the contaminants in the groundwater exceed the interim standards set for drinking water by the federal government, for example, then the water is hazardous for the use for which it was designated under the standards. These standards include, however, only a limited number of chemicals, and thus they do not necessarily protect either man or the environment against either the short-term or the long-term effects of the presence of every contaminant that might be found in groundwater. Drinking-water standards are not the only criteria that might be exceeded.

One of the main criteria usually used in judging risk is the contaminant's effect upon public health. The epidemiological evidence for an association between chronic disease and the use of contaminated groundwater is inconclusive but suggestive of a link with certain diseases. More is known about the acute effects, with regard to disease caused both by pathogenic microorganisms and by chemicals, of ingesting contaminated groundwater. Some of the synthetic organic chemicals that have been detected in groundwater have not been tested for their potential to affect human health, and thus they may pose a hazard which at present is not known.

The effects upon the environment of contaminated groundwater are even less well documented than its effects on human health, although it is well established that certain contaminants may cause stress to vegetation or even its destruction, and that they probably adversely affect animals. For example, water for irrigation should be relatively free of boron and chloride, both of which have a deleterious effect upon plant growth. Many plants selectively accumulate heavy-metal ions from water. Water for human use should ideally be of the highest quality, but livestock may also be particularly sensitive to such factors as the heavy-metal content of the water they drink.

Another way to assess the potential danger of contaminated groundwater is to gauge the persistence of its deleterious effects on the environment. For example, cadmium, which is toxic and believed to be carcinogenic, has an infinite half-life and is not degraded. Some inorganic and organic compounds may be degraded by biological action in the soil zone so that only harmless end-products reach the aquifer. All of the heavy-metal ions and some synthetic organic chemicals associated with manufacturing and service industries would probably not be degraded.

Attenuation

Attenuation processes reduce the severity or toxicity of the contaminating compounds, elements, or pathogens. Different soils have different capacities for attenuation, and affect various chemicals to different degrees. The attenuation of contaminants may take place by biological activity, dilution, volatilization, mechanical filtration, precipitation, buffering, neutralization, and ion exchange. Diffusion and dispersion will bring contaminants into contact with material that may retard their movement and reduce their concentration. Attenuation will therefore vary with the time and distance traveled. Since little dilution ordinarily takes place in groundwater, the concentrations of the contaminants in it often remain much higher in groundwater than they would in surface water.

The Geographical Extent of the Problem

No comprehensive national survey of groundwater contamination has been undertaken, probably because it would be extremely expensive and time consuming. Six studies of drinking-water supplies have been undertaken, however, under the Safe Drinking Water Act. Incidents of contamination have been reported from every state. From the regional assessments completed by the U.S. Environmental Protection Agency (EPA) in the 1970s, it may be concluded that problems indigenous to one area may not occur in another, but that several sources of groundwater contamination occur at a high or moderate degree of severity in each area studied. The four pollutants most commonly reported—chlorides, nitrates, heavy metals, and organics—are probably more of a reflection of the prevailing monitoring practices at the time the surveys were made than they are of the actual incidence of the contaminants that most threaten the quality of groundwater.

For this report ten states (AZ, CA, CT, FL, ID, IL, NE, NJ, NM, and SC) were sampled which had reported incidents of contamination and which were examples of regions with differing levels of industrialization, agricultural activity, climatic conditions, and population density. Human and animal wastes were among the three most frequently reported sources of contamination, and saltwater intrusion was found to be a serious problem in densely populated coastal regions. The industrial Northeast predictably had problems associated with industrial wastes, petroleum products, and landfill leachate. California, Florida, and Nebraska each reported problems arising from agricultural practices, whereas New Mexico and California reported problems with the disposal of oil-field brines. These summaries include, of course, only the known incidents of contamination; a comprehensive national survey might well uncover other important sources of contamination, or different frequencies from the same sources. The problems encountered to date vary regionally and depend upon the type and degree of industrial and agricultural activities carried out and the population density. The known incidents vary from the formation of a single isolated plume of contamination to a high frequency of the occurrence of contamination, and they fall into geographical patterns.

The Severity of the Problem

In order to determine the overall magnitude of the problem, it is necessary to assess the severity of the contamination of groundwater and this can be undertaken in several ways. If the concentration of contaminants exceeds the numerical standards set for a particular use, as, for example, for drinking water, the problem could be called severe. The severity depends on the population affected by well closings, the nationwide percentage of aquifers affected, and the percentage of the known reserves of groundwater that are contaminated. The degree of hazard posed by the contaminants, for example, their toxicity, enters into the evaluation, as does the cost and feasibility of finding an alternative water supply. Many of the data required to assess the severity of the problem by these methods are unavailable.

Since no systematic national survey of the contamination of groundwater has been carried out, the only estimates of the order of magnitude of the amount of groundwater presently contaminated rely upon surveys of the numbers of certain types of potential sources of contamination. EPA did such an estimate for certain selected point sources, such as surface impoundments and landfills, which it considered the most important sources, and also for secondary sources, such as subsurface disposal systems and petroleum exploration and mining. The Agency concluded that up to 1% by area of usable surface aquifers near the land surface may be contaminated by these sources. Lehr (1982) estimated that up to 2% could be contaminated. It should be pointed out that these are nationwide estimates for the entire United States. In certain areas, especially those with a high population density, a much higher percentage of the groundwater may be contaminated. These estimates did not include contamination from non-point sources, such as agricultural activities.

Aquifer Rehabilitation

Remedial action for contaminated aquifers is complex, time-consuming, and extremely expensive. It is feasible under certain circumstances, assuming no additional contamination occurs, and the choice of remedial action determined upon is dictated by the time period during which contamination has taken place, the type and behavior of the contaminants, and the hydrogeology of the site. Often it is more cost-effective to locate a new source of water than to attempt treatment. Contamination that occurs in shallow plumes in unconsolidated rock may be controlled by the excavation and removal of the plume, once the problem of the final disposal of the contaminated material has been solved. There are two other major categories of remedial alternatives: in-situ methods, and conventional methods of withdrawal, treatment, and final disposal. Many in-situ techniques are experimental. They include the detoxification, stabilization, and immobilization of contaminants and require the use of biological cultures, chemical reactants, or sealants. The aim in each case is to detoxify or stabilize the contaminants or to form an impervious barrier around the plume in order to prevent its migration. Methods for withdrawal, treatment, and final disposal may use collection or withdrawal wells, subsurface gravity collection-drains, impervious grout-curtains, and cut-off trenches. Treatment of the water removed could be by reverse osmosis, ultrafiltration, ion-exchange resins, wet-air oxidation, ozonation and ultraviolet radiation, coagulation and precipitation, aerobic biological treatment, or the use of activated charcoal filters.

Costs, ranging from several thousands to several billions of dollars, have to be estimated on a case-by-case basis and are determined by many factors specific to the site. For many problems pertaining to groundwater pollution, the prevention of contamination is far better than curative action.

Measures for Protecting Groundwater

The protection of groundwater from contamination may be cost-effective for valuable aquifers. Many federal and state regulations can be used for this purpose, as summarized below, although the majority of regulations were not specifically designed with groundwater protection as their primary goal. The most efficient way of preventing important aquifers from becoming contaminated is by protecting their recharge areas. For most confined aquifers it would be necessary to prohibit the siting of contaminating activities in specified recharge areas or to ensure that potentially contaminating activities use adequate methods to prevent groundwater degradation. For unconfined aquifers this might be difficult because of their extensive recharge areas. Protection might entail careful regional and local planning since recharge areas may cross county or state boundaries. Other protective measures can be taken, including the careful restriction of groundwater pumping in areas where salt water can intrude into potable aquifers, the capping and sealing of dry bore-holes that traverse one or more aquifers and offer a conduit for contaminants, and the continued stringent supervision of the drilling and maintenance of injection wells and water wells.

Monitoring for Groundwater Contamination

Monitoring groundwater quality and aquifer conditions can bring to light contamination before it becomes a significant problem. The appropriate design of a monitoring system depends upon the hydrology, pollution sources, population density, and climate of the region. The four main types of monitoring systems are those which measure quality in relation to numerical standards, source monitoring for effluent quality and quantity, case-preparation monitoring for enforcement-action data, and research monitoring.

In order that the samples of water withdrawn for analysis are not altered chemically, well-casing materials and sampling procedures must be carefully chosen. Detailed knowledge of groundwater flow-patterns, natural water quality, and the attenuation capacities of the soil and geologic strata would enhance the siting of monitoring facilities so that they produce the most useful data with the minimum of damage and expense. The chemicals analyzed should be the best indicators for the suspected type of groundwater contamination under investigation. They should include organic chemicals from natural and man-made origins as well as inorganic ions, such as chloride, nitrate, and heavy metals.

The sophistication of present-day analytical methods may have outstripped our ability to interpret what they reveal, our ability to determine the significance of low-concentrations of contaminants on the environment and on public health.

Federal Regulations Applicable to Groundwater

Although there is no federal program aimed specifically at the problem of groundwater contamination, there are some programs that provide a measure of protection. The legal framework for federal efforts to protect groundwater is a group of statutes aimed primarily at other environmental problems but focusing indirectly on some groundwater problems.

One of the principal federal statutes affecting groundwater is the Resource Conservation and Recovery Act (RCRA) of 1976. This Act established guidelines for the management of municipal solid wastes and hazardous wastes. Interim-status regulations were issued in May of 1980. Design and performance criteria for landfills that accept hazardous waste became effective in January 1983.

The Safe Drinking Water Act (SDWA) of 1974 contains an underground-injection control (UIC) program designed to prevent groundwater contamination from waste-injection wells. Another program, the sole-source aquifer program, enables EPA to protect those areas of the country which have only one aquifer as their principal source of drinking water. The SDWA also establishes interim primary and secondary drinking-water standards which must be met nationwide.

The Clean Water Act of 1977 (CWA) requires that EPA establish a program to equip and maintain a water-quality surveillance system for surface and groundwater, but little has been done to implement the groundwater provision. The area-wide planning program under section 208 of this Act, which is no longer funded, embodies a potentially effective means of controlling groundwater pollution.

The Toxic Substances Control Act (TSCA) of 1976 and the Surface Mining

Control and Reclamation Act (SMCRA) both have provisions that could offer a measure of protection to groundwater.

The Comprehensive Environmental Response, Compensation and Liability Act of 1980 (CERCLA) authorizes the federal government to clean up contamination caused by inactive waste-disposal sites or spills. Many of these sites represent immediate threats to the quality of groundwater. The revised National Contingency Plan for the cleanup of oil and hazardous substances was published in the Federal Register on 16 July 1982.

Many of the statutes outlined above contain broad imminent-hazard provisions which enable EPA to take immediate action to restrain activities posing a threat to any feature of the environment, including groundwater.

State and Local Groundwater-Quality Regulations

It is only in the last few years that states have made large-scale efforts to prevent, abate, and monitor groundwater pollution, but these efforts receive less attention and fewer resources than do corresponding surface-water programs. Long-standing laws exist in many states to govern the allocation of groundwater. Many regulations for groundwater protection do not recognize the hydrological connection between surface water and groundwater and between land use and groundwater. The considerable variation in the natural quality of groundwater and the regional characteristics of the major sources of the contamination of groundwater may account for the diversity in state regulatory mechanisms and organizational structures.

State regulations that affect the quality of groundwater fall into three broad categories:

- those dealing with particular sources of pollution, such as septic systems and waste-disposal sites
- those establishing and implementing water-quality standards for aquifer water, in which aquifers may be classified according to current or projected uses
- those which regulate the use of land in areas overlying critical aquifer-recharge zones.

As with federal regulations, the state and local controls that effectively protect groundwater often are not designed for that purpose and have several other regulatory objectives.

The Classification of Aquifers

The classification of aquifers is a management tool that is in use in some states and under consideration in others. It establishes water-quality goals for each aquifer and identifies the standards or controls necessary to assure that those goals are met. A policy that chooses selectively to protect different aquifers at different levels of quality is dependent upon a classification system. Because hydrogeologic conditions, water quality, and present and future groundwater use vary from state to state, there is no aquifer classification system in use that could serve as a model for other states wishing to develop such a system. The policies of preserving and restoring aquifers for drinking water and of prohibiting the degradation of existing water quality would not require classification systems.

The benefits provided by using a system of aquifer classification include legal protection for valuable aquifers, a basis for siting potentially contaminating activities in low-risk areas, and guidance for planning programs which would protect the quality of water at all levels of government. The deterrents to establishing a classification system include the difficulty of delineating aquifer boundaries, the difficulty of gaining public acceptance for degradation zones or waste-receiving zones, and the difficulty of projecting groundwater use, needs, and availability for the future.

Groundwater Protection Strategies That Have Been Proposed

In 1980, after more than one year of discussion, EPA proposed a national groundwater-protection strategy. In order to protect groundwater, a comprehensive framework was needed which would develop institutional capabilities at the federal and state levels, would enable consistent policies and priorities to be determined, would expedite the gathering of pertinent data, focusing on high-priority problems, and would provide long-range planning. The proposed strategy issued in 1980 would have protected groundwater quality according to its value and use, and it adopted a technical approach using siting and design criteria, best management practices, effluent standards, innovative and alternative technologies to achieve performance standards and, to a lesser extent, numerical groundwater-quality standards and economic incentives.

With the change of administration in the federal government in 1981, EPA undertook a reassessment of the proposed groundwater strategy. A new policy is expected to be unveiled in the future, one that assigns the primary role in groundwater protection to the states and attempts to resolve inconsistent regulatory issues and set policies on state classification of groundwater. Also to be resolved are institutional arrangements, for example, intrastate and state- and local-government relationships, and EPA's commitment of time and money to the policy.

Conclusions

- Groundwater is essential to the continuance of our present quality of life and for industry and agriculture.
- The quality of groundwater varies considerably because of natural and anthropogenic contamination.
- Groundwater management must recognize the relation among land use, surface water, and groundwater.
- Contamination incidents have been reported from all parts of the country.
- Sources of contamination are varied and include both point and nonpoint sources and may be planned or inadvertent.
- The contaminants range in type from simple inorganic ions to complex synthetic organic chemicals.
- The types of contamination vary from one region of the country to another and are influenced by climate, population density, intensity of industrial and agricultural activities, the hydrogeology of the region, and the status and enforcement of federal and state regulations that can be used to protect groundwater.
- The methods for assessing the severity of the problem of groundwater contamination are varied and include its effects on the environment and on human health, the margin by which water standards are exceeded for a particular use, the percentage of usable groundwater contaminated, and the ease and cost of finding an alternative water supply.
- The risks posed to humans and the environment vary according to the volume and toxicity of the contaminants, their concentration and persistence in the aquifer, and the degree of exposure to them.
- The impact of contamination on humans may be measured by well closings and illness caused by chemical or pathogenic contamination.
- The lack of comprehensive national surveys of the extent of groundwater contamination and the fact that few of the contaminants have been tested for their effects upon human health, make it difficult to assess, in quantitative terms, the national risk of using contaminated groundwater.
- Estimates of the percentage of usable groundwater near the surface that is contaminated range from less than 1% to 2%, which only takes into account contamination from certain point sources. In addition it should be emphasized that any estimate that is a nationwide average is not very meaningful because most areas would exceed or fall below the estimate. In addition, contamination is most likely to exceed these estimates in areas of high population density, where the number of persons affected may be large.

- Aquifer rehabilitation is feasible in certain cases but is expensive and time-consuming, with no guarantee of complete success.
- Aquifer classification based on water quality and present and projected use might be a tool for groundwater management and protection.
- The prevention of the contamination of useful, potable aquifers is far superior to subsequent curative efforts. This can, in part, be achieved by regional planning and the enforcement of federal and state regulations designed to protect groundwater.

Two

Options for Dealing with the Contamination of Groundwater

The number and diversity of potential sources of groundwater contamination make it clear that groundwater contamination will never be totally eliminated everywhere. We can, however, minimize or reduce the impact of many potential sources of contamination to groundwater. Many strategies for the management and protection of groundwater involve policy issues which are generic to the field of resource management in the United States, and in particular to the field of water resources.

The protection of groundwater is not a simple matter because the potential sources of groundwater contamination are numerous and highly diversified, and they vary greatly from region to region or locality to locality. This complexity means that there is no uniform pattern to groundwater problems. Each situation must be analyzed in the context of its particular circumstances. Techniques for the protection of groundwater must be tailored to specific conditions.

Water use and allocation in many parts of the country have been determined by historical practice and by pricing policies, taxes, and land use. Policies aimed at modifying the use of groundwater or surface water may include incentives, such as the alteration of the price of water, tax policies to encourage or discourage water connections and use, and institutional structures to manage or allocate the resource. These policies should recognize that many individuals or groups may presently, or in the future, tap the same aquifer for varying amounts of water for different uses. The policies should also recognize that contaminated aquifers are not easily rehabilitated and that the slow rate of groundwater movement does not result in the rapid dilution of contaminants in the aquifer.

Regulations of land use, either at the local level or as part of a more comprehensive regional-planning endeavor, can also contribute to groundwater-protection and management strategies. Land-use controls, which allocate or zone certain kinds of activities through positive choice or exclusion are able to achieve two goals. They may alter the demand for water in different locations, thus altering as well the runoff or residual flows that affect the quality of groundwater. Land-use restrictions may prohibit the siting of potentially polluting activities in the recharge areas of aquifers which contain water of high quality, while encouraging the siting of potentially contaminating point sources, such as waste-disposal activities, in hydrogeologically suitable or less vulnerable areas.

The management of waste or residuals resulting from human activities must include an assessment of the appropriate method of disposal, whether it be by land, air, or water. For example, a decision to incinerate a waste might well reduce the volume remaining that would need to be placed on the land or in water, but incineration may increase the concentrations of unwanted constituents in that residual, and it may contribute to air pollution. Federal regulation over the past decade has limited air and surface-water contamination, thus restricting the use of these two media for the disposal of wastes. Consequently the land disposal of waste has become prevalent. This, in turn, intensified the problems of management and the dangers of infiltration that may adversely affect the quality of groundwater. The recent regulations concerning landfills and impoundments under the Resource Conservation and Recovery Act of 1976 (RCRA) will undoubtedly change many contaminating practices.

Many products produced by our society are difficult to dispose of without harming the environment. Some sources of groundwater contamination can be ascribed to the existence and use of such products. It is possible, in some instances, to alter the composition of the product in order to reduce or eliminate its undesirable effects on the environment. An example of this approach is the reduction or removal of phosphorus from detergents, which resulted in a reduction of the eutrophication of some surface waters. Water conservation is another strategy that may help to reduce the disposal of wastewater and thereby enhance the protection of groundwater.

Alternative policies for the prevention or mitigation of groundwater pollution might involve a broad range of incentives and disincentives. Among the choices for public policy are different types of regulation at the federal, state, and local levels, market mechanisms, taxes, subsidies, land-use controls, and use modification due to different behavioral patterns and philosophical goals. Many of these potential remedies and tools have long been discussed in the context of water-resource management, in some cases for more than a century. Other approaches are of more recent origin.

The listing of these options is intended to demonstrate the diversity of possible methods or strategies to protect groundwater, as is an examination of a variety of the most common types of groundwater contamination and the steps that might be followed to reduce these problems. No attempt is made in this report to evaluate either the political feasibility or the social desirability of any of the possibilities described below that may result in the protection of groundwater from contamination. It is hoped however, that they will illustrate the range of choices open to society in dealing with this problem, and that they will stimulate further investigation into which approaches will most effectively protect groundwater in different situations.

This report does not set forth a rigid system of priorities but does recognize that without some attention to priorities little progress can be made towards the adoption of intelligent policies for groundwater management. Priorities must take into account the natural occurrence of groundwater, its regional variations both in the volume available and in quality, present and historical demands upon the resource, and prospective demands dictated by the interests and geographic mobility of American society. It may be necessary to determine which aquifers are the most important resource for both present and future uses. An obvious example is an aquifer which has a good yield of high-quality water situated in an area where it provides the major source of available fresh water for a large population. It is also necessary to judge which threats to the quality of groundwater are the most serious. Such a judgement would involve assessing the nature of the threat to the environmental and to public health, the expected time period of the threat, the number of persons involved, the hydrogeology of the site, and the feasibility of mitigating the danger.

In the following discussion we will consider some of the most frequently encountered types of groundwater contamination along with some of the more effective options for dealing with them. It is not intended that these examples should give a complete overview of all the problems that might be encountered, but rather that they will serve as selected illustrations of a range of difficulties.

The Disposal of Hazardous Wastes

Hazardous wastes are generated by industrial, domestic, and governmental activities. They may be part of material disposed of or stored in a landfill, dump, impoundment, or other facility, or they may be generated by chemical reactions or biological activity within the disposal site itself. Under the Comprehensive Environmental Response, Compensation and Liability Act of 1980 (CERCLA), the U.S. Environmental Protection Agency (EPA) requires owners and operators of inactive sites—and under RCRA the present owners and operators of privately owned active industrial sites—to report the site locations and the amount and type of wastes stored. As there may be numerous disused sites whose previous operators are no longer in business, the estimate of the quantity of hazardous wastes generated may not be complete.

Groundwater contamination resulting from the disposal of hazardous wastes has been reported in several parts of the United States, particularly along the eastern seaboard. Contamination occurs when leachate formed in a landfill or dump percolates down to an aquifer or when a surface impoundment develops a leak that allows its contents to percolate through the soil into an aquifer. Deep-well injection of hazardous wastes may also present a threat to deep, confined, potable aquifers if this means of disposing of wastes is improperly used. Many impoundments and landfills are lined with impermeable plastic or clay seals to separate their contents from the soils below, but these seals may develop leaks over time. The quantity of leachate produced is further increased by rainfall and snowmelt as it percolates through the disposed wastes. As leachate passes through the soils, some is attenuated, or taken up, by the soils. The extent to which this occurs is dependent on the type of soil. Thus, deeper aquifers, both confined and unconfined, are less vulnerable to serious contamination by hazardous wastes than are shallow aquifers. Shallow unconfined aquifers in the vicinity of hazardous-waste disposal sites are extremely difficult to protect.

The control of the contamination of groundwater by hazardous wastes can be approached in several ways. The most obvious, but usually unrealistic, solution is the complete removal of the problem by banning the production, use, and disposal of hazardous material. Even a reduction in the amount of hazardous wastes generated is, however, very important. A reduction can be achieved by recycling, detoxifying, dewatering, and by the substitution of non-hazardous materials. A second method of control is to change the means of disposal, either by incinerating the wastes or by discharging them into bodies of surface water, but to do so would only alter the focus of the pollution problem from groundwater to the air or surface water. A third possibility is to use the best management practices known in the siting, design, and operation of facilities for the disposal of hazardous waste. Sites could be chosen that are away from shallow unconfined aquifers, in areas of low population density, and on relatively impermeable geologic formations. A system of monitoring wells should be installed to detect leaks, as is required under RCRA, since liners and other sealants are not necessarily leak proof. These and numerous other controls are called for by recent federal regulations, although the application of such requirements to existing facilities is at an early stage. Monitoring systems should be allied with the capacity for an effective response to both actual and threatened contamination of groundwaters. One way to reduce the risk of contamination is to retire old facilities that cannot meet the new safety requirements.

The reuse of water is also becoming increasingly attractive. Recycle reuse technology is considered by industry to be the ultimate solution to the problem of disposing of contaminants as it can reduce those problems by converting wastes into usable products or into energy.

The disposal of wastes by injection wells raises specialized problems. There are probably less than 300 deep-well disposal sites operating in the United States, excluding the wells used for the reinjection of brines in the petroleum industry. The injected fluid is usually of a hazardous nature; often it is radioactive or a toxic chemical, petrochemical, or pharmaceutical waste that is difficult to treat. Care must be taken to site deep disposal wells where they can neither inject waste into potable aquifers nor pose the threat of contamination by the upward migration of contaminants through unplugged dry bore holes. The proper construction and maintenance of such wells is also essential.

Perhaps the best method for preventing the contamination of groundwater by hazardous wastes is to consider carefully adopting ways to reduce the use and production of hazardous wastes. In addition, different types of disposal for different types of hazardous wastes should be considered. Landfills, dumps, or impoundments may be more suitable for certain wastes than for others, such as those that are easily leached by water. An effort could be made to compact or condense extremely harmful wastes and place them in inert media such as glass or ceramics before disposing of them.

Septic Tanks

Septic tanks are a widely used method of disposing of residential or other domestic wastewater and sewage, and they are sometimes used to dispose of commercial and industrial wastes. When operating correctly, they efficiently renovate wastewater, as the sewage is decomposed by bacterial action and other natural processes. The use of septic tanks is widespread in the United States. Approximately 30% of the population of the United States uses septic tanks, and it is estimated that these tanks handle about 3.5 billion gallons of waste per day. This is the largest discharge of waste from any source that goes directly into the ground and that may enter an aquifer. In the eastern United States, where the population density is high and there are many shallow unconfined aquifers, the potential for groundwater contamination is greater than in any other part of the country.

Septic tanks are regulated by all states. Owners of new septic tanks are usually required to have a permit for their construction and to report on the soil, percolation rate, and the details of the design and maintenance of the equipment. There is often a minimum-lot-size regulation which prevents septic tanks from exceeding a certain density. In some instances the lot size is sufficiently large to discourage any excessive development over particularly susceptible aquifers. Some states also require that septic-tank installers and pumpers be registered, and some have maintenance and sludge-disposal rules. Thus, a measure of protection against groundwater contamination is provided by regulations currently in place, although we do not have an accurate idea of how well these regulations are enforced, nor of the efficiency of the systems that were installed prior to the existence of the regulations.

There are several options which can further reduce the potential of septic tanks to contaminate groundwaters. Of these, the major solution to the problem is the installation of sewers. This is a costly alternative to septic-tank usage, especially to new users in low-density areas. In addition, it obviously creates a need for the construction and operation of sewage-treatment plants, which entails great expense and yet still requires the discharge of certain waste matter, such as nutrients, heavy metals, and complex organic chemicals, into bodies of surface water.

Another choice which might be feasible in some situations is the use of waterless toilets, which operate by acid incineration, gas incineration, or composting. This would eliminate the organic solids and liquids produced by septic tanks, but would not deal with the majority of domestic wastewater which results from bathing, laundry, and food preparation, etc. In addition the use of these toilets results in the formation of ash or compost, the disposal of which would still present a problem.

If home sites are on soil that is not suited to the use of traditional septic tanks, there are alternate designs that can be used. These designs include a dosing system, which distributes effluent evenly over a drainage area, and a mound system, which may be used in sandy or clay soils. The latter method uses a built-up mound of permeable soil for a drain field.

Agricultural Practices

Modern agricultural practices have resulted in the increased production of food and feed grain, and in an increase in domestic animal husbandry.

The large increase in the use of agricultural chemicals and the prevalence of irrigation in the last twenty years has made agriculture a significant non-point source of groundwater contamination, particularly by the nitrate in fertilizers.

Non-point sources of contamination are more difficult to control than are point sources, and often in these cases the goal would be to minimize the effect of such contamination rather than to seek its total prevention. Contamination from the nitrate in fertilizers could be minimized by avoiding excessive applications of fertilizers, by supplying only the amount of nutrients that the plants require, by applying it only in the growing season, by using slow-release fertilizers, and by employing crops rotation systems utilizing nitrogen-fixing plants. Pesticides have been found in groundwater in Arizona, California, New York, and elsewhere. Again the threat of contamination from pesticides could be reduced by closely controlling their application rates and timing, by the use of biodegradable pesticides, and by the use of pesticides only as part of an integrated approach to pest management in order to reduce the applications of such chemicals.

Confined animal feedlots and their disposal facilities, a relatively recent innovation, are a potential source of groundwater contamination through runoff and infiltration and from the waste products they generate. When a great many animals are confined to little acreage, the natural assimilative capacity of its soil and vegetation is severely stressed. Various animals produce different ratios of ammonia and phosphate, while nearly all animal waste contains large amounts of nitrate. Nitrate is not attenuated in the soil but may percolate down into the groundwater. A certain amount of attenuation does take place naturally in the underground environment which reduces the level of other pollutants. The management and control of concentrated animal feedlots, including stock-rate and density, play an important role in protecting groundwater against contamination. Siting restrictions and a reduction in the density of livestock are both ways in which it is possible to alleviate the problem. Other safeguards against contamination include mandatory specifications for water diversion and containment, for operation of the facility, and for the storage and disposal of wastes.

The total of irrigated land in the United States is about 50 million acres, and the irrigation of agriculture requires nearly 70% of the groundwater used annually. Irrigation in arid areas may cause an increased mineralization of groundwater. Bouwer (1981) has discussed some options for dealing with these problems. The ways to avoid mineralization include a reduction of the volume of water used and the growing of a crop with a lower evapotranspiration rate. Water use could be reduced by maximizing crop yields per unit of irrigation water, by growing cool-season crops rather than warm-season ones, by growing crops with low water requirements, and by developing and using antitranspirants. Certain vegetables might not be available at certain times of the year if those practices were followed. The use of subirrigation systems, which are not susceptible to evaporation, in place of furrow and sprinkler systems is one method for reducing solute concentrations in irrigation return flow. A method of reducing the amount of salts that reach the aquifer is the use of underground drains when the groundwater does not lie far below the surface of the land. The water thus removed can be recycled or disposed of elsewhere. Where the aquifer is deep, the water percolating down can be removed by pumping wells that penetrate only the upper portion of the aquifer, ensuring that the bulk of the groundwater remains uncontaminated. This method is costly and requires a high-energy input. The overpumping of groundwater in agricultural areas has caused saltwater intrusion in coastal areas, and it has also reduced the quality of groundwater in inland areas where water of poor quality has migrated into a usable aquifer. Overpumping may be reduced by conservation methods such as lining irrigation canals. Land subsidence, for example in California and Texas, has been documented in regions where the withdrawals of groundwater exceed the recharge of its aquifer. One way to avoid such an overdraft is to make the pumping of large quantities of groundwater uneconomical, which could be achieved, in some instances, by eliminating subsidies, imposing high water charges, or limiting the amount of water that can be used.

Accidental Spills and Leaks

Spills and leaks may occur at airports, industrial sites, highways and railroads, gas stations and refineries. There is always an inherent risk of leaks and spills in the storage and transportation of liquids. Organic chemicals are the most frequently reported groundwater contaminant resulting from spills and leaks. Pipelines are widely used to transport a variety of fluids, the most common one being petroleum. In 1976 there were 174,000 miles of petroleum pipelines which transported 9.63 billion barrels, or 20 million tank cars, of petroleum product. Between 1968 and 1981 there were 4,112 reported pipeline accidents, 1,372 of which were due to corrosion and 1,101 to equipment rupturing the pipeline. It is not known how many of these incidents resulted in contaminated groundwater.

Small hydrocarbon spills may be absorbed by the unsaturated soil zone, but larger ones may reach the aquifer. Very low concentrations of hydrocarbons in water render it unpalatable and unfit to drink. Immediate response and proper cleanup procedures are therefore essential to prevent groundwater contamination. If spills are soaked up with absorbent substances, which are then properly disposed of, spilled materials could be prevented from entering the soil and subsequently contaminating the aquifer.

Methods for detecting leaks in underground storage tanks, such as the careful inventorying of stock to bring to light unexplained losses that could be due to leaks reduce the threat of groundwater contamination. Siting storage facilities on natural or constructed impermeable material could also reduce the problem. The use of non-corrodible materials or liners for pipelines can assist in preventing or minimizing leaks. Many pipelines now have pressure gauges at regular intervals that facilitate the speedy detection of leaks. Pipelines are often located close to the surface of the land so that evidence of leaks can be spotted by aerial surveillance that is carried out at frequent intervals. Positioning pipelines deeper would not only decrease the possibility of detecting leaks, but it would also place them closer to the groundwater. It is therefore important to protect pipelines from rupture by heavy equipment, and this could be achieved by educating and licensing the operators of heavy equipment. Careful maintenance and inspection of storage and pipeline facilities could detect system failures before they become a major problem.

The Land Spreading and Spraying of Sludges

Sludges are the semi-solid residues that remain after the disposal of wastewater from domestic, commercial, and industrial operations. Groundwater may be contaminated by sludge when it is disposed of by land spreading because precipitation may leak chemical constituents, bacteria, and viruses into the soil.

Sludges can be disposed of by spreading or spraying over land. The use of municipal sludge on agricultural land is more readily accepted in Europe than in the United States. Sludges from manufacturing processes may contain agricultural fertilizers, but they also may contain toxic chemicals and heavy metals that vary from degradable to very refractory. The major hazardous constituents of sludges are heavy metals, organic chemicals, and biological components such as bacteria or viruses.

Groundwater contamination caused by the land spreading or spraying of sludges could best be controlled by a careful consideration of the site and its physical capacity to handle the wastes. The rate of application should be dependent on the depth and richness of the soil, its attenuation capacity, and the use of the land. Sludge disposal may best be sited on land where there is a mild gradient and a good soil cover that both allows slow percolation and has a high attenuation capacity, where there is a low water table, and where the vegetation is not to be used for food. The rate of application and loading of sludge needs to be carefully regulated so that the soils' capacity for renovation is not exceeded.

Mining

Domestic mining for minerals and coal are multibillion-dollar industries in the United States. Mining operations change the natural environment, either permanently or temporarily, and may disturb groundwater. Waste products from mining can also cause a variety of problems in the quality of groundwater. Because the contamination of surface water by mining activities is of such a serious nature, relatively little attention has been given to the contamination of groundwater, although it too may be a serious problem.

Mining can be hazardous to the quality of groundwater in several ways. Uncontrolled mining may pollute streams and rivers in the aquifer-recharge area, or it may contaminate an aquifer by intersecting it, thereby introducing contaminants. The artificial lowering of the water table, especially in coal-mining operations, may expose sulfur-bearing minerals to oxidation, leading to the formation of an acid solution which may enter the groundwater. Mining for metals may introduce toxic or radioactive contaminants into groundwater. The tailings ponds used for the disposal of wastes from a mine can contribute significantly to the contamination of groundwater. Quarrying may increase the total amount of suspended solids in groundwater.

There are many ways in which the threat of contamination from mining operations could be reduced or, in some cases, eliminated. Since mining and its products are important to society, it would be unrealistic to restrict mining activities nationwide. Nevertheless, it may be beneficial to restrict these activities in particularly sensitive areas. Unlike many contaminating activities, mining cannot usually be shifted to a site that is less vulnerable hydrogeologically. Mining has to take place where the minerals occur, although most minerals occur at more than one location. Instead, the best management techniques known and the best technology applicable to mining could be used to minimize groundwater pollution. This can be, and often is, achieved in part by requiring permits for mining operations, well drilling, and the disposal of mine wastes. The Surface Mining Control and Reclamation Act requires that all permitted surface coal-mining operations be in compliance with environmental-protection performance standards, including the special measures designed to minimize disturbances to the hydrologic balance and to prevent toxic drainage from entering the groundwater. The Act also gives the Secretary of the Interior the authority to carry out whatever actions are necessary to abate the adverse effects of past coal-mining practices upon water resources. This Act does not cover mining operations other than coal.

Other methods of mitigating the threat to the quality of groundwater from mining include the neutralization of acid mine drainage where practicable and the sealing of aquifers that have been cut through wherever it is technically feasible. The use of impermeable liners and berms in tailings ponds is important, as it is for hazardous waste impoundments. When the ponds are back filled, the surface should be covered by soil and revegetated. Long-term monitoring and maintenance is required to keep the heavy metals in the ponds from migrating into the groundwater. The use of quarry sites and abandoned mines as disposal sites should be discontinued unless it can be proven that the disposal technology employed at these sites poses no serious threat to the quality of groundwater.

Highway Deicing-Salts

The use of salts (sodium chloride and calcium chloride) to melt ice on highways is a common practice in many of the northern states. In the winter of 1978–79, over 12 million tons of salt were used on roads in the United States. Groundwater is particularly vulnerable to salt contamination because salts are highly soluble and relatively mobile in groundwater.

Salts may be washed off of paved surfaces into storm drains or onto adjacent ground, where they may percolate down into an aquifer. Salts for use on highways are often stored in uncovered piles along roadsides and can cause further contamination when the salt is dissolved by rain and snowmelt. Since salt is cheap, the loss of deicing salt by this means was largely ignored until recently.

It is unlikely that the use of highway deicing-salts will ever be eliminated. At present, it is the cheapest and most effective method of clearing ice from highways. There are several ways to minimize their use, however, and thereby to minimize groundwater contamination. Mechanical options include increasing the accuracy of spreading equipment, covering piles of stored salt, and in some situations even installing heat elements under the pavement. Efforts are being made to make spreading equipment more precise and accurate in the application of deicing salts so that smaller quantities of salt can be used. More and more states are storing salt in enclosed structures in order to minimize its exposure to precipitation. Planning to develop priority systems for salting so that primary and secondary roads are treated according to their use can be encouraged. Heavily used roads require better deicing than roads receiving less use.

The Infiltration of Surface Water

Aquifers are often in hydraulic connection with bodies of surface water. Under certain conditions, the polluted surface water of lakes or streams can percolate into a water table aquifer beneath the body of surface water, thereby degrading the quality of the groundwater. The development of groundwater near a body of surface water may also draw contaminated water into the aquifer.

A major national effort is now under way to reduce the pollution of surface waters under the mandate of the Clean Water Act. That effort includes the use of pollution-control equipment to reduce discharges of pollutants into public water bodies and a particular emphasis on cleansing the wastewater from municipal sewage-treatment plants and from industrial facilities. As improvements are made in the quality of surface waters, additional protection will also be afforded to groundwater.

Brine Disposal Associated with the Petroleum Industry

Oil production is accompanied by the production of brine wastes. Groundwater contamination resulting from the disposal of oil-field brines has been documented in 17 states. In the past it was common practice to dispose of brines in evaporation pits, which often leaked their contents into the soil and raised the possibility of groundwater contamination. This procedure is now normally prohibited.

Current practices in most oil fields have made progress towards eliminating present and future problems associated with brine disposal. The practices include the injection of the brine into deep formations that are generally deemed unsuitable for other uses and the reinjection of brines into oil-producing formations to enhance oil recovery. Both of these practices may pose a potential threat to groundwater quality if they are not properly regulated or if the regulations are not enforced. Reinjection of brines is considered to be potentially a less contaminating method of disposal than the use of evaporation pits.

The Development of Groundwater

The simple action of pumping water from wells may bring lesser quality water into their zone of influence. In inland areas pumping can cause saline water to migrate from saline aquifers through leaky aquitards into potable water. In coastal regions the problem is often one of saltwater intrusion on potable water.

With a clear understanding of the hydrogeologic conditions of the area where groundwater is pumped, these problems can be anticipated and pumping accordingly restricted to a safe level. The restriction of pumping can itself limit the growth of communities, and land zoning may also be used to prohibit excessive development in areas where saltwater intrusion may occur. In coastal areas the injection of freshwater barriers can reverse the hydraulic gradient so that the flow is toward the sea rather than toward the pumping wells, thus effectively reducing or eliminating saltwater intrusion. The injection wells required to create a freshwater barrier are an expensive undertaking, however, and their efficient operation requires a source of water of reasonable quality which is sufficient for continuous injection. In some situations physical barriers between the aquifer and the seawater can be built in the ground to protect groundwater from saltwater intrusion.

Contamination from Radioactive Sources

Radionuclides occur both naturally and as waste products from hospitals, utilities and other commercial reactors, defense operations, uranium milling operations, and fuel-recycling facilities. All can contaminate groundwater. The primary way to protect groundwater from naturally occurring radioactive contaminants is to avoid the development of groundwater in those areas where the minerals occur. The possibility of contamination from radioactive wastes can be mitigated by their proper storage.

No permanent method for the disposal of high-level radioactive wastes has been agreed upon, but several options are being actively investigated. Heavy concentrations of high-level radioactive wastes will be solidified in a stable medium, recently identified as borosilicate glass. They may then be buried in a geologic repository that can withstand the heat generated by fission, and that is isolated from the flow systems of groundwater, which could transport radioactive material. To delay the permanent burial of radioactive wastes until a better method of disposal can be identified is another viable option. Temporarily stored wastes are, however, more vulnerable to exposure to the biosphere.

Conclusion

This review of options for protecting groundwater from various types of contamination illustrates the complexity of establishing effective overall programs which will protect the quality of groundwater. The dominant characteristic both of the potential sources of contamination and of the alternative approaches for the protection of groundwater is their diversity. Each situation must be evaluated clearly in its own particular context. Any comprehensive range of programs developed to deal with the problem of groundwater contamination must be prepared to deal with the wide range of the situations described.

Three

The Groundwater Resource

- Groundwater occurs in two types of aquifers, confined and unconfined, and is usually within 2,500 feet of the ground surface.
- The susceptability of an aquifer to recharge varies greatly.
- Aquifer water mixes very slowly compared to surface water.
- Groundwater varies greatly in quantity and quality.
- Groundwater is a source of drinking water for 40–50% of the population of the conterminous United States. It is used in large quantities for irrigation and by industry.

What Is Groundwater?

Groundwater may be defined as subsurface water that occurs beneath the water table in soils and geologic forms that are fully saturated (Freeze and Cherry, 1979). It is an integral part of the hydrologic cycle, and any approach to groundwater problems should recognize this. Groundwater is not only an important natural resource but also an essential part of the natural environment. Much of the folklore and many of the widely held misconceptions about the nature of groundwater—for example, that it occurs in underground lakes, rivers, and veins and can be detected by listening for the noise–are dispelled by Lehr and Pettyjohn (1975) in their description of groundwater and its flow patterns.

The global hydrologic cycle consists of the movement of water between the oceans and other surface water, the atmosphere, and the land. The process is illustrated by Figures 3–1 and 3–2. A part of the precipitation, either as rainfall or melting snow, infiltrates the ground and percolates down through the unsaturated soil, known as the aerated zone, to the zone of saturation or the water-table level. Table 3–1, an estimate of the water balance of the world, shows the relative volumes of water contained in each part of the hydrologic cycle. Only 2.7% of all the water on the planet is fresh, and of that only 0.36% is easily available to users (Leopold, 1974). It has been estimated that about 40,000 billion gallons per day (bgd) pass over the conterminous United States, the 48 states within a common boundary, as water vapor. Approximately 10% of this, 4,200 bgd, is precipitated as rain, snow, sleet, or hail, equivalent to an average uniform annual rainfall of 30 inches nationwide. About two-thirds of the precipitation evaporates or is transpired by vegetation. The remaining 1,450 bgd accumulates in ground and surface waters, flows to the sea or across national boundaries, is consumed, or evaporates from reservoirs (U.S. Water Resources Council, 1978a). Of the 1,450 bgd only 675 bgd are usually available for intensive beneficial uses.

The ability of an aquifer to store and transmit water is a function of its permeability and porosity (Freeze and Cherry, 1979; U.S. EPA, 1977). When the saturated substratum is sufficiently permeable to store and transmit significant quantities of water, the geological formation is called an aquifer. There are two main types of aquifers, confined and unconfined. An unconfined or water-table aquifer contains water under atmospheric pressure; the upper surface of the water is called the water table and

Table 3–1. Estimate of the Water Balance of the World

Parameter	Surface area (km^2) × 10^6	Volume (km^3) × 10^6	Volume (%)	Equivalent depth (m)*	Residence time
Oceans and seas	361	1370	94	2500	~4000 years
Lakes and reservoirs	1.55	0.13	<0.01	0.25	~10 years
Swamps	<0.1	<0.01	<0.01	0.007	1–10 years
River channels	<0.1	<0.01	<0.01	0.003	~2 weeks
Soil moisture	130	0.07	<0.01	0.13	2 weeks–1 year
Groundwater	130	60	4	120	2 weeks–10,000 years
Icecaps and glaciers	17.8	30	2	60	10–1000 years
Atmospheric water	504	0.01	<0.01	0.025	~10 days
Biospheric water	<0.1	<0.01	<0.01	0.001	~1 week

*Computed as though storage were uniformly distributed over the entire surface of the earth.

Source: R. Allan Freeze, John A. Cherry, *Groundwater* (Engelwood Cliffs, N.J.: Prentice Hall, Inc., 1979), p. 84. Reprinted by permission of the publisher.

may rise and fall according to the volume of water stored, which is dependent upon seasonal cycles of natural recharge. A perched aquifer is one in which a limited layer, or lens, of impermeable material occurs above the water table, forming a thin zone of saturation above it. It is a type of water-table aquifer. The second major category of aquifer is the confined or artesian aquifer. These are bounded top and bottom by layers of relatively impermeable geologic formations termed aquitards or confining layers (Figure 3–1). The aquifer is completely saturated with water which is under greater than atmospheric pressure. An artesian aquifer is not recharged everywhere uniformly, but in one or more general recharge areas. Water levels in non-pumping wells of unconfined aquifers correspond to the level of the water table and therefore vary according to the volume of water in storage. Water levels in non-pumping wells tapping confined aquifers are dependent upon the artesian pressure of the water in that aquifer, and in some cases the water may exceed the top of the well casing, thus causing a flowing well. The hypothetical projection of such water levels is known as the potentiometric surface (Figure 3–1). The aquitards, or confining layers, are not totally impermeable and permit some recharge or discharge to lower confined aquifers. Aquifers can occur in unconsolidated materials such as sand and gravel or in consolidated material or bedrock. The latter may consist of carbonate rock, volcanic rock, or fractured igneous, metamorphic, and sedimentary rocks. Sand and gravel aquifers usually contain the most groundwater, but high-yield wells can also occur in carbonate and volcanic rocks.

Groundwater moves in response to gravity, pressure, and friction, the first two driving the water, the latter resisting motion. Due to the complexity of the channels through which groundwater flows, it is difficult to construct a model of the movement of groundwater at a microscopic level. The French engineer, Darcy, however, formulated an empirical law in the mid-nineteenth century which effectively averages the microscopic complexities, providing a macroscopic model for groundwater movement. Darcy's Law relates the rate at which groundwater flows across a surface to the rate of change of energy of the groundwater along the flow path. This law is central to the derivation of equations used to model the flow of groundwater. The resulting partial differential equations, with boundary conditions imposed by the particular groundwater basin being studied, can be solved to complete a groundwater model. Bear (1972) discusses the application of the three methods used for solving such boundary-value problems, namely analytical, analog, and numerical. Analytical methods result in explicit mathematical expressions of the solution and are useful for problems where the governing equations may be simplified and the boundaries of the basins idealized. Analog models are scaled physical models which simulate groundwater flow. Numerical models offer the widest range of generality and require the use of digital computers. The two most widely used numerical methods for solving groundwater equations are the finite-difference technique and the finite-element technique.

The main difference between groundwater and surface water is that the movement of groundwater is slow and occurs under laminar flow. The flow rates of groundwater are governed by hydraulic gradients and aquifer permeabilities and range from a fraction of an inch to several feet per day. Movement of groundwater occurs from points of recharge towards points of discharge along lines of hydraulic head. The laminar flow of groundwater would result in little mixing taking place, in contrast to the good mixing potential in the turbulent flow of most surface water. This factor is extremely important when considering the fate of contaminants. The rates of contaminant movement are determined by groundwater flow-rates, chemical and physical interaction between the aquifer materials and the contaminant, and changes in water chemistry. Contaminated water would not be diluted by the entire body of groundwater, as would happen with contaminated surface water. In fractured rock or carbonate aquifers, little dilution takes place, and in unconsolidated deposits dilution is primarily by hydrodynamic dispersion (Miller, 1981a).

The Occurrence and Natural Quality of Groundwater

Most aquifers occur within 2,500 feet of the surface of the land. They may be thick or thin, extensive or local, very near the land surface or at considerable depths. It has been estimated that 30% of the stream flow of the United States is supplied by groundwater that emerges as natural springs or other seepage. In certain areas in times of drought, all the stream flow in the low-flow months may be due to groundwater (U.S. Water Resources Council, 1978a). The interrelatedness of surface and groundwater is further underlined by the fact that surface water can recharge groundwater. Under certain conditions seepage from lakes, rivers, streams, reservoirs, and canals may recharge aquifers.

The quantity of groundwater in storage is much greater than the volume of surface water available in streams and lakes. It comprises more than 96% of all the fresh water in the United States, the remaining 4% occurring in lakes, rivers, and streams (Weimar, 1980). Estimates of groundwater within 2,500 feet of the land surface in the conterminous United States range from 33 quadrillion to 59 quadrillion gallons (U.S. Water Resources Council, 1978a) to as much as 100 quadrillion gallons (Lehr, 1982). As a point of comparison, Lake Michigan contains 1.3 quadrillion gallons of water. Not all of the groundwater in storage is available for use, however, because some is bound to soil particles. The cost of extraction may also be an inhibiting factor in certain areas. The geographical extent of the main groundwater resources in the United States is shown in Figure 3–3. It would be possible to drill a well with a yield sufficient for domestic use in almost every region of the country (U.S. EPA, 1977). The country has been divided up into 10 groundwater regions, Figure 3–4 (Lehr et al., 1976). They are considered the best broad classification of the groundwater situation in the conterminous United States. The division is based on the types of aquifers.

1. The western mountain ranges consist mainly of igneous, metamorphic, and consolidated sedimentary rocks. Most of the groundwater occurs in rock fractures. The large amount of precipitation that falls in this area is released and recharges aquifers in adjacent regions.
2. Alluvial basins consist of valleys surrounded by mountains in the arid southwest. Water levels in many aquifers have declined over recent years due to the use of large volumes of groundwater for agricultural irrigation.
3. Columbia Lava Plateau consists of lava flows and unconsolidated sediments. In some areas there are large supplies of groundwater.
4. The Colorado Plateau has high, dry plateaus of sedimentary shale and sandstone and has a scarcity of productive aquifers.
5. The High Plains are extensive and semi-arid to sub-humid. The unconsolidated sedimentary rocks form the Ogallala aquifer. Due to extensive agricultural irrigation, withdrawals have greatly exceeded groundwater recharge in some areas.
6. The glaciated central lowlands consist of glacial drift, sand, and gravel which form major groundwater reservoirs. In some heavily populated or highly industrialized areas the groundwater has been overdeveloped or polluted.
7. The unglaciated Central Region is composed of horizontal consolidated sedimentary rocks, with limestone and sandstone formations providing the major aquifers. The yields are low to moderate and adequate for domestic supply but would not be sufficient for irrigated agriculture.
8. The unglaciated Appalachians have high-yielding limestone and sandstone aquifers and shale which does not give as high a yield as the other two. The water table may occur at a considerable depth below the surface. This region has an abundance of surface water year round.
9. The glaciated Appalachians is a region which is similar to the unglaciated Appalachians.
10. The Atlantic and Gulf Coast Plain has an abundance of groundwater and surface water. The geology consists of unconsolidated gravel,

sand, silt and clay, and limestone. Supplies of groundwater may not be abundant in some areas of Texas, Louisiana, Mississippi, and Alabama. Florida has a prolific aquifer.

Unfortunately there is more than one classification system for dividing the country up into water regions. The system used by the U.S. Water Resources Council (1978b) is shown in Figure 3–5. For the purpose of compiling and analyzing water-resources data for both surface water and groundwater, the U.S. Water Resources Council divided the nation into 21 major water-resources regions, eighteen within the conterminous United States, the other three being Alaska, Hawaii, and the Caribbean area. These 21 regions are further subdivided into 106 subregions. The regional divisions are areas that contain either the drainage area of a major river or the combined drainage of a series of rivers.

The U.S. Environmental Protection Agency (EPA) used another classification system in compiling data on groundwater pollution for various regions of the United States (Fuhriman and Barton, 1971; Miller, DeLuca, and Tessier, 1974; Miller, Hackenberry, and DeLuca, 1977; Scalf, Keeley, and LaFevers, 1973; and Van der Leeden, Cerrillo, and Miller, 1975). The EPA system most closely resembles that described by Lehr et al. (1976), which is summarized above.

Along with the geological characteristics of the groundwater regions, climatic conditions—in particular precipitation and temperature—have effects upon the quantity and quality of the groundwater available. Variations from average precipitation may cause droughts or floods. Figure 3–6 shows the average annual precipitation in the United States. Water is lost from the land to the atmosphere by evaporation and transpiration, or evapotranspiration. When evapotranspiration exceeds precipitation, groundwater recharge by percolation does not occur (U.S. EPA, 1977). The arid areas of the Southwest are examples where annual precipitation is less than 10 inches, and potential evaporation could exceed this 4 to 20 times. In such areas groundwater recharge occurs mainly in wet, or multi-year cycles. In the eastern states, the annual precipitation exceeds the evaporation, thus providing surpluses which contribute to stream flow. Regional variations in temperature may also affect groundwater in ways unrelated to surface evaporation. Frozen ground does not permit infiltration of rain, thus causing floods and preventing groundwater recharge.

The United States Geological Survey (USGS) has completed and published summary appraisals of the nation's groundwater resources for each of the regions that were briefly outlined above in the U.S. Water Resources Council scheme. A listing of the titles is given in Table 3–2. These geological survey professional papers list groundwater usage for each region by categories of use, e.g. municipal water supply and agricultural irrigation. They list the natural groundwater quality and any problems that may be

Table 3–2. Summary Appraisals of the Nation's Groundwater Resources, by Region

(A)	Ohio—R. M. Boyd, Jr., 1974.
(B)	Upper Mississippi—R. M. Boyd, Jr., 1975.
(C)	Upper Colorado—Don Price and Ted Arnow, 1974.
(D)	Rio Grande—S. W. West and W. L. Broadhurst, 1975.
(E)	California—H. E. Thomas and D. A. Phoenix, 1976.
(F)	Texas-Gulf—E. T. Baker, Jr. and J. R. Wall, 1976.
(G)	Great Basin—Thomas E. Eakin, Don Price, and J. R. Harrill, 1976.
(H)	Arkansas-White-Red—M. S. Bedinger and R. T. Sniegrocki, 1976.
(I)	Mid-Atlantic—Allen Sinnott and Elliott M. Cushing, 1978.
(J)	Great Lakes—William G. Weist, Jr., 1978.
(K)	Souris-Red-Rainy—Harold O. Reeder, 1978.
(L)	Tennessee—Ann Zurawski, 1978.
(M)	Hawaii—K. J. Takasaki, 1978.
(N)	Lower Mississippi—J. E. Terry and C. T. Bryant, 1979.
(O)	South Atlantic-Gulf—D. J. Cederstrom, E. H. Boswell, and G. R. Tarver, 1979.
(P)	Alaska—Chester Zenone and Gary S. Anderson, 1978.
(Q)	Missouri Basin—O. James Taylor, 1978.
(R)	Lower Colorado—E. S. Davidson, 1979.
(S)	Pacific Northwest—Bruce L. Foxworthy, 1979.
(T)	New England—Allen Sinnott, 1982.
(U)	Caribbean—Fernando Gómez-Gómez and James E. Heisel, 1980.

Source: U.S. Geological Survey Professional Paper 813. U.S. Government Office.

encountered due to the presence of natural iron in the water or to its salt content and hardness. In addition, they list present and potential anthropogenic threats to the quality of groundwater.

The quality of groundwater is often described in terms of hardness and salinity. Hardness reflects its calcium and magnesium content and is usually expressed as the equivalent amount of calcium carbonate. It can be viewed as a measure of usefulness for domestic and industrial purposes. Naturally occurring hardness values are shown in Figure 3–7.

Water quality, however, is usually defined in terms of the concentration of its chemical constituents (Tables 3–3 and 3–4). As water moves through the hydrologic cycle (Figures 3–1 and 3–2), it interacts with the atmosphere, soils, and subsurface geologic formations, all of which affect its chemical composition. Thus, there is a natural background level for the chemical content of the water which varies regionally and which may be

Table 3–3. Simple Groundwater Classification Based on Total Dissolved Solids

Category	Total dissolved solids (mg/l or g/m^3)
Freshwater	0–1000
Brackish water	1000–10,000
Saline water	10,000–100,000
Brine water	More than 100,000

Source: Freeze and Cherry, 1979.

subsequently augmented from industrial and domestic sources. Freeze and Cherry (1979) discuss the natural chemical content of groundwater in detail. Rainwater is saturated with oxygen, nitrogen, and carbon-dioxide gases and is usually slightly acidic, having a pH of about 5.6. The acidity may be increased by industrial pollutants, namely the oxides of sulfur and nitrogen. The more acid the rainwater, the more likely it is to react with the geologic materials with which it comes into contact.

Rainwater percolating through the soil may increase in acidity due to the biological processes that occur in that zone. Plant and microbial respiration produce carbon dioxide which increases acidity. It would be possible for the percolating water to become supersaturated with carbon dioxide. Acidity may also be increased by products of decomposition such as humic and fulvic acids, nutrient uptake by roots, and nitrifying bacteria, but these are minor factors compared with the amount of carbon dioxide produced by respiration. Thus, the water undergoes a chemical change during its passage through the soil to the underlying water-bearing formations.

In the saturated zone, the water reacts with the geologic formations, increasing the content of total dissolved solids. Thus, the chemical quality of groundwater depends both upon its age and the geological formations encountered in its flow history. Carbonate formations would increase the magnesium and calcium content and also the concentration of bicarbonate due to the dissolution of calcite ($CaCO_3$) and dolomite ($Mg{\cdot}CaCO_3$). Aluminosilicate minerals would increase the concentrations of sodium, potassium, magnesium, calcium, and silicon hydroxide ($Si(OH)_4$) in the water.

In consolidated deposits consisting of minerals from a range of sedimentary, igneous, and metamorphic sources, the order of encounter of the groundwater with the different assemblages determines the chemical constituency at a particular point in time. Sulfate-bearing minerals such as gypsum and anhydrite, although they occur less frequently than the carbonate and crystalline formations, are characterized by high solubilities.

Table 3–4. Classification of Dissolved Inorganic Constituents in Groundwater

Major constituents (greater than 5 mg/l)	
Bicarbonate	Silicon
Calcium	Sodium
Chloride	Sulfate
Magnesium	Carbonic acid
Minor constituents (0.01–10.0 mg/l)	
Boron	Nitrate
Carbonate	Potassium
Fluoride	Strontium
Iron	
Trace constituents (less than 0.1 mg/l)	
Aluminum	Molybdenum
Antimony	Nickel
Arsenic	Niobium
Barium	Phosphate
Beryllium	Platinum
Bismuth	Radium
Bromide	Rubidium
Cadmium	Ruthenium
Cerium	Scandium
Cesium	Selenium
Chromium	Silver
Cobalt	Thallium
Copper	Thorium
Gallium	Tin
Germanium	Titanium
Gold	Tungsten
Indium	Uranium
Iodide	Vanadium
Lanthanum	Ytterbium
Lead	Yttrium
Lithium	Zinc
Manganese	Zirconium

Source: S. N. Davis and R. J. M. DeWiest, *Hydrogeology* (New York: John Wiley and Sons, Inc., 1966). Reprinted by permission of the publisher.

Thus, in older groundwater that has encountered sulfur-bearing minerals, the sulfate anion may dominate the bicarbonate anion. In very deep, old groundwater, the chloride anion may dominate both the bicarbonate and sulfate ones due to the presence of readily soluble minerals such as halite (NaCl) and sylvite (KCl).

The U.S. Public Health Service (USPHS) standard for total dissolved solids (TDS) in drinking water is 500 ppm, although the 1974 Safe Drinking Water Act considers waters containing up to 10,000 ppm TDS as potential sources of drinking water (U.S. EPA, 1977). The four types of naturally occurring groundwater that often exceed 10,000 ppm TDS are connate water, intruded seawater, magmatic and geothermal water, and water affected by salt leaching and the products of evapotranspiration. In many areas of the United States, groundwater can be used for drinking with no pretreatment, in which case it is said to be a raw resource. In other areas pretreatment to correct hardness or color may be necessary. Where contamination by pathogenic organisms is a potential threat, chlorination may be indicated. Water from some aquifers is unusable due to its salinity or to the presence of naturally occurring toxic substances such as arsenic or radionuclides. Most of the fresh water aquifers are underlain by brackish or saline aquifers and, in general, salinity may be said to increase with depth.

The Use of Groundwater

Groundwater is a major natural resource in the United States and is often more easily available than surface water. It is estimated that between 40 and 50% of the population uses groundwater as its primary source of drinking water (U.S. Water Resources Council, 1978a; U.S. EPA, 1977). Groundwater delivered by community systems supplies 29% of the population and a further 19% has its own domestic wells. The water quality of the latter is not routinely assessed. Figure 3–8 shows the population served by groundwater and surface water for drinking purposes; a total of 48% relies on groundwater. These are unpublished data for 1970 from the USGS (U.S. EPA, 1977). Approximately 36% of the municipal public drinking-water supplies come from groundwater. Of the rural population, 95% is dependent upon groundwater for drinking purposes. Of the total groundwater usage, 60% is for public supplies and 40% for rural supplies. Of the major cities in the United States, 75% depend upon well water for most of their supplies. The states vary in their dependence upon groundwater for drinking, as shown in Table 3–5, which also presents unpublished data from USGS for 1970. New Mexico has the highest level of dependence, with 92% of its population using groundwater as its source of drinking water, as compared with 30% of Maryland's population. Figure

Table 3–5. Dependence of the United States Population on Groundwater as a Source of Drinking Water for 1970

State	Total Population (Thousands)	% Of Total Population Relying On Groundwater	Population Served By Groundwater From Public Supplies (Thousands)	Population Served By Groundwater From Rural Supplies (Thousands)	% Of Public Supply Population Relying On Groundwater	% Of Rural Population Relying On Groundwater
Alabama	3,444	59	884	1,139	38	100
Alaska	302	63	62	130	49	74
Arizona	1,772	71	989	274	66	100
Arkansas	1,923	67	605	681	49	100
California	19,953	46	8,000	1,164	43	93
Colorado	2,207	23	306	197	16	87
Connecticut	3,032	37	590	531	24	98
Delaware	548	65	217	138	53	100
Florida	6,789	91	4,819	1,379	89	100
Georgia	4,590	70	825	2,376	38	98
Hawaii	770	87	662	11	95	14
Idaho	713	88	407	218	87	90
Illinois	11,114	38	3,880	358	36	82
Indiana	5,194	58	1,497	1,494	43	87
Iowa	2,825	82	1,524	794	75	100
Kansas	2,249	62	817	565	50	93
Kentucky	3,219	39	304	936	14	88
Louisiana	3,643	62	1,291	927	48	100

Table 3–5 (continued)

State	Total Population (Thousands)	% Of Total Population Relying On Groundwater	Population Served By Groundwater From Public Supplies (Thousands)	Population Served By Groundwater From Rural Supplies (Thousands)	% Of Public Supply Population Relying On Groundwater	% Of Rural Population Relying On Groundwater
Maine	994	37	153	219	20	91
Maryland	3,922	30	368	803	12	100
Massachusetts	5,689	31	1,464	286	27	100
Michigan	8,875	38	1,365	2,006	20	100
Minnesota	3,805	67	1,498	1,057	55	100
Mississippi	2,217	90	1,177	827	85	100
Missouri	4,677	31	942	529	24	74
Montana	694	47	152	174	30	93
Nebraska	1,484	86	908	365	81	100
Nevada	489	64	265	46	60	97
New Hampshire	738	61	261	191	48	98
New Jersey	7,168	53	3,032	746	47	100
New Mexico	1,016	92	645	293	91	96
New York	18,191	32	4,152	1,734	25	100
North Carolina	5,082	60	660	2,374	25	99
North Dakota	618	66	189	222	48	99
Ohio	10,652	40	2,475	1,754	29	80
Oklahoma	2,559	40	551	475	28	85

Oregon	2,091	56	355	821	30	92
Pennsylvania	11,794	30	1,351	2,144	14	100
Rhode Island	950	33	213	103	25	100
South Carolina	2,591	61	221	1,359	18	100
South Dakota	666	79	284	240	69	94
Tennessee	3,924	51	1,194	805	38	100
Texas	11,197	58	4,584	1,949	50	100
Utah	1,059	58	502	113	53	99
Vermont	445	56	100	150	35	96
Virginia	4,648	34	477	1,109	14	98
Washington	3,409	44	1,072	433	38	78
West Virginia	1,744	53	380	551	32	97
Wisconsin	4,418	64	1,536	1,311	49	100
Wyoming	332	61	130	73	52	89
District of Columbia	757	0	0	0	0	0
Puerto Rico	2,712	26	396	302	17	80
United States Total	205,897	48	60,600	38,568	37	94

Source: U.S. EPA, 1977.

3–9 shows groundwater as a percentage of total water use for all purposes in 1975. It is clear that the states west of the Mississippi, in the area where irrigated agriculture is prevalent, depend heavily on groundwater. The more humid eastern portion of the country is far less dependent on groundwater. Figure 3–10 shows the actual usage figures for the various states in millions of gallons per day, for public water systems (1970) and total groundwater usage for all purposes (1975). The western states are again the main users of groundwater.

The most recent figures for groundwater use are for 1975, although unpublished USGS data for 1980 are available, subject to revision. Table 3–6 shows the historical trends in groundwater use as a percentage of withdrawals. The total use in 1975 was 82 bgd, up from 68 bgd in 1970, an increase of just over 20%. Most of this increase is accounted for by increases in agricultural irrigation. The percentage used by public and rural and industrial supplies actually decreased from 1970 to 1975. An idea of the actual water use in 1975 is given in Table 3–7, which includes saline groundwater withdrawals and water used for the generation of thermo-electric power, thus giving a total of over 85 bgd. Of this, 57 bgd was used to irrigate 54 million acres of land. Figure 3–11 shows, for comparison, the historical trends in the use of both ground- and surface water.

To give an idea of the way water is used in a typical community, the figures in Tables 3–8 and 3–9 are useful. In an average American community, the average per-capita water consumption is approximately 159 gallons per day (Last, 1980). In an American home, depending on the nature of the residence and the climate, exterior residential use may range from 5 to more than 150% of the interior use, averaging about 75%. This is primarily for watering lawns. Personal use of water, excluding laundry, toilet flushing,

Table 3–6. Historical Trends in Groundwater Uses as a Percent of Withdrawals: 1950–1980

	1950	1960	1970	1975	1980*
Total Fresh Groundwater Withdrawals (bgd)	34	50	68	82	88.5
Public Supplies (%)	12	13	14	13	13
Rural Supplies (%)	8	6	5	5	5
Irrigation (%)	62	68	66	69	68
Industry (%)	18	13	15	14	14

Note: May not total 100% due to rounding.

*USGS unpublished preliminary data, subject to revision, 1982.

Sources: Murray and Reeves, 1972, 1977; MacKichan and Kammerer, 1961. Based on USGS data.

Table 3–7. Groundwater Use for the U.S.: 1975, 1980

	1975	1980*
Population served by groundwater for public supplies	64,700,000	74,600,000
Total groundwater withdrawn, mgd, for public supplies	11,000	11,701
Rural use of groundwater, mgd		
Domestic	2,700	3,296
Livestock	1,200	1,189
Total withdrawn for irrigation, mgd, to irrigate a total of 54,000,000 acres (1975) and 63,125,000 (1980)	57,000	60,400
Groundwater withdrawals for industrial use, mgd		
Fresh	11,000	10,297
Saline	980	927
Water use for generation of thermoelectric power, mgd	1,390	1,597
Total withdrawals of groundwater, mgd	85,270	89,407

*USGS unpublished preliminary data, subject to revision, 1982.

Sources: Murray and Reeves, 1977.

and so forth, accounts for 40% of the internal residential use and averages out to 6.3 gallons per capita per day.

The safe yield of a groundwater basin is defined as the amount of water that can be withdrawn annually without producing an undesired effect (Todd, 1959). Undesired results include depletion of the groundwater reserves, intrusion of water of an undesirable quality, contravention of water rights, the deterioration of the economic advantages of pumping, excessive

Table 3–8. Allocation of Water Used in U.S. Communities

Use	Percentage
Residential	40
Commercial	15
Industrial	25
Public	5
Unaccounted for	15
Total	100

Source: J. M. Last, *Maxcy-Rosenau Public Health and Preventive Medicine,* 11th ed. (Norwalk, Conn.: Appleton-Century-Crofts, 1980), p. 976. Reprinted by permission of the publisher.

Table 3–9. Allocation of Interior Residential Water Use

Use	Percentage
Drinking and cooking	5
Bathing	30
Toilet flushing	40
Laundry	15
Dishwashing	5
Miscellaneous	5
Total	100

Source: J. M. Last, *Maxcy-Rosenau Public Health and Preventive Medicine,* 11th ed. (Norwalk, Conn.: Appleton-Century-Crofts, 1980), p. 976. Reprinted by permission of the publisher.

depletion of stream flow, and land subsidence (Domenico, 1972; Freeze and Cherry, 1979). Any withdrawal in excess of a safe yield is termed an overdraft. It has been suggested that the optimal yield would be a more useful concept and should be determined by an optimal groundwater-management scheme that includes and best meets economic and social objectives associated with the use of water. Under certain conditions, optimal yields may involve the mining of groundwater to depletion or complete conservation (Freeze and Cherry, 1979).

Increased demands on groundwater have strained the supply in certain regions, resulting in reduced artesian pressure, land subsidence, reduced spring and stream flow, and the intrusion of saltwater. This kind of groundwater overdraft is occurring in the High Plains from Texas to Nebraska, parts of California, Arizona, Louisiana, Arkansas, Wisconsin, Illinois, and North Carolina. Figure 3–12 shows the extent of the areas affected by groundwater overdraft and related problems. In the Second National Water Assessment, the U.S. Water Resources Council (1978a) lists actions that could be taken before pumping becomes uneconomical in the areas with declining water levels. These include locating alternate water sources, developing artificial recharge of the aquifers, relocation of water-requiring activities, and reduction of water use through better water management. Groundwater overdraft is considered to be serious when it continues indefinitely (U.S. General Accounting Offices [GAO], 1980), causing the exhaustion of the resource and associated economic and social dislocations and perhaps general weakening of a region's economy. Such potential problems are developing in California, the High Plains regions, Florida, New Mexico, Colorado, and Arizona, but many of these states are successfully dealing with the problem (U.S. GAO, 1980). Although this book deals with changes in groundwater quality, changes in quantity through overdraft are briefly mentioned here as they can affect the quality of the remaining groundwater in the region.

The Profile of an Aquifer

In order to provide a picture of the importance of groundwater, it is useful to describe a specific aquifer, its characteristics and uses, and the problems which are encountered that affect it as a natural resource. A recent study undertaken by the High Plains Study Council provides such data for the Ogallala Aquifer. The Ogallala is an exceptional aquifer in both extent and volume, running as it does through parts of eight states. It is an integral part of the burgeoning economy of those states, as well as of the environment. Because of its unusual size and certain other characteristics, however, it should not be viewed as a representative aquifer.

The Ogallala Aquifer is a major source of groundwater in the High Plains region, underlying a land area of approximately 150,000 square miles. Three times the size of New York State, or about the size of California (Bittinger 1981), the formation extends from southern South Dakota to northwestern Texas and transects portions of six other states including Nebraska, Wyoming, Colorado, Kansas, Oklahoma, and New Mexico (Figure 3–13) and contains an estimated quadrillion gallons of water, the equivalent of Lake Huron (Stengel, 1982). The aquifer fuels a $30 billion-a-year agricultural economy (B. Turner; Camp, Dresser & McKee; personal communication), irrigates over 12 million acres of farmland (Bittinger, 1981), or 20% of the irrigated acreage in the United States (Banks, 1981), and helps support a population of nearly half a million people (Press and Siever, 1978). Furthermore, 40% of the beef consumed in this country is fattened in the aquifer area (Banks, 1981). Such heavy exploitation of the vast groundwater resources in the Ogallala has resulted in serious depletion in some areas. These problems are now the subject of intensive study.

The Ogallala was formed during the early Pleistocene time, some two million years ago, from glacial outwash of the ancestral Rocky Mountains which consisted of gravel, sand, and finer debris that was caught up by streams of meltwater running away from the glacier (Press and Siever, 1978). The outwash settled unevenly throughout the High Plains, giving the aquifer water-storage capacities that varied according to the depth and content of the outwash. In Nebraska, where two thirds of the Ogallala's waters lie, the aquifer has a considerably greater storage capacity per unit of area than in the South Plains of Texas being 1,000–1,500 feet thick as opposed to less than 100 feet thick in Texas (H. O. Banks; Camp, Dresser & McKee; personal communication). At present, there are an estimated 2 billion acre-feet of water in storage in Nebraska (H. O. Banks; Camp, Dresser & McKee; personal communication) compared with 350 million acre-feet in Texas and 100 million acre-feet in Oklahoma (Scalf et al., 1973). Annual withdrawals from the entire aquifer average 5 or 6 million acre-feet (U.S. Water Resources Council, 1980).

The Ogallala's extensive groundwater resources were virtually unknown until the early part of this century. The first wells were drilled into the formation over 90 years ago (Press and Siever, 1978), but the land was used primarily for cattle grazing and dryland wheat production well into the 1900s (Warren et al., 1982). The start of irrigated farming, with the use of high-capacity pumps, after World War II brought rapid economic growth but also caused the water table of the aquifer to decline steadily, in some areas by as much as 100 feet (Press and Siever, 1978), and even to the point of drying up. Gaines County, Texas, has dried up its groundwater resources entirely (H.O. Banks; Camp, Dresser & McKee; personal communication). The aquifer is very slow to recharge. Because of its high rate of evaporation and its high percentage of impermeable soils, the water is not replenished at the rate at which it is used. The depth of the water table nearly everywhere in the Ogallala formation is 50 feet or more below the roots of plants. Plants get the first opportunity at capturing any infiltrating rainfall, making that portion unavailable for pumping (U.S. Water Resources Council, 1980). Overall, the amount of water being overdrawn annually from the aquifer exceeds 3 million acre-feet (Mapp and Eidman, 1976). Annual recharge from precipitation averaging 12 to 22 inches per year (Warren et al., 1982), irrigation return-flows, and some stream-bed percolation is estimated to be 0.27 million acre-feet (Bekure, 1971). The state of Texas has estimated that, at the current rate of use and without an imported water supply, approximately 40% of the now irrigated acreage in the High Plains of West Texas will have to revert to dryland farming or be abandoned by the year 2000, and 60% will have to be abandoned by the year 2020 (Banks, 1981).

The depletion of the Ogallala began to attract public attention in the early 1970s (Banks, 1981). Members of Congress representing the Great Plains states of Colorado, Kansas, Nebraska, New Mexico, Oklahoma, and Texas encouraged the development of legislation that would mandate intensive study of the problem. A $6-million study was authorized by public law in 1976, and the High Plains Study Council was formed under contract with Camp, Dresser & McKee. The Council approved a study design with the following objectives in 1977 (Warren et al., 1982):

1. to determine the potential development alternatives for the High Plains,
2. to identify and describe policies and actions required to carry out promising development strategies, and
3. to evaluate the local, state, and national implications of these alternative development strategies.

It is a comprehensive resource and economic-development study of the area served by the Ogallala (Banks, 1981). Major emphasis is being given to improving the water supply by local conservation and by improved practices of irrigation and agricultural management and to interbasin transfers of surplus water from adjacent basins, the Missouri River, and streams in the Arkansas. Effective, comprehensive, interstate management of the Ogallala groundwater resource is a further major element of the study.

Currently there is little or no public support for comprehensive, interstate management of the aquifer, although interdependencies are widely recognized (Banks, 1981). Laws in the states vary widely. In Texas state agencies have little or no authority to control or manage groundwater. Rights to the use of groundwater are based on the "rule of capture" established by the Texas Supreme Court in 1904. In New Mexico the doctrine of prior appropriation governs the development and use of groundwater. The State Engineer has exclusive administrative control over the acquisition of rights to groundwater. In Oklahoma the Water Resources Board issues permits for groundwater use. Kansas and Colorado require permits for appropriation of groundwater, with limitations on the amounts to be extracted, the objective being to prolong the life of available supplies. Groundwater-management districts have regulatory authority. In Nebraska natural resource districts have management authority, but they are hampered by limited financial resources.

Contamination of the Ogallala aquifer does not, to date, appear to be a major problem or concern (B. Turner; Camp, Dresser & McKee; personal communication). There has been some contamination around major population centers like Lubbock, Texas, but the depletion problem is of more immediate concern (Fig. 3–14). A just-completed study by Camp, Dresser & McKee predicts that 5.1 million acres of irrigated land in six Great Plains states will dry up by the year 2020 (Stengel, 1982). A continuation of present trends will mean the loss of 1.6 million irrigated acres in Kansas, 1.2 million in Texas, 260,000 in Colorado, 224,000 in New Mexico, and 330,000 in Oklahoma. Twenty recommendations have been made for remedial action, but only one is an actual cure. The Army Corps of Engineers has proposed a system of huge canals that would import water from South Dakota, Missouri, and Arkansas. The cost of the project (from $3.6 billion to $22.6 billion) is prohibitive, however, and stopgap efforts like conversion to dryland farming will probably be the most immediate solutions to the depletion problem.

Use of the Ogallala Groundwater Resources in a Few Selected States

In New Mexico the aquifer is heavily developed from southern Quay County to southern Lea County (Scalf et al., 1973). The thickest and most productive part of the aquifer is in northern Lea County. Individual well yields in this area can be as much as 1,600 gpm. In southern Lea County, where the aquifer is thinner, wells yield from 300 to 1,000 gpm, but water levels have been declining at a rate of almost 3 feet per year since 1950.

In Oklahoma the Ogallala is the most important aquifer in the state, underlying most of the panhandle (Scalf et al., 1973). Deposits of sand, gravel, and minor amounts of clay store high-quality groundwater. The aquifer is as much as several hundred feet thick, contains more than 100 million acre-feet of available water, and supplies most of the water requirements of the panhandle. It is used to irrigate 135,000 acres, to supply water for the industrial needs of the Keyes helium plant and the natural gas industry in the panhandle, and to supply all the public and domestic needs in the area.

In Texas the aquifer formation consists of interfingered and intergraded lenses and layers of sand, gravel, silt, clay, and caliche, a crust of calcium carbonate (Scalf et al., 1973). The High Plains is divided by the Canadian River into the northern High Plains and the southern High Plains. The northern area comprises approximately 9,300 square miles. The zone of saturation in most places is 100 to 500 feet thick. Irrigation has developed more slowly here than in the southern High Plains, which is the area of greatest groundwater development in Texas. This area includes about 25,000 square miles and has the most serious depletion problems of the entire aquifer. According to a 1975 USGS report, groundwater withdrawals in the southern High Plains have been averaging 7,142.9 million gallons a day (mgd) (U.S. GAO, 1980). The rate of recharge has been 125 to 134 mgd.

The Texas Department of Water Resources has made estimates and projections of groundwater availability in the Ogallala through the year 2030 (Texas Department of Water Resources, 1979). They have determined the annual effective recharge to be 97 billion gallons. The amount of water in recoverable storage in 1974 was determined to be 110,840 billion gallons. (Recoverable storage is defined as that portion of the underground reservoir capacity which, it is estimated, is physically capable of yielding water economically.) The projected average availability of groundwater annually was then determined through 2030, with average annual groundwater availability being defined as the estimated sustainable annual yield, or effective recharge, plus that amount of water which can be recovered from storage over a specified period of time without causing irreversible harm, such as land-surface subsidence or water-quality deterioration. The projections are as follows:

1980–1989	1,527.04 billion gallons
1990–1999	1,242.61 billion gallons
2000–2009	1,242.61 billion gallons
2010–2019	837.85 billion gallons
2020–2029	837.85 billion gallons
2030	789.84 billion gallons

The remaining recoverable storage in 2030 is projected to be 24,804.43 billion gallons.

Figure 3–1. Illustration of Relationships Within the Hydrologic System
Adapted from figure used in U.S. EPA., 1977.

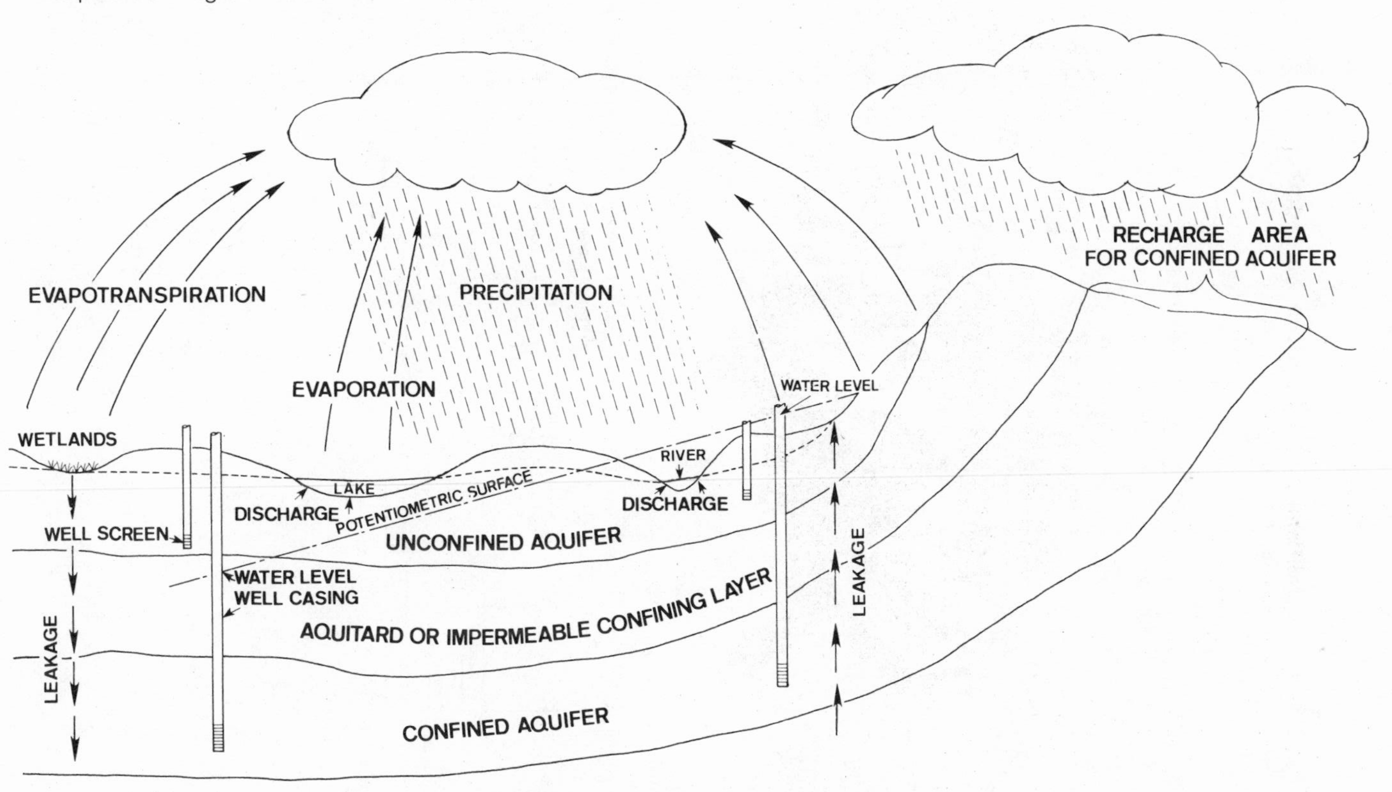

Figure 3–2. Geochemical Cycle of Surface Water and Groundwater
Source: Lehr et al., 1976.

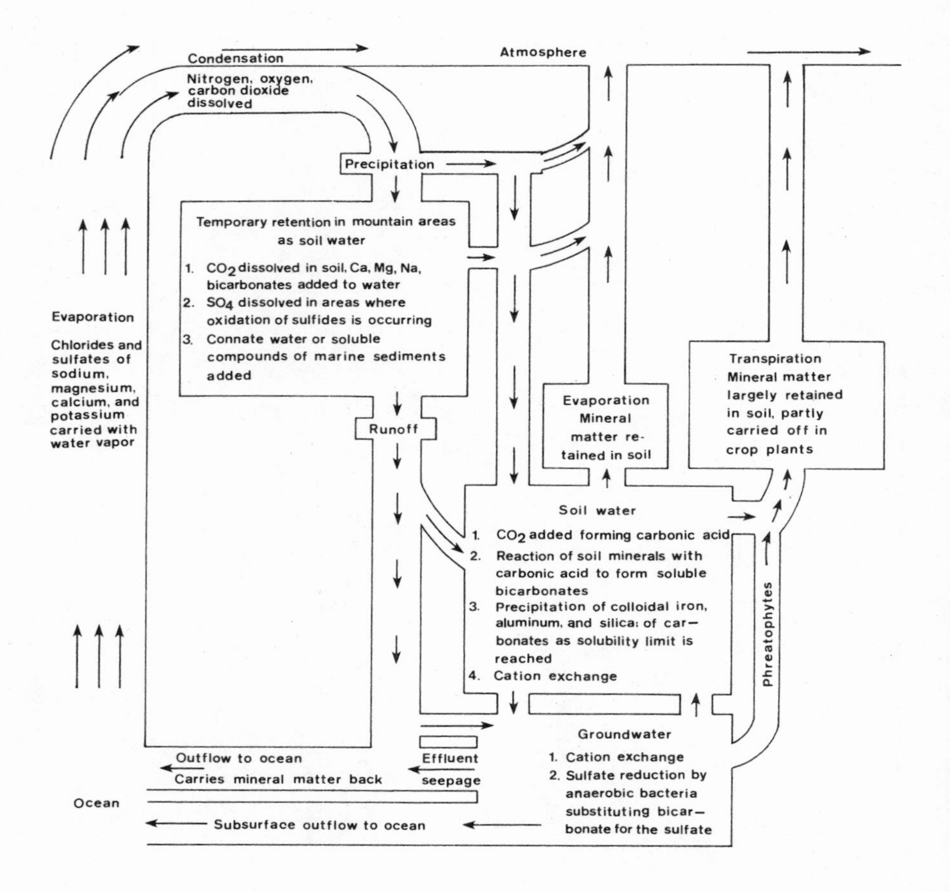

Figure 3–3. Groundwater Resources of the United States
Source: U.S. Water Resources Council, 1978b.

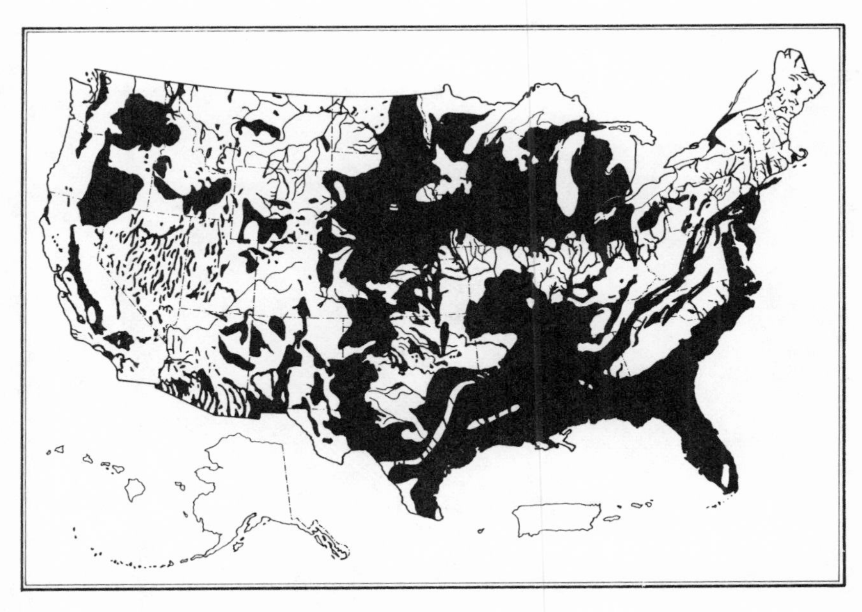

Watercourse related aquifers

Areas of extensive aquifers that yield more than 50 gallons per minute of freshwater

Areas of less extensive aquifers having smaller yields

Figure 3–4. Ten Major Groundwater Regions of the United States, excepting Alaska and Hawaii
Source: Lehr et al., 1976.

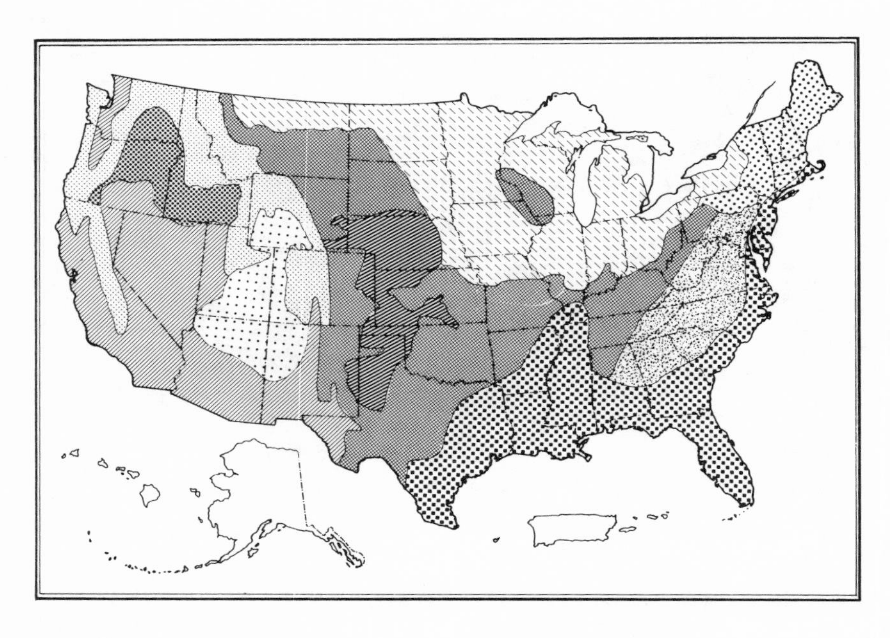

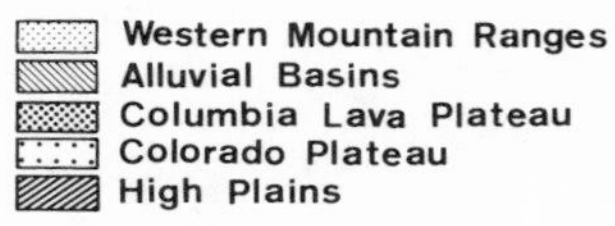

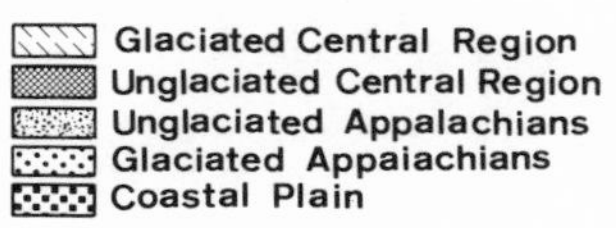

Figure 3–5. Water Resources Regions
Source: U.S. Water Resources Council, 1978.

Figure 3–6. Average Annual Precipitation
Source: U.S. EPA, 1977.

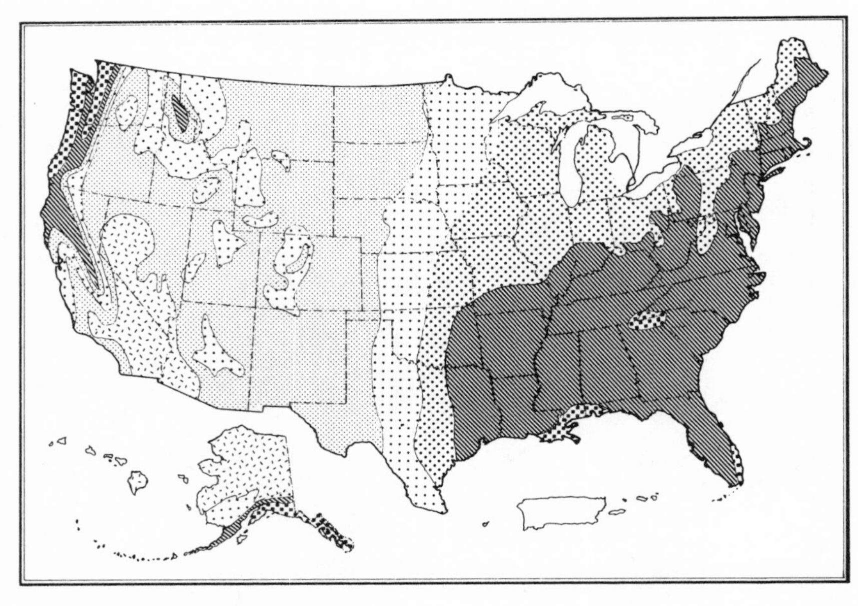

Average Annual Precipitation in inches

0–10	30–40
10–20	40–60
20–30	60 and over

Figure 3–7. Hardness of Groundwater

Geraghty et al., *Water Atlas of the United States*, 1973.

Used with permission of the Water Information Center, Inc., Syosset, New York

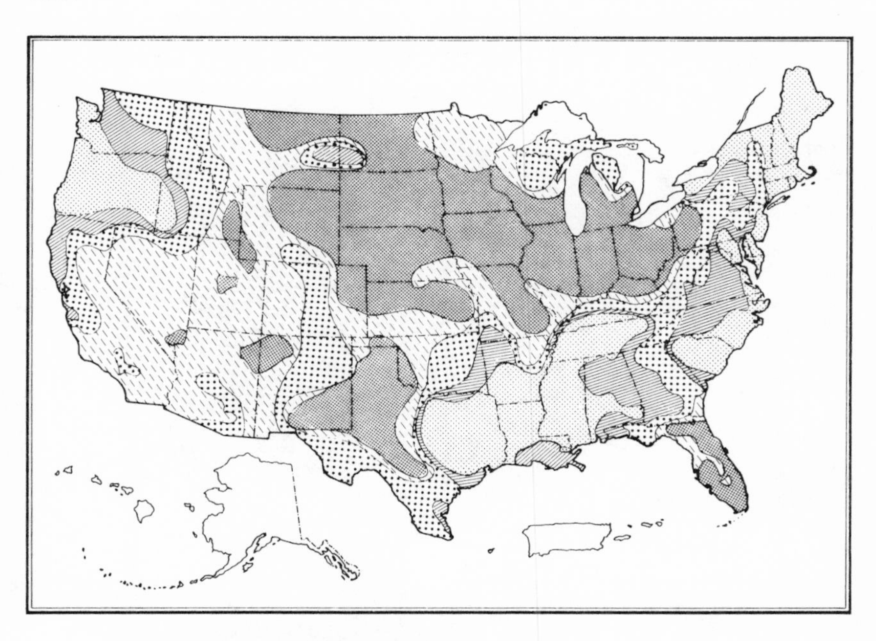

Hardness as $CaCo_3$ in parts per million

Pattern	Range
dotted (light)	< 80
diagonal lines	80 - 120
dotted grid	120 - 180
dashed lines	180 - 240
dense shading	> 240

Figure 3–8. Population Served by Source and Supply, 1970
Source: U.S. EPA, 1977.

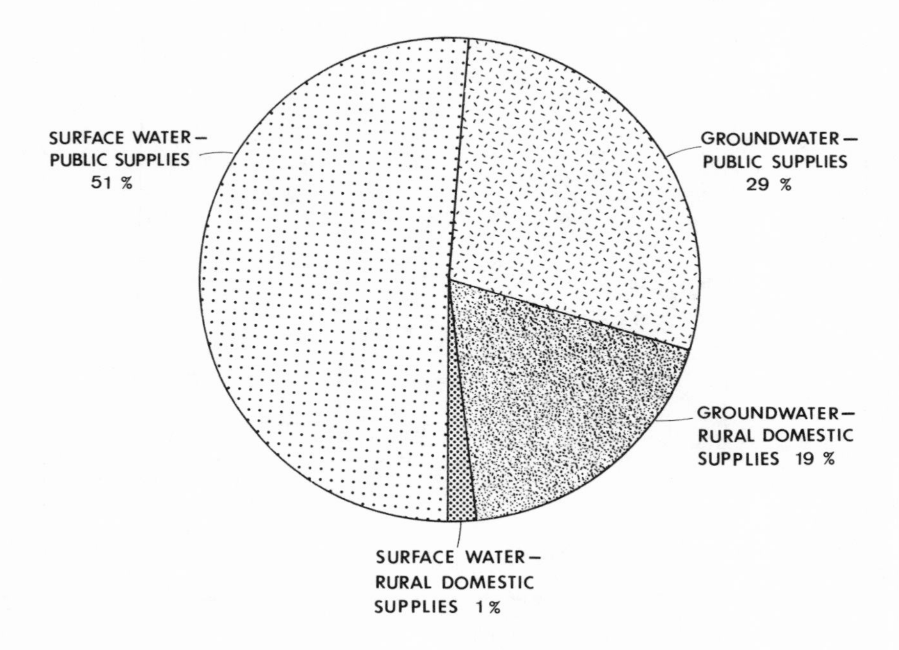

Figure 3–9. Groundwater as a Percentage of Total Water Use in 1975
Source: Lehr, 1981.

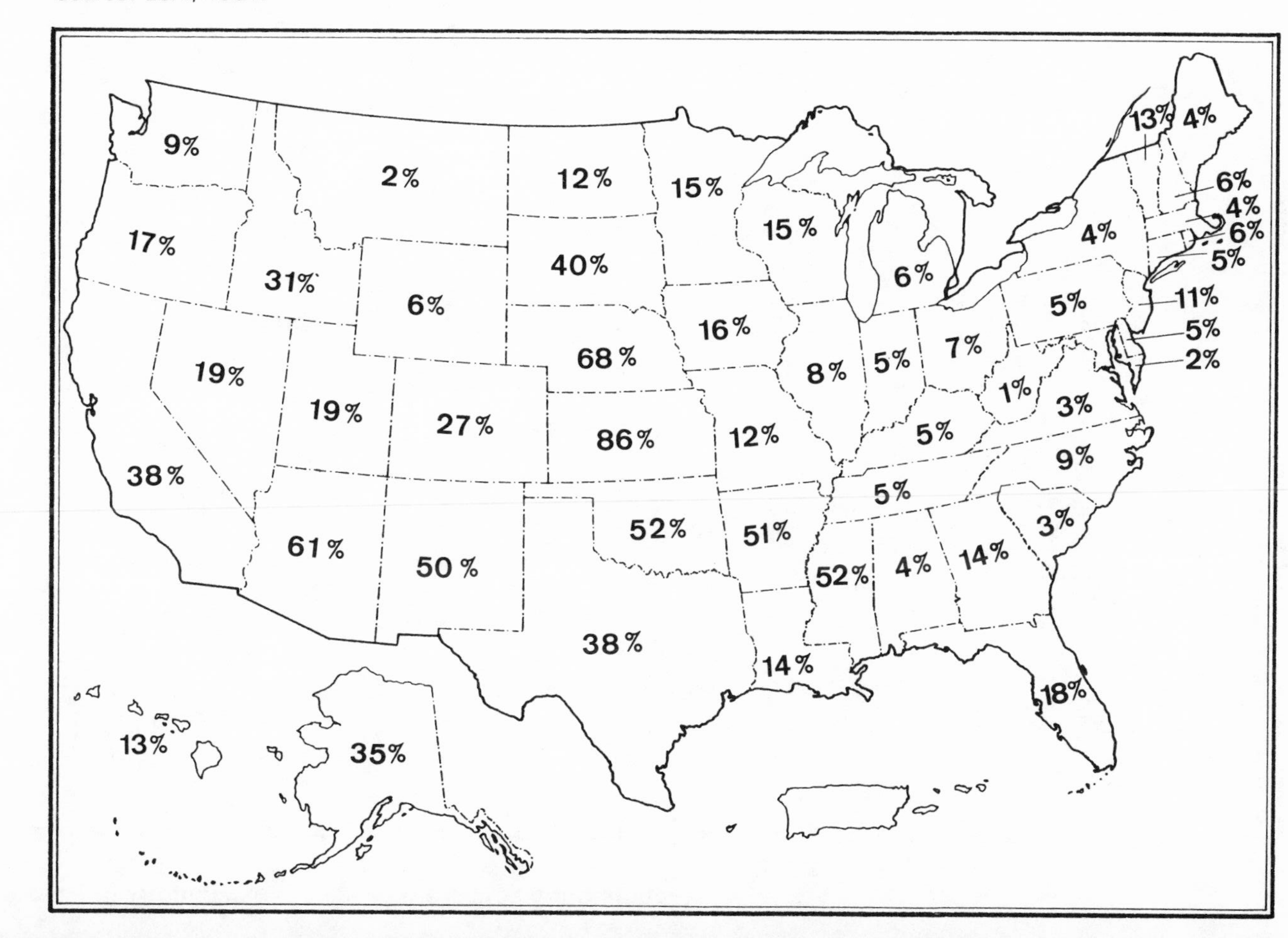

Figure 3–10. Groundwater Usage in the United States, mgd.
Source: U.S. EPA, 1977 and Lehr, 1981.

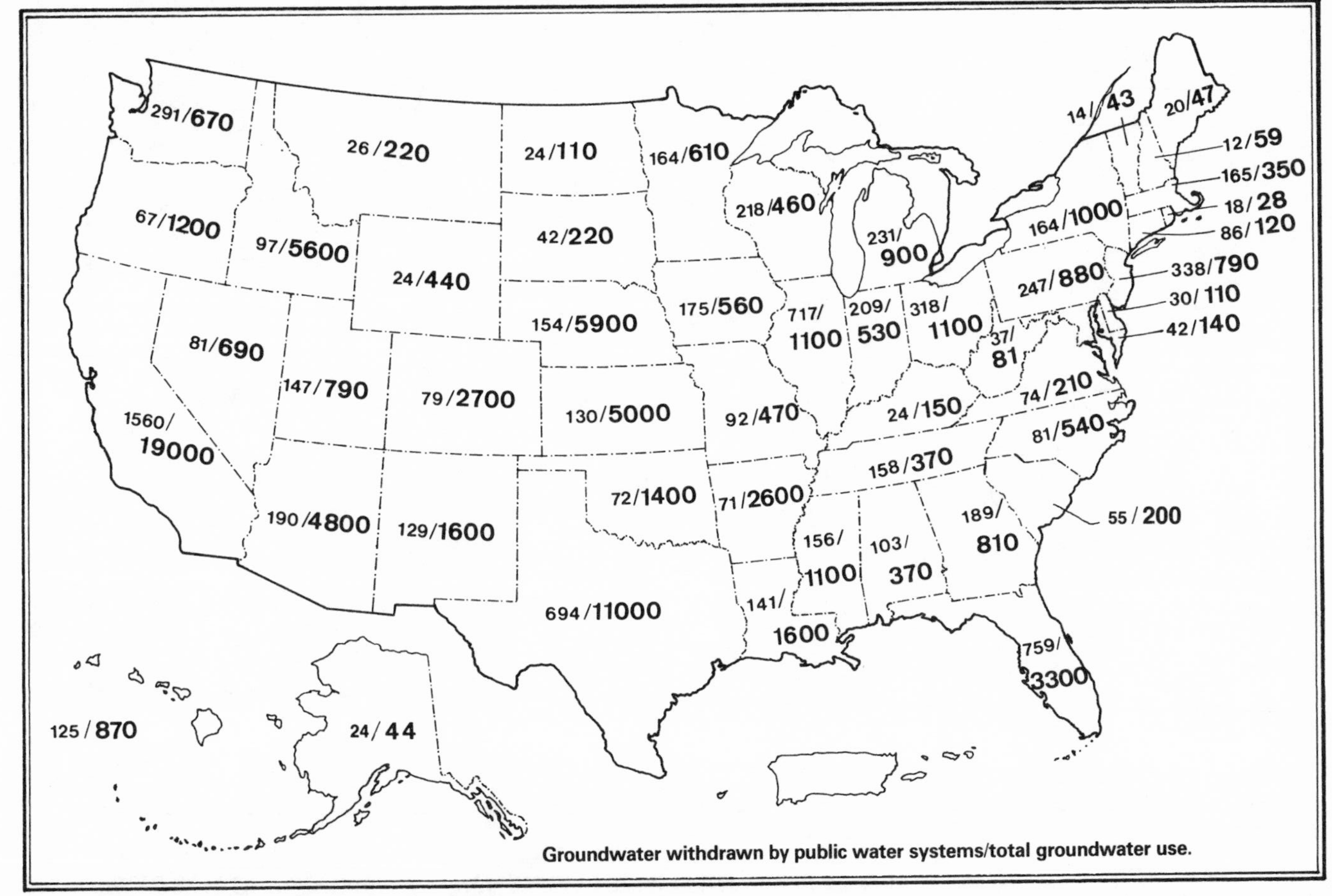

Figure 3–11. Graphs Showing Trends in Use of Water for Public Supplies, Rural Supplies, Irrigation, and Self-Supplied Industry, 1950–75
Source: Murray and Reeves, 1977.

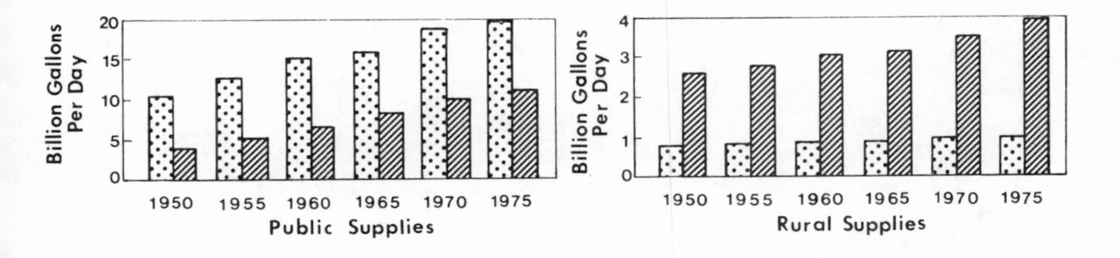

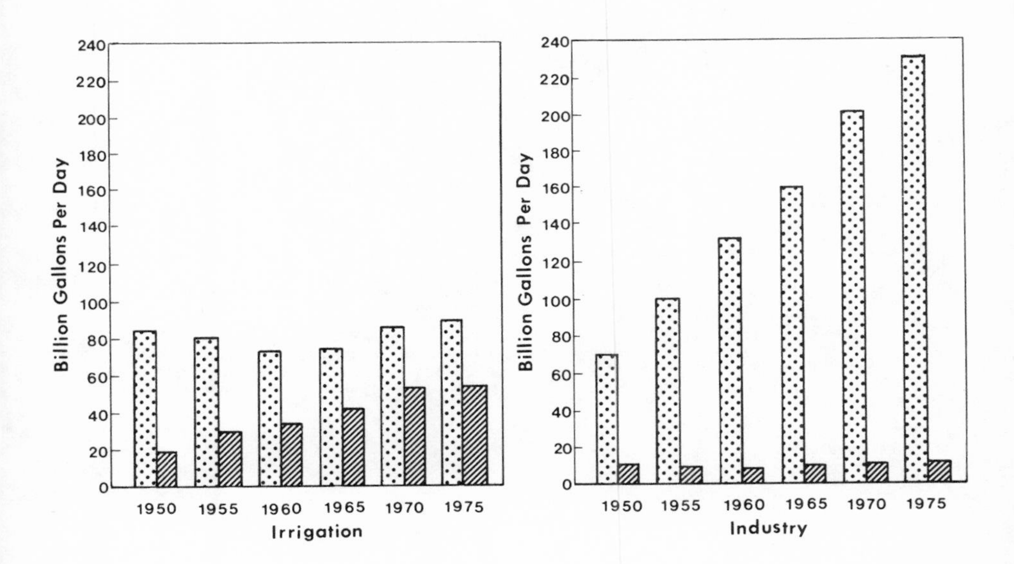

Surface water
Groundwater

Figure 3–12. Groundwater Overdraft and Related Problems
Source: U.S. Water Resources Council, 1978a.

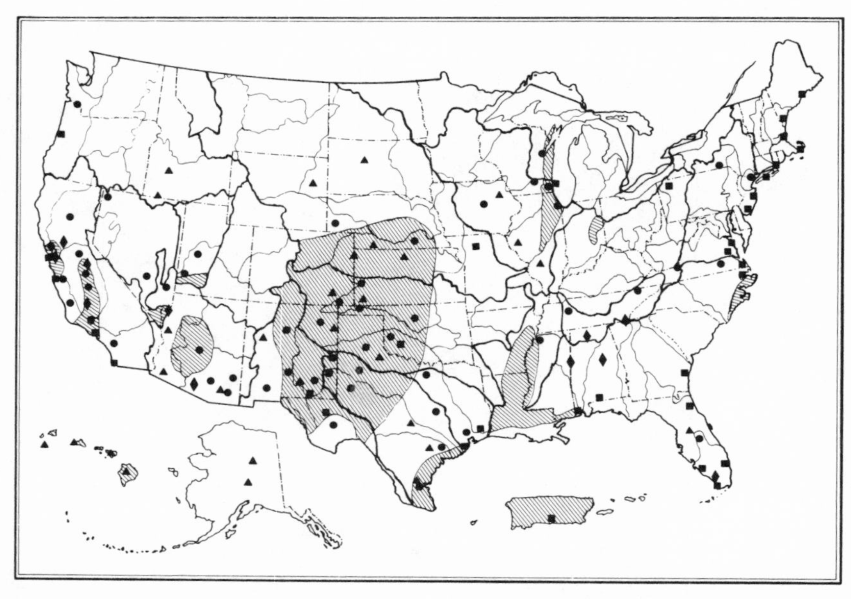

AREA PROBLEM

- Area in which significant groundwater overdraft is occurring
- Unshaded area may not be problem-free, but the problem was not considered major

BOUNDARIES

- Water resources region
- Subregion

SPECIFIC PROBLEMS (as identified by Federal and State/Regional study teams)

- ● Declining groundwater levels
- ▲ Diminished springflow and streamflow
- ♦ Formation of fissures and subsidence
- ■ Saline water intrusion into fresh-water aquifers

Figure 3–13. Ogallala Aquifer
Source: Banks, 1981.

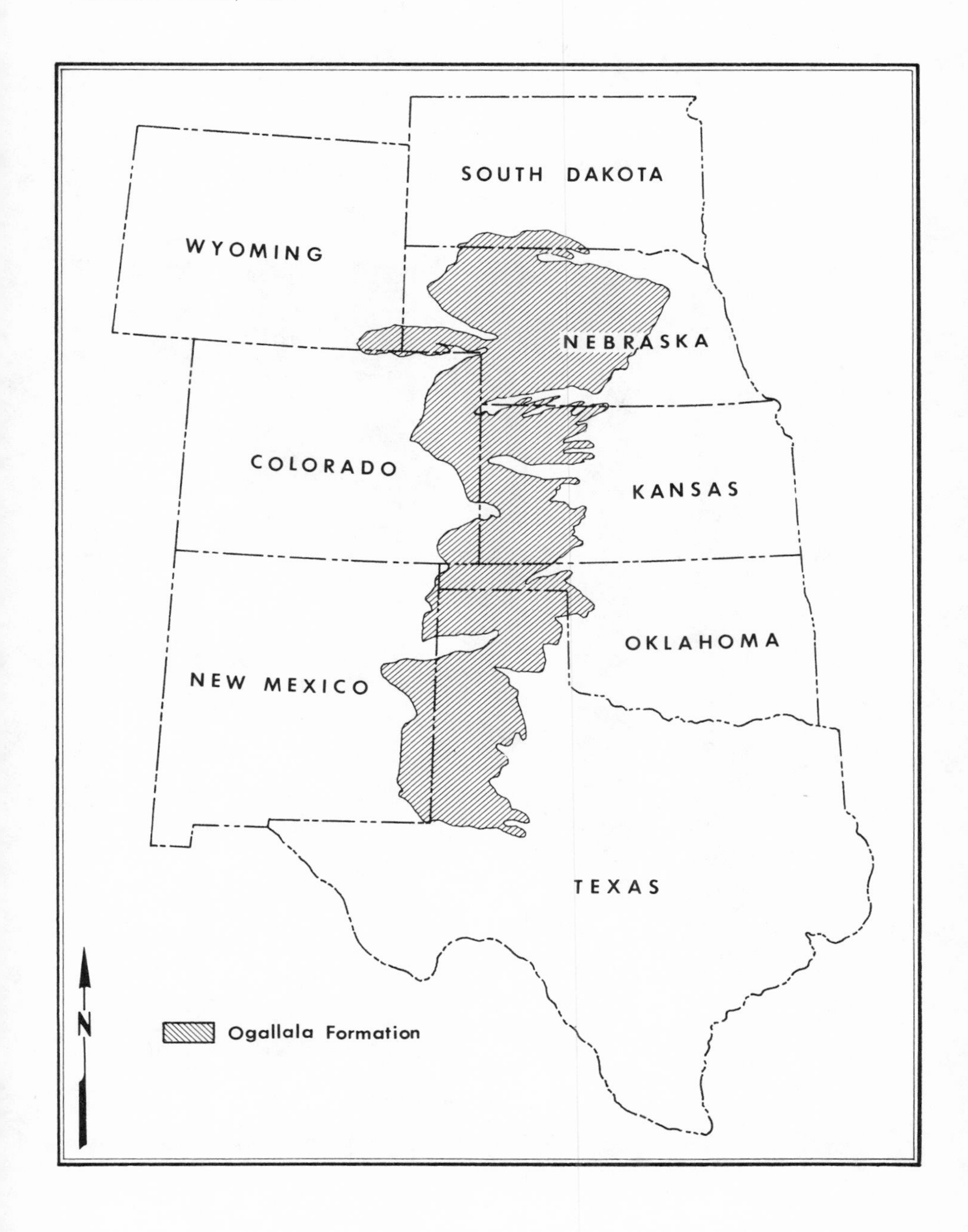

Figure 3–14. Projected Groundwater Depletion from the Ogallala Aquifer, 1977–2020
High Plains Associates: Camp Dresser & McKee Inc., Black & Veatch, and Arthur D. Little, Inc., "Six State High Plains—Ogallala Aquifer Regional Resources Study, March, 1982," Austin, Texas. Used with permission.

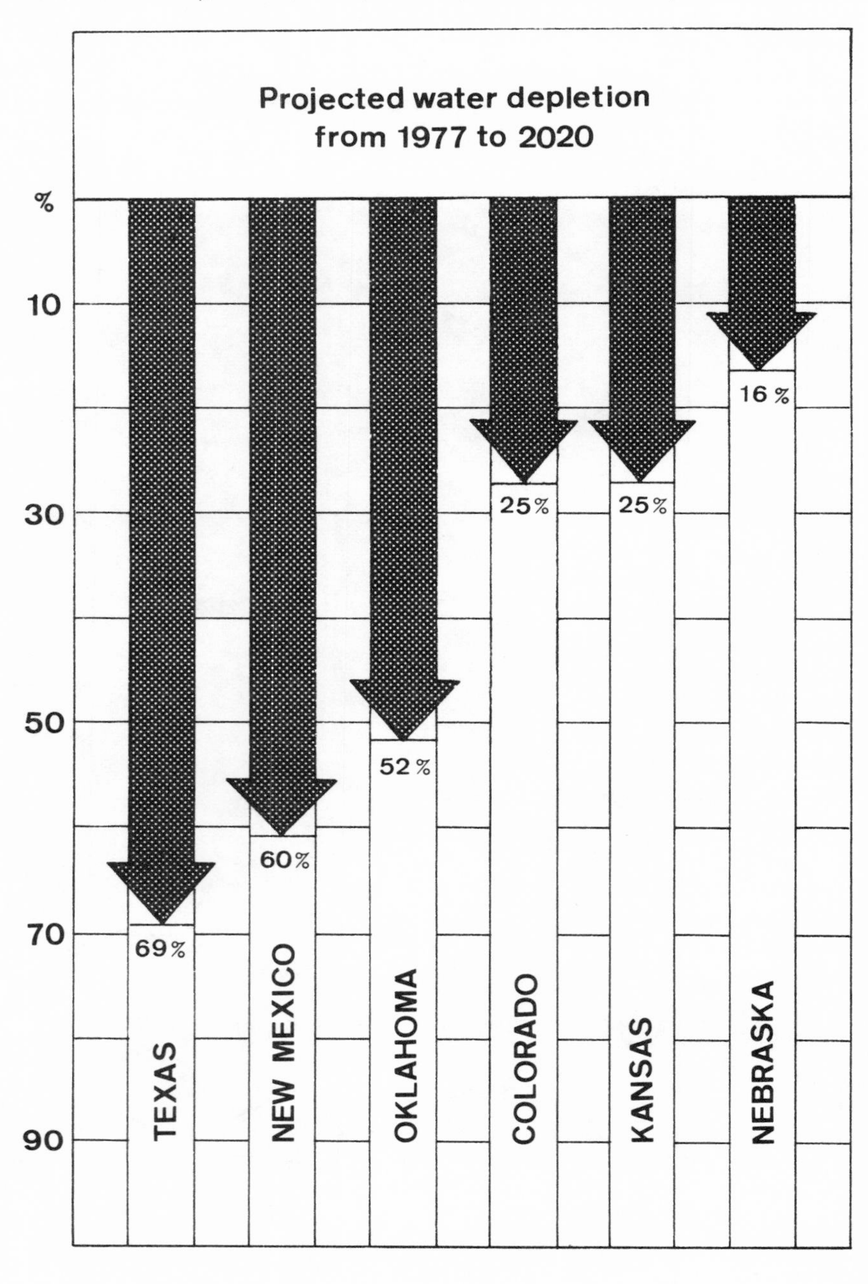

Four

Groundwater Contamination

- Groundwater contamination incidents have been reported from all parts of the United States.
- More contamination is likely to be discovered in the future, especially if a comprehensive national survey is undertaken.
- There are many and varied sources of contamination; natural and anthropogenic, point and non-point, planned and inadvertant.
- Types of contaminant found in groundwater range from simple inorganic ions, such as chloride, nitrate, and heavy metals, to complex synthetic organic chemicals.
- The types of reported contamination problems, and their sources, vary from one region of the country to another and are influenced by climate, population density, intensity of industrial and agricultural activities, and the hydrogeology of the region.

The mobility of our society, as well as the distribution of industry and agriculture, depends upon an available supply of clean water. Nevertheless, instances of groundwater contamination have been found in most sections of the country (Kerns, 1977; U.S. EPA, 1980a, c). For the purpose of this book groundwater contamination will be defined as the addition to water of elements, compounds, or pathogens that alter its composition. The pollution of groundwater occurs when the concentrations of the contaminants render the water unfit for present and future uses. A geographic distribution of groundwater pollution is shown in Figure 4–1 from the Second National Water Assessment.

One of the major difficulties with groundwater contamination is that it occurs underground, out of sight. The sources of pollution are not easily observed, nor is the effect of pollution often seen until irreversible damage has occurred. There are no obvious warning signals such as fish kills, discoloration, or stench that are often early indicators of surface-water pollution. Where contamination affects pumping wells, such indicators may occur, although many commonly found contaminants are both colorless and odorless, which makes detection difficult. They occur in concentrations that, if ingested, may cause long-term chronic illness, rather than acute poisoning, although many chemicals now found in groundwater have not been tested for their effects on human health. The tangible effects of groundwater contamination usually come to light long after the incident causing the contamination has occurred. The long time lag between occurrence and detection is a major problem.

Groundwater can be contaminated by a variety of compounds, both natural and man-made. Contamination due to man has occurred for centuries, but industrialization, urbanization, and increased population have greatly aggravated the problem in some areas. Miller (1981a) and Braids (1981a) summarized the mechanisms of contamination and attenuation. Freeze and Cherry (1979) give a detailed account of these mechanisms, as well as of the movement of a contaminant in an aquifer. Groundwater moves slowly along a definite route determined by the hydraulic-head relationships in the aquifer. Very little dilution takes place, and that which does occurs by hydrodynamic dispersion and diffusion. A contaminant usually enters the groundwater system from the surface of the land, percolating down through the aerated soil and non-saturated zone. The root zone may extend two or three feet into the soil as shown in Figure 4–2, and many reductive and oxidative biological processes take place in this zone that may degrade or biologically change the contaminants. Plant uptake can remove certain heavy metals; microbial fixation and other biological processes can also remove a fraction of the contaminants, the size of the fraction being dependent on the nature of the contaminant. For example, iron and manganese can be affected by microbial oxidation and reduction in the soils, depending upon conditions. In the deeper geologic material that consists mainly of humus and weathered rocks, there is a reduction in such biological processes. Attenuation may occur by surface adsorption as cations in the contaminant are attracted to the charge of the clay particles. Soils are said to have a cation-exchange capacity. Other contaminants may be removed by insoluble organic-matter complexing, giving rise to complexed humic acids. Microbial action may influence redox potentials and cause the release of inorganic ions during decomposition (Braids, 1981a). The susceptibility of different contaminants to differential attenuation varies. The attenuation of positively charged cations and bacteria is far greater in the unsaturated soil zone than in the aquifer, where very little attenuation takes place. Negatively charged anions may be attenuated in the refuse zone (Horizon A in Figure 4–2), in the unsaturated zone and, in some instances, for example, phosphate, actually in the aquifer. Adsorption of contaminants on soil particles is reversible. The flow of water resulting from well pumping will cause desorption from the particles, which will release the contaminants into the groundwater. Removal of all traces of the contaminant may require the passage of many volumes of water over a long period of time.

The movement of a contaminant in the aquifer is affected by its solubility in water, which for ionic compounds depends upon their crystalline structure and their ability to form complexes with other compounds. There are some compounds classified as having low solubility that will nevertheless yield solutions that may be toxic and offensive. An idea of a contaminant's movement in groundwater may be obtained from its relative solubility or, for an organic compound, its partitioning coefficient between water and octanol (Braids, 1981a). A high coefficient, indicating a high solubility in octanol, would indicate that the contaminant would not be very mobile in groundwater as it is not very soluble in water. In the case of gasoline spills, a difference of solubility exists between the aromatic and aliphatic chain, and cyclic compounds create more problems. The density of the contaminating compound also plays a role (Miller 1981a). Low-density fluids will tend to float on top of the water table, while higher density contaminants would sink to the bottom of the aquifer.

Once in the aquifer a contaminant, depending upon its density, will move with the groundwater at a rate varying between a fraction of an inch to a few feet per day, forming, under certain idealized conditions of homogeneity, an elliptical plume of contamination with well-defined boundaries (Figure 4–3). This dispersion process causes a spreading of the solute in a longitudinal flow direction and also transverse to the flow path (Freeze and Cherry, 1979); thus the plume will widen and thicken as it travels. Movement and dispersion of the contaminant are affected by the density of the contaminant, the geologic formation through which the contaminant passes, and the reactive nature of the contaminant. The more dense the contaminant, the greater will be its downward migration in a uniform geologic formation in relation to the movement in the flow direction of groundwater. Prediction of plume movement and behavior is made difficult as geologic formations are not often uniform. Layered beds and lenses may cause fingering or separation of the plume. Different geologic materials may retard or enhance the movement of the plume. The nature of the plume is further affected by the reactivity of the constituents of the contaminant. Concentrations can be altered by a variety of chemical and biochemical reactions including adsorption-desorption reactions, acid-base reactions, solution-precipitation reactions, oxidation-reduction reactions, ion pairing, and microbial cell synthesis (Freeze and Cherry, 1979). The plume continues to move with groundwater flow unless it is blocked and eventually reaches points of groundwater discharge such as streams, wetlands, lakes and tidal waters. Because very little dilution takes place, concentrations of contaminants are often much higher in groundwater than in surface water (Miller, 1981a).

52 Sources of Contamination

Sources of groundwater contamination may be divided into three main categories:

1. natural pollution
2. waste-disposal practices
3. non-disposal sources due to man's activities.

The degree of threat posed by these sources of contamination depends upon the concentration of the contaminant, its toxicity at that concentration, the volume of groundwater affected, the hydrogeological conditions, the uses made of the water from that particular aquifer, the population affected by such uses, and whether an alternate water supply is readily available.

Groundwater-pollution problems and their sources have been the object of numerous summaries. An incomplete, but illustrative listing includes Keeley, 1976; Fuhriman and Barton, 1971; Van der Leeden et al., 1975; Miller et al., 1977; Scalf et al., 1973; Miller et al., 1974; U.S. EPA, 1980a, 1978a and b; U.S. GAO, 1978, 1980; U.S. Water Resources Council, 1978a, b, and c. The only comprehensive survey of the sources of contamination due to waste-disposal practices was completed for the 1977 Report to Congress (U.S. EPA, 1977).

Changes in the Composition of Groundwater Due to Natural Processes

All groundwater contains some dissolved salts. Mineralization of groundwater due to leaching is a significant source of saline groundwater in the arid areas of the country and is greatest in the areas of lowest precipitation (Figure 3–6). In areas where the water table is near the surface, evaporation and transpiration further concentrate the salts in the remaining water. Natural leaching has been identified as the most significant source of contamination in the arid southwest and south-central area comprising Arizona, California, Nevada, Utah, Arkansas, Louisiana, New Mexico, Oklahoma, and Texas, exceeding in importance anthropogenic sources of groundwater contamination (Fuhriman and Barton, 1971; Scalf et al., 1973). Chlorides are the most widespread contaminant, but sulfates, nitrates, fluorides, and iron are also common natural contaminants, occurring in localized natural deposits and causing the groundwater in those areas to exceed EPA standards for those ions. Radioactivity from uranium causes problems in Texas, Oklahoma, and New Mexico (Scalf et al., 1973). Arsenic may be a local problem in the thermal springs of the northwest region (Van der Leeden et al., 1975). Other examples of such localized problems occur throughout the country. Water from fault zones or of volcanic origin can contain high levels of salts or toxic chemicals. As mentioned in the section characterizing groundwater, the aquitards which confine the aquifers are not totally impermeable. A change in the composition, thickness, or continuity of the aquiclude would permit leakage from one aquifer to another. The leaking of a saline aquifer into a potable aquifer causes deterioration of the quality of water in the potable aquifer. Although natural alteration of chemical composition cannot be prevented, the groundwater thus affected may be fit for some uses with or without pretreatment.

Contamination Due to Waste-Disposal Practices

The 1977 Report to Congress on Waste-Disposal Practices and Their Effects on Groundwater (U.S. EPA, 1977) provides an account of these various sources of contamination which, at the time the report was compiled, was the best estimate of the source and extent of groundwater contamination. The major sources described there and elsewhere will be summarized here. It should be noted that many of the numbers given in the 1977 Report are estimates and that definitive data on waste-disposal practices often were not, and are not, readily available. In addition, the recent implementation of the Resource Conservation and Recovery Act of 1976 would be expected to have affected waste-disposal practices, but such recent data or estimates are not available. Waste from natural and manufactured products is often stored on or beneath the land surface, in fact to bury wastes seems an ingrained cultural phenomenon (Braids, 1981a). Such burial of wastes is now regulated by the statutes described in Chapters 12 and 13. Sources of contamination are derived from all aspects of our lives, including industry, agriculture, and government. One estimate is that over 30,000 chemicals are now being used and distributed through the environment and that an additional 1,000 are being added each year (Weimar 1980). The Council on Environmental Quality (CEQ, 1981c) estimates that about 55,000 chemicals are now in commercial production and about 700 to 800 are added each year. For disposal, however, most are reacted with other chemicals, immobilized, or otherwise treated and burned. The ways waste-disposal practices may impinge upon the purity of groundwater are shown in Figure 4–4.

Individual Sewage-Disposal Systems

Thirty percent of the population of the United States, or seventeen million families, use septic tanks (Keeley, 1977; Scalf and Dunlap, 1977). They are regulated by various state and local requirements. Assuming a 50 gallon per-capita discharge per day, it is estimated that septic tanks handle 3.5 billion gallons of waste per day, excluding contributions from commercial and industrial sources (Keeley, 1977). They are the highest ranking source of wastewater which is discharged directly into groundwater. The three methods of on-site domestic waste disposal are septic tanks, with their subsurface disposal system, the less satisfactory cesspool, commonly found in older installations where there is a deep layer of permeable soil, and finally the pit privy. Properly constructed septic-tank systems and privies permit effective treatment of human waste. Cesspools work only in coarse or highly fissured materials and have a high potential for contamination. The septic tank has several important functions. It separates solid and liquid wastes, stores solids and floatable materials, and treats aerobically both stored solids and nonsettleable material (Canter et al., 1982). Soils which have slow percolation rates, shallow soils, soils over the permeable bedrock, and soils with permanent or periodic high water tables are not suitable for the use of conventional septic-tank systems.

The leach beds for septic tanks typically consist of 500 to 600 square feet of drain bed, 18 to 24 inches below the surface of the ground. The effluent is thus distributed over a wide area, and the shallow depth of the bed permits some evaporation and some uptake of contaminants by plants. Because it is near the surface, the drain field operates under aerobic conditions, with the result that good quality water reaches the groundwater. It is important that a zone of unsaturated soil occur between the leach bed and the water table so that the effluent from the septic tank is not discharged directly into the groundwater and hence into the aquifer.

The degree of potential risk posed by these systems depends in large measure upon their design and installation and upon the hydrogeology of the area. When sited correctly they operate efficiently, renovating wastewater and returning good-quality water to the watershed. When operating incorrectly, pollutants could enter the groundwater. This would be particularly troublesome in areas where drinking-water wells tap the same aquifer in the vicinity of the leach bed.

The advantages of septic tanks include the following (Canter et al., 1982):

- Minimal maintenance is required.
- The cost of individual or community septic tanks is less than the cost of central wastewater collection and treatment plants.
- It is a low-technology system.
- The energy requirements are low when compared with centralized wastewater-treatment facilities.

The disadvantages include:

- The potential for groundwater contamination when the tanks are incorrectly sited, either with regard to density or soil characteristics or both.
- The systems require proper maintenance. Failure to provide this results in system overflows or pollution of nearby wells.
- Septic-tank cleaners may severely contaminate groundwater.

The typical composition of domestic sewage is shown in Table 4–1. The constituents which pose the greatest threat to the quality of groundwater are nitrates, phosphates, heavy metals, inorganic ions (Na^+, Cl^-, SO_4, K^+, Ca, and Mg), and pathogenic organisms. In addition, toxic synthetic organic chemicals are becoming a more significant hazard due to the increased use over the last five years of cleaning products containing such chemicals. The geographic extent of the problem is shown in Figures 4–5. It is difficult to show by mapping how regions are affected by sources of contamination. All contamination incidents are indicated by points on a map, but not all the groundwater in the area indicated is contaminated. Since the most

Table 4–1. Characteristics of Domestic Sewage

Constituent	Concentration* Typical Domestic Sewage
Total Suspended Solids	200
Conductivity	700
Chemical Oxygen Demand (COD)	500
Biochemical Oxygen Demand (5-day BOD)	200
Total Organic Carbon (TOC)	200
pH	8.0
Alkalinity (as Ca CO_3)	100
Acidity (as Ca CO_3)	20
Total Phosphorus	10
Total Nitrogen	40
Chloride	50
Calcium	50
Magnesium	30
Iron	0.1
Manganese	0.1

*Mg/1 except for conductivity (micro-mhos/cm), and pH (pH units).

Source: U.S. EPA, 1973a.

important factors affecting the contamination of groundwater by sewage are the density of the individual units and the soil characteristics, the greatest potential for contamination is in the eastern region of the country. A septic-tank density of greater than 40 per square mile is a region of potential contamination to groundwater (U.S. EPA, 1977).

The Land Disposal of Solid Wastes

According to the Resource Conservation and Recovery Act of 1976, solid wastes are defined as any garbage, refuse, sludge from waste-treatment plants, water-supply treatment plants, or air-pollution control facilities, and other discarded materials, including solid, liquid, semi-solid, or contained gaseous materials resulting from industrial, commercial, mining, and agricultral operations, and from community activities. They do not include solid or dissolved material from domestic sewage, irrigation return-flows or industrial discharges which are point sources, or products and by-products of the nuclear industry. Solid wastes are considered hazardous when their quantity, concentration, or physical, chemical, or infectious characteristics cause, or significantly contribute to, an increase in mortality or an increase in serious illness, or pose present or potential hazards to human health or the environment when improperly treated, stored, transported, disposed of, or otherwise managed.

The solid portion of household wastes contains a high proportion of putrescible matter that is broken down by biodegradation, releasing carbon dioxide and methane gas (UNESCO, 1980). The leachate contains high concentrations of sulphate, chloride, and ammonia. Abundant quantities of cellulose from paper products may retard the movement of halogenated hydrocarbons by absorption. Solid commercial wastes have a similar composition to household wastes. They may, however, contain greater quantities of oils, phenols, and hydrocarbon solvents. Phenols are the most resistent to biological breakdown and may be leached. Domestic and commercial wastes are serious groundwater contaminants because of the numerous dissolved constituents and the high biological oxygen demand (BOD) of many of the constituents. Tables 4–2 and 4–3 shown how variable leachate composition may be depending upon the wastes deposited in a landfill. The tables do not include synthetic organic chemicals (see p.103–11).

The solid components of industrial wastes vary with the source of production (UNESCO 1980). Cyanide wastes are produced in metallurgical operations; sulfite wastes come from paper and pulp manufacturing; mercury is a waste product in the electrical industry; and the petrochemical industry produces several solid residues ranging from polychlorinated biphenyls (PCBs) to pesticides and herbicide residues to phenol-rich tar wastes.

Table 4–2. Summary of Leachate Characteristics Based on 20 Samples from Municipal Solid Wastes

Components	Median value (ppm)[a]	Ranges of all values (ppm)[a]
Alkalinity ($CaCO_3$)	3,050	0 –20,850
Biochemical Oxygen Demand (5 days)	5,700	81 –33,360
Calcium (Ca)	438	60 – 7,200
Chemical Oxygen Demand (COD)	8,100	40 –89,520
Copper (Cu)	0.5	0 – 9.9
Chloride (Cl)	700	4.7 – 2,500
Hardness ($CaCO_3$)	2,750	0 –22,800
Iron, Total (Fe)	94	0 – 2,820
Lead (Pb)	0.75	<0.1 – 2.0
Magnesium (Mg)	230	17 –15,600
Manganese (Mn)	0.22	0.06 – 125
Nitrogen (NH_4)	218	0 – 1,106
Potassium (K)	371	28 – 3,770
Sodium (Na)	767	0 – 7,700
Sulfate (SO_4)	47	1 – 1,558
Total Dissolved Solids (TDS)	8,955	584 –44,900
Total Suspended Solids (TSS)	220	10 –26,500
Total Phosphate (PO_4)	10.1	0 – 130
Zinc (Zn)	3.5	0 – 370
pH	5.8	3.7 – 8.5

a) Where applicable.

Source: U.S. EPA, 1977.

Other serious solid-waste contaminants can result from thermal-power generation from the burning of coal forming fly ash which, due to its high surface area volume ratio, is fairly reactive. Leaching may initially give rise to high concentrations of arsenic, chromium, selenium, and chloride. Another contaminating product resulting from the burning of coal is the sludge formed by the aqueous scrubbing of flue gases. Sludges typically contain cyanide and heavy metals and are of low pH unless neutralized by the addition of lime. It has been found that mixtures of sludge, fly ash, and lime rapidly set into a low-permeability solid which leaches less readily.

Contamination occurs when precipitation infiltrates and percolates through solid wastes at poorly designed land-disposal sites, forming a leachate of dissolved minerals, heavy metals, and organic chemicals (Tables 4–2 and 4–3). Leachate formed at disposal sites which are located in wetlands,

Table 4–3. Components of Industrial Waste

	Metals mining	Primary metals	Pharmaceuticals	Batteries	Inorganic chemicals	Organic chemicals	Pesticides	Explosives	Paints	Petroleum refining	Electroplating
Ammonium salts		X								X	
Antimony	X				X				X		
Arsenic	X	X	X		X					X	
Asbestos					X				X		
Barium									X		
Beryllium	X									X	
Biological waste			X								
Cadmium	X	X		X	X				X	X	X
Chlor. hydrocarbons					X	X			X		X
Chromium		X	X	X	X				X	X	X
Cobalt									X	X	
Copper	X	X	X	X					X	X	X
Cyanide		X			X					X	X
Ethanol waste, aqueous			X								
Explosives (TNT)								X			
Flammable solvents						X			X		
Fluoride		X			X						
Halogenated solvents			X								
Lead solvents	X	X		X	X				X	X	X
Magnesium	X										
Manganese		X									
Mercury		X	X	X	X				X	X	
Molybdenum										X	
Nickel		X		X	X					X	
Oil		X								X	X
Organics, misc.						X					
Pesticides (organo-phosphates)							X				
Phenol		X								X	X
Phosphorus					X						X
Radium	X										
Selenium	X	X	X							X	
Silver				X						X	X
Vanadium										X	
Zinc	X	X	X	X	X				X	X	X

Source: U.S. EPA, 1977.

flood plains, or where there is a shallow water table and which are constructed without natural or artificial barriers is likely to contaminate groundwater.

The types of land-disposal sites for solid wastes include dumps, landfills, sanitary landfills, and secured landfills—listed in increasing order of their ability to protect the environment from the adverse effects of their use. Landfill regulations promulgated under the Resource Conservation and Recovery Act (RCRA) were issued in July 1982. The Comprehensive Environmental Response, Compensation and Liability Act (CERCLA) requires remedial actions at inactive sites that pose a threat to the environment and to human health. In 1977 there were 18,500 land-disposal sites accepting municipal waste (U.S. EPA, 1977). A 1978 Waste Age survey identified 15,000 active municipal landfills, of which only 35% met state regulations (U.S. EPA, 1980d). There has been no national survey of privately owned industrial land-disposal sites although, as of November 1980, EPA has inventoried hazardous-waste facilities in connection with the interim status permits granted under the Resource Conservation and Recovery Act.

The amount of solid waste generated in this country has been estimated to be enough to cover 400 acres of land to a depth of 10 feet each day (Schneider, 1972). It is estimated that in 1973, 3.75 pounds of solid waste were generated per person per day, amounting to 144 million tons across the nation for the year (U.S. EPA, 1974). Resource recovery reduced this total by only 9 million tons per year.

Hazardous wastes may be disposed of in a landfill dump or impoundment (see below). Under CERCLA, EPA requires owners and operators of inactive sites, and under RCRA present owners and operators of active privately owned industrial sites, to report site locations and amounts and types of wastes stored. However, as there may be numerous old disused sites whose previous operators are no longer in business, the estimate of the quantity of hazardous wastes generated in this country may not be complete.

The Collection, Treatment, and Disposal of Municipal Wastewater

The collection, treatment, and disposal of municipal wastewater may be a problem in urban areas. Municipal wastewaters include domestic wastewater, storm water and its associated debris, and industrial wastes. They are collected by sanitary sewer systems and transported to treatment sites. Leaks may occur in the system due to age, disruption by tree roots, seismic activity, or poor construction. The lagoons and ponds used in wastewater treatment operate under anaerobic, aerobic, or facultative conditions. The total volume of sewage handled by these plants is approximately 15 bgd (U.S. EPA, 1977). Lagoons are often constructed without adequate seals, thus promoting leakage under certain geologic conditions and posing a threat to groundwater. The third possible route of groundwater contamination is by the land disposal of treated wastewater, which could alter the chemical constituents of the natural groundwater. Land-disposal methods include agricultural irrigation, rapid infiltration ponds, overland runoff, and discharge into dry stream beds and ditches. Methods involving spraying onto land are not suitable for use in freezing winter months. Figure 4–6 shows the geographic distribution of various densities of population that are served by municipal sewage-treatment facilities that utilize the land disposal of effluent.

Industrial and Other Wastewater Impoundments

Under the Safe Drinking Water Act of 1974, EPA undertook a national survey of surface impoundments, which was carried out from 1976 to 1978, and the interim report was published in 1978 (U.S. EPA, 1978b). This report defines surface impoundments as depressions in the land (pits, ponds, lagoons, and pools) containing liquid, semi-solid, and solid wastes. It was estimated that there were nearly 133,000 sites and that of these, 75% were for industrial, 15% for agricultural, and 10% for municipal, institutional, or private use. In its final report, completed in 1980 but as yet unreleased, EPA stated that the number of sites that had been located in the United States totalled approximately 80,000 and contained over 180,000 impoundments. Of these, 31,000 have been assessed as potentially hazardous (Inside EPA, 1980). Of the sites located, 31% are oil and gas brine-pits, 23% are municipal sites, 18% are agricultural, 14% industrial, and 9% mining sites. Of the total number, about 4,500 were abandoned sites. Table 4–4 shows EPA's assessment of these sites. At the time of the survey it was estimated that 70% of the industrial sites were unlined, less than

Table 4–4. EPA Surface-Impoundment Assessment: Identifying Potential Hazards

	Located Sites	Assessed Sites	Located Impoundments
Industrial	11,359 (14%)	8,583 (27%)	26,534 (15%)
Municipal	18,559 (23%)	10,292 (33%)	35,163 (20%)
Agricultural	14,294 (18%)	6,471 (21%)	18,600 (10%)
Mining	6,860* (9%)	1,262 (4%)	23,876 (13%)
Oil & gas brine pits	24,857* (31%)	3,407 (11%)	65,964 (37%)
Abandoned sites	2,378 (3%)	677 (2%)	4,480 (2%)
Other	1,295 (2%)	483 (2%)	5,593 (3%)
TOTAL	79,602	31,175	180,210

*Site numbers for the mining and oil & gas brine pit sites are not necessarily related to actual ownership and should not be referred to as the actual number of legal sites. The number of located impoundments would be a closer approximation for these two categories.

Source: *Inside EPA* (9 May 1980). Reprinted by permission of Inside Washington Publishers.

10% had groundwater monitoring, and 30% were both unlined and located on permeable ground overlying usable aquifers. Of this 30%, one-third are within one mile of a water-supply well (Inside EPA, 1980). The new regulations under RCRA may have affected the validity of these estimates, but no recent figures are available. New Mexico was estimated to have the largest number of sites with 16,176, and Rhode Island the fewest with 30. Table 4–5 shows the total estimated number of impoundment sites by state; the number of sites actually located has not been released. The character of the wastes in these sites varies from harmless to very toxic. The impoundments are used for the treatment, storage, or disposal of wastes, are natural or man-made, and may or may not be lined. Discharging impoundments are designed to discharge regularly into bays, oceans, lakes, or streams. The liquid in non-discharging impoundments is lost by evaporation or by seepage into the soil. The types of wastes received by these sites range from sewage wastes, industrial wastes—including those from air scrubbers, cooling tower blow-down, and ash residues—and oil- and gas-extraction wastes to animal-feedlot and other agricultural wastes. Of these, the largest users of surface impoundments are the oil and gas industries (U.S. EPA, 1978a and b; Inside EPA, 1980). Evaporation ponds were used extensively in the South for oil-brine disposal. Evaporation ponds usually lose more fluid by infiltration than by evaporation, especially in the more humid regions of the country (Miller, 1981a, Pettyjohn, 1972). EPA promulgated regulations for hazardous-waste surface impoundments in July 1982. In addition, state regulations exist in most oil-producing states. The chemical character of the waste varies enormously and may include suspended and dissolved solids, pathogenic organisms, oil and grease, detergents, heavy metals, and toxic organic chemicals. It may have a high biological oxygen demand (BOD), chemical oxygen demand (COD), and total organic carbon (TOC). The pH, acidity, or alkalinity each vary. Not all surface impoundments contain hazardous wastes, some are used as holding ponds prior to the treatment of the fluids. Because the chemical character of the wastes varies, only a minimal number of impoundments would hold each of the contaminants listed. The type of groundwater contamination known to occur as a result of leaking impoundments reflects the nature of the fluids in the impoundments. Dissolved materials, both inorganic and organic, move into groundwater by direct seepage, while solids may be leached by precipitation or waste fluids. As with all sources of contamination, the sorptive capacity and low permeability of some soils may slow or impede the movement of some of the contaminants.

Land Spreading of Sludge

When the wastewater from municipal and industrial wastes is treated (see above), a residue of sludge remains. In 1977 less than 1% of the

Table 4–5. Estimate of Numbers of Impoundment Sites for All Categories, by States

State	No.
Alabama	1,590
Alaska	130
Arizona	332
Arkansas	953
California	3,721
Colorado	5,237
Connecticut	96
Delaware	63
Florida	2,035
Georgia	1,438
Hawaii	78
Idaho	584
Illinois	3,667
Indiana	2,538
Iowa	1,466
Kansas	6,086
Kentucky	2,141
Louisiana	9,997
Maine	237
Maryland	523
Massachusetts	73
Michigan	3,229
Minnesota	1,540
Mississippi	1,676
Missouri	2,757
Montana	1,363
Nebraska	2,329
Nevada	261
New Hampshire	105
New Jersey	277
New Mexico	16,176
New York	960
North Carolina	1,038
North Dakota	2,784
Ohio	13,196
Oklahoma	2,006

Oregon	757
Pennsylvania	15,341
Rhode Island	30
South Carolina	911
South Dakota	650
Tennessee	776
Texas	8,436
Utah	669
Vermont	329
Virginia	2,116
Washington	1,045
West Virginia	2,803
Wisconsin	985
Wyoming	5,179
	132,709

Source: U.S. EPA, 1978a and b.

municipal sludge-disposal facilities were monitored for possible groundwater contamination and even fewer industrial sites were (U.S. EPA, 1977). As of 19 November 1981 any facility that disposes of sludge that is considered hazardous on land must have a ground-water-monitoring system in place under Resource Conservation and Recovery Act regulations. The purpose of land treatments is to biodegrade the organics and to immobilize the inorganics. The potential for contamination exists, however, since the chemical constituents and viruses in sludge may be leached by precipitation after the sludge is spread on the land. Sludge from manufacturing industries may contain either useful agricultural chemicals or toxic compounds, and it varies from degradable to very refractory. Sludge is stabilized and may be dewatered before land application. The higher the proportion of clay and organic colloids in the soil, the greater the capacity for the heavy-metal ions present in sludge to be immobilized. The main hazardous constituents of the sludges include heavy metals and organic chemicals, such as dyes, inks, oils, pesticides, detergents, organic solvents, and polynuclear aromatic hydrocarbons (PAHs), although organic chemicals are typically trace contaminants. Sludges from the municipal treatment of wastewater or the biotreatment of industrial wastewater include biological components such as bacteria, viruses, fungi, algae, protozoans, rotifers, and other parasites such as worms and flukes. The constituents that may be found in various types of industrial wastes are enumerated in the 1977 Report to Congress (U.S. EPA, 1977).

Land farming of sludge has been used for nearly thirty years by the petroleum industry. The Solid Waste Management Committee of the American Petroleum Institute concludes from its research on this method of disposing of oil sludge, that if the area farmed is carefully matched to the amount of organic material that must be degraded, the type of land farming practiced, and the degradation rate of the sludge, then the underlying soil and groundwater will not be significantly contaminated (Knowlton and Rucker, 1979).

64

Brine Disposal Associated with the Petroleum Industry

Groundwater contamination associated with oil production has been documented in 17 states (U.S. EPA, 1977). Brief mention of the disposal of brines by the use of surface impoundments was made above. Oil production is usually accompanied by the production of saline wastewater in amounts that vary with production procedures. One estimate is that an old well may produce 100 barrels of brine for each barrel of oil (U.S. EPA, 1977). Others estimate that the production of 8 million barrels of crude oil produces 30 million barrels of saltwater and that the ratio of brine to crude oil recovered is 10:1 (Keeley, 1977). In 1969 Oklahoma, Texas, Louisiana, Arkansas, and New Mexico accounted for 70% of the total American production of crude oil from their 300,000 wells (Scalf et al., 1973).

In the early days of oil and gas production the brine was disposed of in unlined pits. The extensive use of such "evaporation" pits that leaked their contents has caused groundwater contamination in the oil-producing regions (Scalf et al., 1973; Fuhriman and Barton, 1971; U.S. EPA, 1977). Use of unlined pits has been completely eliminated in some states and partially so in others. For example, unlined pits were banned in Texas in 1969. Other states permit the use of small pits in remote areas if they pose no threat to groundwater.

Present practices for brine disposal include injection of the brine into deep underground formations that are deemed unsuitable for other purposes and reinjection of brines into oil-producing formations to enhance oil recovery. These injection practices, if not properly controlled, pose a potential threat to groundwater.

Past methods of production such as well drilling, completion, and abandonment practices also were not so strictly controlled as they are now. Some wells were improperly equipped, and abandoned wells were improperly plugged, thereby providing a potential for groundwater contamination. In 1973 alone, 10,000 miles of dry, non-producing wells were drilled. Between 1965 and 1973 there were 90,000 fewer producing oil wells (API, 1975). The need to protect groundwater was recognized, however, and state oil and gas regulatory agencies now have regulations concerning brine injection, well completion, and plugging practices. The Interstate Oil Commission sponsored a study in 1978 which concluded that in Texas, Arkansas, Louisiana, New Mexico, and Oklahoma reinjection of brines had resulted in fewer instances of groundwater contamination than had the use of evaporation pits. It therefore believes that the practice does not pose a major threat to the groundwater supplies.

Most oil-field brines are corrosive, but the corrosion rate of old and new well casings is unpredictable, therefore frequent monitoring and surveillance is carried out. Although brine is the main threat to the quality of groundwater, minor threats are also posed by the oil and gas themselves, by drilling fluids, chemicals used in treating wells, corrosion inhibitors, and other chemicals (U.S. EPA, 1977). Oil drilling may entail drilling through freshwater aquifers, thus raising the potential for contamination.

The Disposal of Mine Wastes

Mining creates conditions and products conducive to groundwater contamination. The recharge and movement of groundwater may be affected by the mining process. Domestic mining for minerals other than organic fuels was a $10-billion-dollar industry in 1974 (U.S. EPA, 1977). Coal has enjoyed a comeback as an energy source due to the self-sufficiency in the energy program, and it is estimated that between one-third to one-half of the world's total reserves is found in the United States. Figure 4–7 shows the distribution of coal fields in the conterminous United States. Techniques of surface and underground mining pose different threats to groundwater quality, although the threat from waste disposal from the two is similar. Although such mining changes the environment, good reclamation may stabilize some of these changes without causing serious damage to the groundwater (Thompson, 1977). Sand, clay, gravel, and stone quarrying are not considered a serious threat to groundwater quality (U.S. Congressional Research Service, 1980). Threats from the remaining categories of mines include those posed by leachate from tailings piles and drainage from strip, surface, and underground mines (van der Leeden et al., 1975). Dewatering of mines, involving a regional lowering of the water table, may have three results: a decrease in the amount of groundwater supplied, a lowering of the water level below the intakes of productive wells, and the oxidation of exposed minerals (Miller et al., 1974). Coal is often found in conjunction with iron pyrites (FeS_2) and other sulfides, and the oxidation of these sulfides and the presence of percolating waters produce sulfuric acid and an increase in Fe^{++} and $SO_4=$, leading to acidic groundwater, a serious problem in the coal-mining areas of Pennsylvania and Appalachia. It is very costly either to neutralize acid mine-drainage or to backfill abandoned mines in order to prevent the problem. Sealing the mines with air- or with water-tight seals has not proved very successful (Miller et al., 1974). A recent report by the National Academy of Sciences summarizes these and other effects that coal mining may have on groundwater quality (NAS, 1981b).

Metal mining produces drainage waters that have lower concentrations of iron and sulfate than do colliery waters, but they have higher concentrations of dissolved heavy metals due to the lower pH caused by the oxidation of metal sulfides. Wastewater from metal mining may also contain organic flocculants from the on-site processes of screening and dressing the ores. The wastes from such operations, which can be both toxic and radioactive, may contaminate groundwater. The tailings ponds used in the waste-disposal operations of mines may contribute contaminated leachate.

The waste products of quarrying for stone, lime, gypsum, and the like are generally inert, and their only contributions to the water that percolates through them is the possibility of an occasional increase in suspended-solids if crushed material is present. Quarrying does, however, increase the potential for local groundwater contamination in other ways. The removal of soil reduces the possibility of an attenuation of any spills or leakages that may occur in the area and increases the potential for contamination, especially if the bedrock is fractured.

Because of the serious nature of surface-water contamination by mining activities, more attention has been given to that than to groundwater contamination, although aquifers in regions with a long history of mining have been written off as sources of water supply (U.S. EPA, 1977). Figure 4–8 shows the states in which significant volumes of wastewater are discharged from mining and ore-processing operations excluding coal and petroleum, and Figure 4–9 shows similar data for coal mining and processing for 1972. Since then coal mining on a large scale has been initiated in the West, particularly in North Dakota, Wyoming, and Montana. Mining of metal and non-metal minerals other than coal produced over 2.5 billion tons of ore and nearly 1.5 billion tons of waste rock in 1972 (U.S. EPA, 1977). The metal mines pose the most serious threat to groundwater, particularly uranium and copper mines, which produce waste containing dissolved toxic materials (e.g., arsenic, sulfuric acid, copper, selenium, and molybdenum), as well as radioactive materials.

Deep-Well Disposal of Liquid Wastes

The injection of a variety of liquid wastes into deep wells to avoid having them contaminate the biosphere was becoming a widely adopted waste-disposal practice in the late 1970s (Freeze and Cherry, 1979) mainly because there were stringent regulations governing disposal into surface waters. Such wells are less widely accepted now in certain states (J. W. Keeley, Kerr Environmental Research Laboratory, personal communication). Waste injection wells in 24 states increased from 30 in 1964 to 280 in 1973 (Warner and Orcutt, 1973), the latter figure probably representing a peak (J. W. Keeley, Kerr Environmental Research Laboratory, personal communication). Because of the hazardous nature of the injected fluid—often radioactive, toxic chemical, petrochemical, and pharmaceutical wastes that are difficult to treat—deep-well disposal may pose a great threat if improperly practiced. It was thought likely to be well controlled, however, as the risks have been well publicized (Lehr, 1975; U.S. EPA, 1977). The Underground Injection Control Program of the Safe Drinking Water Act, which prohibits direct injection into drinking-water aquifers, and regulations recently issued under the Resource Conservation and Recovery Act provide such controls. All injection wells are in the depth range of 660 to 13,200 feet, most being between 990 to 6600 feet. Injection zones are usually located in sandstone, basalt, and carbonate rocks. Injection occurs under pressure and injection rates vary from 500 to 370 gallons per minute. Injection causes hydrodynamic changes in the aquifer including the formation of a mound in the potentiometric surface extending in the direction of the regional flow in the aquifer (Freeze and Cherry, 1979). This is essentially the reverse of what happens when a well is pumped in a confined aquifer. Until 1976 documented cases of disposal-system failure were rare, but they may increase if underground injection becomes more common and occurs over longer periods of time. Underground injection in the vicinity of old unplugged wells, the locations of which are often not known, may lead to the upward leakage of the wastes (Van Everdingen and Freeze, 1971). These authors estimate that there may be more than one million unplugged, unlocated wells in North America which were used for purposes other than disposal. Another hazard associated with the practice of waste injection but only indirectly linked to groundwater contamination is the triggering of earthquakes due to increased pore-water pressures along fault lines (Freeze and Cherry, 1979). The most publicized occurrence, at the Rocky Mountain Arsenal in Colorado, occurred after injection of chemical-warfare waste, using a 12,000-foot well, into fractured pre-Cambrian rocks. The earthquakes thus caused stopped when injection ceased (Ballentine et al., 1972; van der Leeden et al., 1975). Other problems may arise if an injection well becomes clogged with injected suspended solids, corrosion products, precipitation occurring between injection fluid and connate water in the aquifer, insufficient treatment of injected water leading to bacterial clogging, and the swelling of the mineral constituents of the geologic formation (Lehr, 1975). The Report to Congress (U.S. EPA, 1977) stated the injection wells can cause groundwater contamination through the following mechanisms:

- direct injection into drinking-water aquifers
- leakage into potable aquifers due to well-construction faults or failure
- leakage through confining beds by hydraulic fracturing or insufficient thickness
- displacement of saline water into potable aquifer
- migration to potable water zone of the same aquifer

The Report concluded, however, that properly constructed, sited, and monitored waste injection-wells can be operated with little danger of groundwater contamination, but that only one half of the states had regulations controlling the construction and operation of injection-well systems in 1977. Within the last five years there has been an accelerated control of underground injection that has significantly changed the numbers of states having such controls.

The Disposal of Wastes from Animal Feedlots

Groundwater contamination by the manure from high-density animal-feeding operations is a relatively new phenomenon. In addition to the threat to groundwater from the vast quantities of manure thus generated, there is also a threat from the food additives, such as hormones and antibiotics, which it may contain (Keeley, 1977). As recently as 1977 Miller et al. claimed that feedlots pose no danger of groundwater contamination in the southeastern states due to the soil's ability to denitrify the wastes. Feedlots for poultry and hog farms in Arizona, California, Nevada, and Utah were thought to lead to water-quality problems from bacteria, viruses, nitrate concentrations and with general color, taste, and odor (Fuhriman and Barton, 1971). The main beef-raising areas, however, are the Corn Belt and the High Plains. Until the 1950s and '60s, while beef was raised on pasture, the wastes were easily assimilated naturally and posed no problem. The need for more meat at reasonable cost led to the establishment of feedlots, with capacities of between 1,000 and 50,000 head of cattle. During the 4 to 5 months each animal spends in the lot, it produces 0.5 tons of manure (dry weight). This can lead to high nitrate concentrations in the groundwater under some conditions. Where the feedlots are located in areas with a deep water table, the risk of contamination is minimized (Scalf et al., 1973). The distribution of cattle-feeding operations in the United States is shown in Figure 4–10. The main poultry-rearing region is the South, in Delaware, Maryland, Virginia, Arkansas, Georgia, and Mississippi, for hogs it is the Midwest, and for sheep the Far West. Of the potential contaminants in manure, nitrate is the most important as it is soluble in water and its concentration is unchanged by passage through the soil. The other contaminants from manure—bacteria and phosphate—are highly attenuated by the soil and pose no significant threat. Feedlot management, including stocking rate, density, and manure removal, plays an important role. Heavy manure accumulations may produce an impermeable mat, which in turn produces anaerobic conditions which favor denitrification. Thus nitrate is volatilized, and also little infiltration takes place, minimizing the nitrate-contamination potential (U.S. EPA, 1977). Concentrated animal-feeding operations are regulated by the Federal Water Pollution Control Act Amendments of 1972 and may require a permit as a point source under the National Pollutant Discharge Elimination System (NPDES).

Groundwater Contamination from Radioactive Sources

The contamination of groundwater from radionuclides may occur from contact with naturally occurring radioactive minerals such as uranium. Radioactive wastes from hospitals, utilities, and defense operations may cause contamination from spills, accidental discharge of low-level radioactive wastewater, and storage-basin leaks.

Groundwater contamination by high-level radionuclides has been reported in a few instances, largely due to the improper storage of wastes. In the early 1950s, one hundred gallons of high-level radioactive wastes leaked from a tank at the Savannah River defense storage site, contaminating some groundwater (Hileman, 1982). In 1973 a 115,000-gallon leak of high-level radioactive wastes occurred at the Hanford Nuclear Reservation (Lindorff and Cartwright, 1977). No groundwater contamination resulted, although the soil beneath the site remains radioactive. Another extensive leak of high-level radioactive wastes occurred in 1956, spilling 450,000 gallons of high-level radioactive wastes in the ground at Hanford, Washington, but with no serious contamination resulting.

Contamination from low-level radioactive wastes is less well documented. The uranium mining and milling industry is a major producer of low-level radioactive wastes and, until 1978 when the Uranium Mine Tailings Radiation Control Act was passed, uranium-tailings piles were left uncovered and unprotected (Hileman, 1982). The impact of mining and milling on surface and ground-water is only beginning to be assessed by extensive monitoring. New Mexico, for example, had installed 15 observation wells by 1981 and has plans for 35 more (Gallaher et al., 1981).

Ways to avoid the leaks which contaminate groundwater are being actively researched. Many sites and various methods of storage are being investigated. For low-level radioactive-waste disposal, it is generally agreed that the technology exists for siting and safe packaging, handling, transport, and isolation of the wastes (Hileman, 1982). Currently, low-level radioactive wastes are concentrated at a few commercial and defense sites across the country and are well monitored. By 1986, under the National Low-Level Radiation Waste Policy Act of 1980, each state will be responsible for the disposal of all low-level radioactive wastes generated by commercial operations within its borders (D. Siefken, Nuclear Regulatory Commission, personal communication). The ultimate disposal for high-level radioactive wastes is actively being sought. These wastes are presently in temporary storage facilities at utility and defense sites.

There is a great deal of research to determine the best method for isolating large concentrations of highly radioactive wastes from the biosphere. The wastes will be solidified and may be buried in geologically stable formations that can withstand high heat for at least 10,000 years (Hileman, 1982). It was recently decided that borosilicate glass would be the medium for solidification of the wastes (Federal Register, 14 January 1983), and research is now focused on repository sites. Several deep-mined burial sites (1,980 to 2,970 feet deep) are being considered, including the old basalt lava flows of the Columbia Plateau at the Hanford Nuclear Reservation in Washington; volcanic welded tuff at the Nevada Test Site, and bedded and dome salt formations in Utah, Texas, Louisiana, and Mississippi (Carter, 1983). Other possibilities include granitic formations beneath blankets of sedimentary rock where the groundwater-flow system is well understood and can act as a barrier between the wastes and the biosphere (Bredehoeft and Maini, 1981). It is also possible to delay burial until the most suitable method of burial can be determined.

Other Sources of Contamination

Accidental Spills and Leaks

Accidental spills and leaks can occur due to breaks in pipelines, tanker truck, and other accidents involving transport of materials and failure of storage tanks. They commonly occur at airports, industrial sites, highways and railroads, gas stations, and refineries. There is an inherent risk in storing fluids. Organics, including hydrocarbons, are the most frequently reported groundwater contaminant due to spills or leaks (U.S. EPA, 1977). Emergency measures to deal with spills often consist of flushing the spilled compound away, thus permitting or even assisting in the contamination of groundwater (Harris, 1982). Flushing usually reduces the immediate threat of fire and explosion. Such practices are more likely to create surface-water pollution than groundwater pollution, as most storm sewers and ditches flow into surface water. If the spill is large enough and is not properly cleaned up, however, groundwater contamination can result. Under the Clean Water Act, Spill Prevention Countermeasure Control (SPCC) plans have been required of every facility since 1975 for spills to the ground. The National Contingency Plan, under CERCLA, effective as of December 1982, details cleanup procedures for spills of oil and hazardous materials on land, into surface water or into groundwater. In addition, releases of quantities of oil or hazardous material in excess of stated amounts must be made known to the National Response Center. Many of the industrial trade associations have researched cleanup and containment, and published manuals; an example would be the American Petroleum Institute manual for the cleanup of underground spills (API, 1980).

Pipelines are used to transport a variety of fluids, but the most common one is petroleum. In 1972 there were 174,000 miles of petroleum pipelines which transported a total of 8.5 billion barrels of petroleum products (U.S.

Department of Commerce, 1974). In 1976 the same amount of pipeline transported 9.63 billion barrels of petroleum products (U.S. Department of Commerce, 1977). In 1971 there were 308 interstate pipeline accidents involving a loss of about 245,000 barrels of liquids. Pipeline failure due to external corrosion caused 33% of these accidents, and damage to pipeline from excavating machines caused an additional 22% (Meyer, 1973). In 1980 there were 275 accidents and in 1981, 198 accidents. The decrease in incidents may be due to extensive regulations from the Department of Transportation regulating transportation of liquids by pipeline, which became effective in July 1981, as well as to improved industry practices. Of the 4,112 accidents that occurred between 1968 and 1981, 1,372 were due to corrosion and 1,101 to ruptures in the pipeline. No information was given about the number of barrels involved in the incidents in 1980 and 1981 (U.S. Department of Commerce, 1982).

Small hydrocarbon spills may be absorbed by the unsaturated soil zone, but large ones can reach the water-table aquifer and float on the surface. Very small concentrations of petroleum products will render groundwater unfit to drink due to its objectionable odor and taste, thus reducing the possibility of its being used for drinking water and posing a threat to health.

Other chemicals have toxic properties. Ammonia, for example, increases the nitrification of groundwater, and acids speed up the solution of heavy metals and soil solids.

In some regions deliberate leakage and spillage, so-called "midnight dumping," of contaminants has occurred. This source of contamination, which is a criminal offense, is considered to be a major problem in New England (D. Burmaster, consultant on surface and groundwater quality, personal communication).

Agricultural Activities

Irrigation return-flow, the use of pesticides, fertilizers, and manure, and changes in vegetative cover have all been known to cause changes in groundwater quality. Agriculture is considered to be an important non-point source of such changes, especially in the increase in nitrate, mainly due to the large increase in the use of agricultural chemicals over the last 20 years (Porter, 1977). Less nitrate-nitrogen is available for leaching in the loamy fine-sand soils of subirrigation systems than in furrow and sprinkler systems. Thus, subirrigation systems provide a method for reducing solute concentrations in irrigation return-flow (Wendt et al., 1976). In addition pesticide contamination has been reported from some areas including California, Arizona, New York, and New Jersey. The pesticide dibromochloropropane (DBCP), now banned in the United States, adversely affects human health and causes reproductive dysfunction in laboratory animals when given at high concentrations. There is no direct evidence for adverse effects on human health at the concentrations found in contaminated groundwater (CEQ, 1981a). Although not really an agricultural activity, suburban lawn care can cause groundwater contamination (Miller et al., 1974). Dry-land farming in the northern Great Plains does not utilize irrigation. These plants have lower evapo-transpiration rates, and more water may move down through the soil and thus contaminate the groundwater. In some cases this salty water produces saline seeps.

Mining

The formation of acid mine-drainage water has been described above. In areas where coal mining has been carried out over long periods of time, in Appalachia and Pennsylvania, for example, it is estimated that due to its low pH, the groundwater there would be unusable for decades after the cessation of mining activities. Metal-mine leachate has increased manganese in wells in Washington, caused arsenic poisoning in cattle in Idaho, and increased the radioactivity of groundwater in Wyoming (U.S. EPA, 1977).

Highway Deicing-Salts

Many of the northern states use large quantities of salt in combination with abrasives such as sand on icy and snowy highways. The salt-solution runoff can percolate through adjacent soils or otherwise find its way into the groundwater via storm drains. Due to its low cost, salt is often stored in uncovered piles. Precipitation dissolves the stored salt, which may then infiltrate shallow aquifers. Large amounts of salt are used on northern highways each winter. Over 12 million tons were used in the winter of 1978–79 (Salt Institute 1980). The forecasted salt usage during 1983–84 is nearly 11 million tons. In addition to salt, varying amounts of calcium chloride and abrasives are used also. In 1965–66 over 20 tons of salt per single-lane mile were used by Illinois, Massachusetts, Pennsylvania, and Washington, D.C. (U.S. EPA, 1977). In 1978–79 the amounts used were considerably less, namely 8.9 tons per lane mile in Illinois, 12.9 tons in Massachusetts, 7.0 tons in Pennsylvania, and 3.04 tons in Washington, D.C. The amount of salt used depends, of course, upon the severity of the winter, upon the amount of abrasives used, and upon driver education. Nevertheless, salt usage in the Northeast has resulted in chloride contamination of many drinking-water wells adjacent to highways.

The dangers to public health of high salt concentrations in drinking water are not well known. Water is considered contaminated with chloride when the concentration of chloride exceeds 250 mg/liter because concentrations above that leave a salty taste in the water (NAS, 1980b). High concentrations of sodium have been linked with hypertension and have been implicated in the exacerbation of certain health problems of the liver and kidney. The American Heart Association has suggested a maximum level of 20 mg/liter in drinking water. High concentrations of salt can also be severely detrimental to most plant life.

Atmospheric Contaminants and Acid Rain

Very little is known about the effects of atmospheric contaminants and acid rain on the quality of groundwater. In Michigan chromium in the dust from an industrial plant was leached into an aquifer and contaminated a well (Deutsch, 1963). Hubert and Canter (1980b) have reviewed the literature concerning the relation between acid rain and groundwater, and they conclude that acid rain may react with soils and surface waters in such a way as to increase the leaching of metals and nutrients. Thus, the potential for groundwater contamination is present and should be investigated further, especially the potential for lead and cadmium contaminations via leaching because of their long environmental-residence time.

The Infiltration of Surface Water

Aquifers are often in hydraulic connection with bodies of surface water. Under certain conditions, polluted surface water from lakes or streams can percolate into a water-table aquifer beneath the body of surface water, thereby degrading the quality of the groundwater. Also, groundwater development near a body of surface water may draw contaminated water into the aquifer.

The Development of Groundwater

Pumping of water wells may bring water of lesser quality into their zone of influence. In inland areas serious problems may be caused by the migration of water of a lower quality from saline aquifers through leaky aquitards into potable supplies. In coastal regions, extensive groundwater development has led to saltwater intrusion. Saltwater encroachment is an important source of groundwater contamination in many populated coastal regions, particularly in parts of California, Texas, Louisiana, Florida, and New York. Saltwater occurs naturally in the aquifers in coastal areas, and pumping freshwater from wells may cause saltwater intrusion into potable aquifers, rendering them unfit for use. In 1977 a USGS inventory reported 114 cases of saltwater intrusion (U.S. EPA, 1977), but this number has probably increased significantly in recent years. Attempts to prevent such contamination have included the injection of freshwater "barriers" to reverse the hydraulic gradient in the aquifer so that the flow is towards the sea rather than towards the pumping wells. This method has met with some success in the Los Angeles area.

Improper Construction and Maintenance of Wells

Faulty, corroded, or ruptured well casings, the linking of two aquifers by a well screen, or open wells can cause contaminants to move from one aquifer to another.

Sources of contamination from the three main categories described above have been documented from all parts of the country. Whether they cause localized problems or whether the groundwater-contamination problems fall into larger regional patterns has been a matter of dispute. Our conclusions, based on a study of the documented cases of groundwater contamination available, are given in Chapter 7 of this report, together with examples of known occurrences of groundwater contamination for selected states. It may be said, however, that groundwater contamination is not usually direct, and in most cases the contaminant must pass through the soil layer. Attenuation of contaminants is greater in the unsaturated zone because of the greater possibility for aerobic degradation, adsorption, complexing, and ion exchange of organics and inorganics (Page, 1981). Even after a contaminant has reached the water table, dilution, buffering, precipitation, reduction or oxidation, mechanical filtration, volatilization, sorption, and other processes may operate to purify chemical wastes (Page, 1981).

Figure 4–1. Groundwater Pollution Problems (as identified by Federal and State/Regional Study Teams)

Source: U.S. Water Resources Council, 1978a.

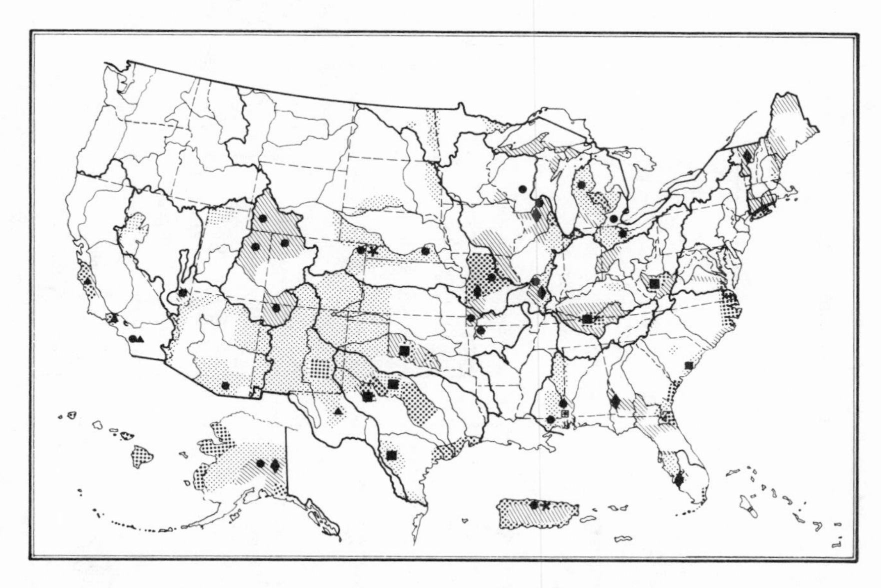

AREA PROBLEMS

- Significant groundwater pollution is occurring
- Salt-water intrusion or ground water is naturally salty
- High level of minerals or other dissolved solids in groundwater
- Unshaded area may not be problem-free, but problem was not considered major

BOUNDARIES

- Water resources region
- Subregion

SPECIFIC SOURCES OF POLLUTION

- Municipal and industrial wastes including wastes from oil and gas fields
- Toxic industrial wastes
- Landfill leachate
- Irrigation return waters
- Wastes from well drilling, harbor dredging, and excavation for drainage systems
- Well injection of industrial waste liquids

Figure 4–2. Major Hydrochemical Processes in the Soil Zone of Recharge Areas

R. Allan Freeze and John A. Cherry, *Groundwater* (Englewood Cliffs, N.J.: Prentice-Hall, Inc., 1979), p. 204. Reprinted by permission of the publisher.

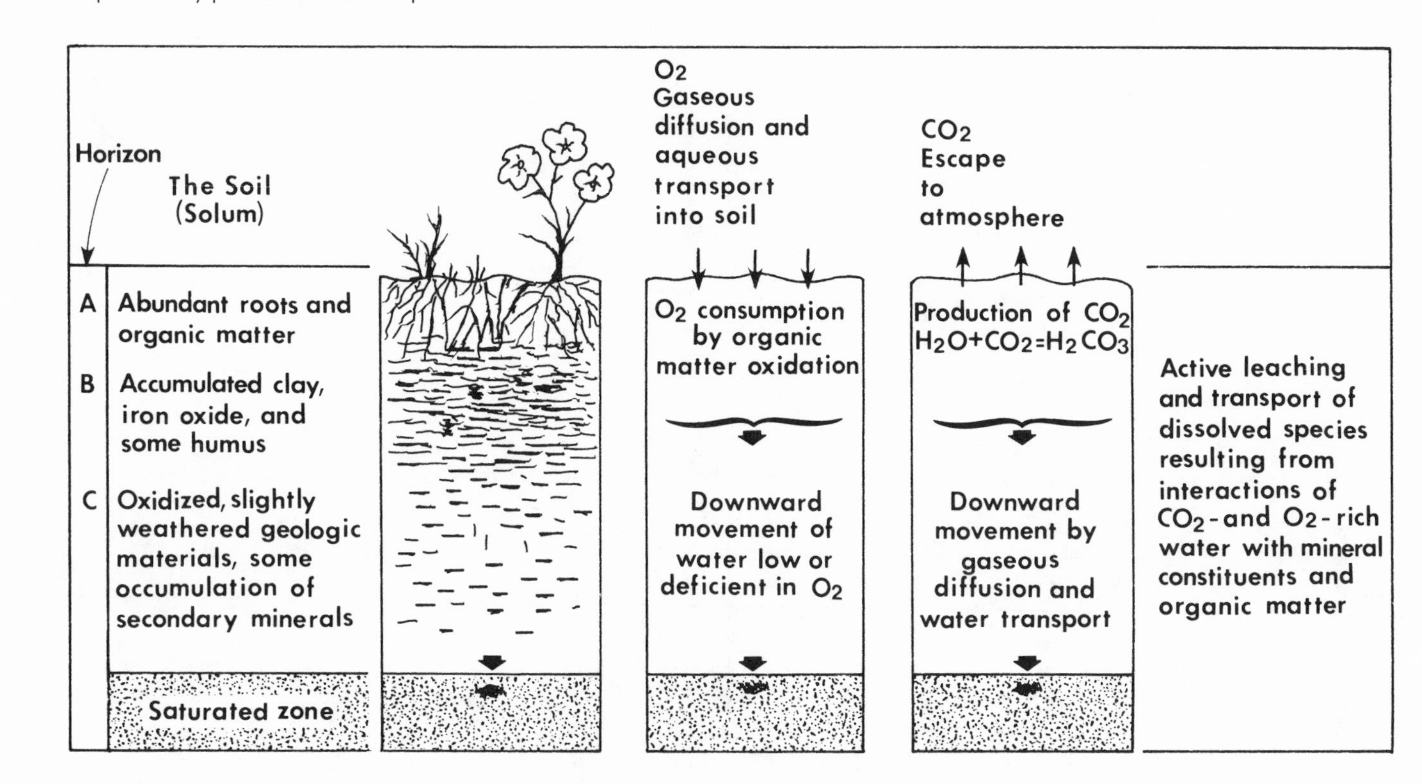

Figure 4–3. Changes in Plumes and Factors Causing the Changes
Source: U.S. EPA, 1977.

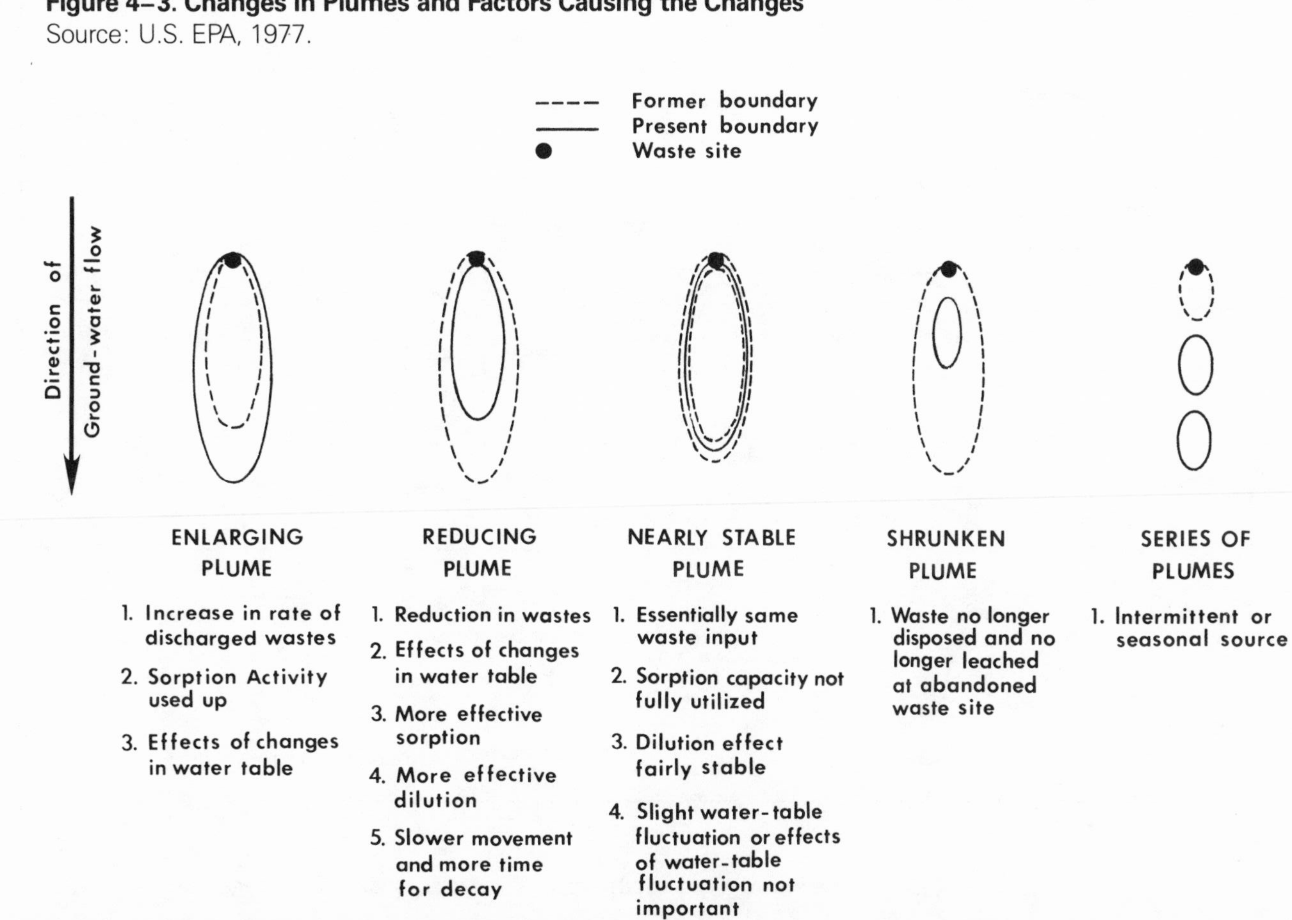

Figure 4–4. How Waste-Disposal Practices Contaminate the Groundwater System
Source: U.S. EPA, 1977.

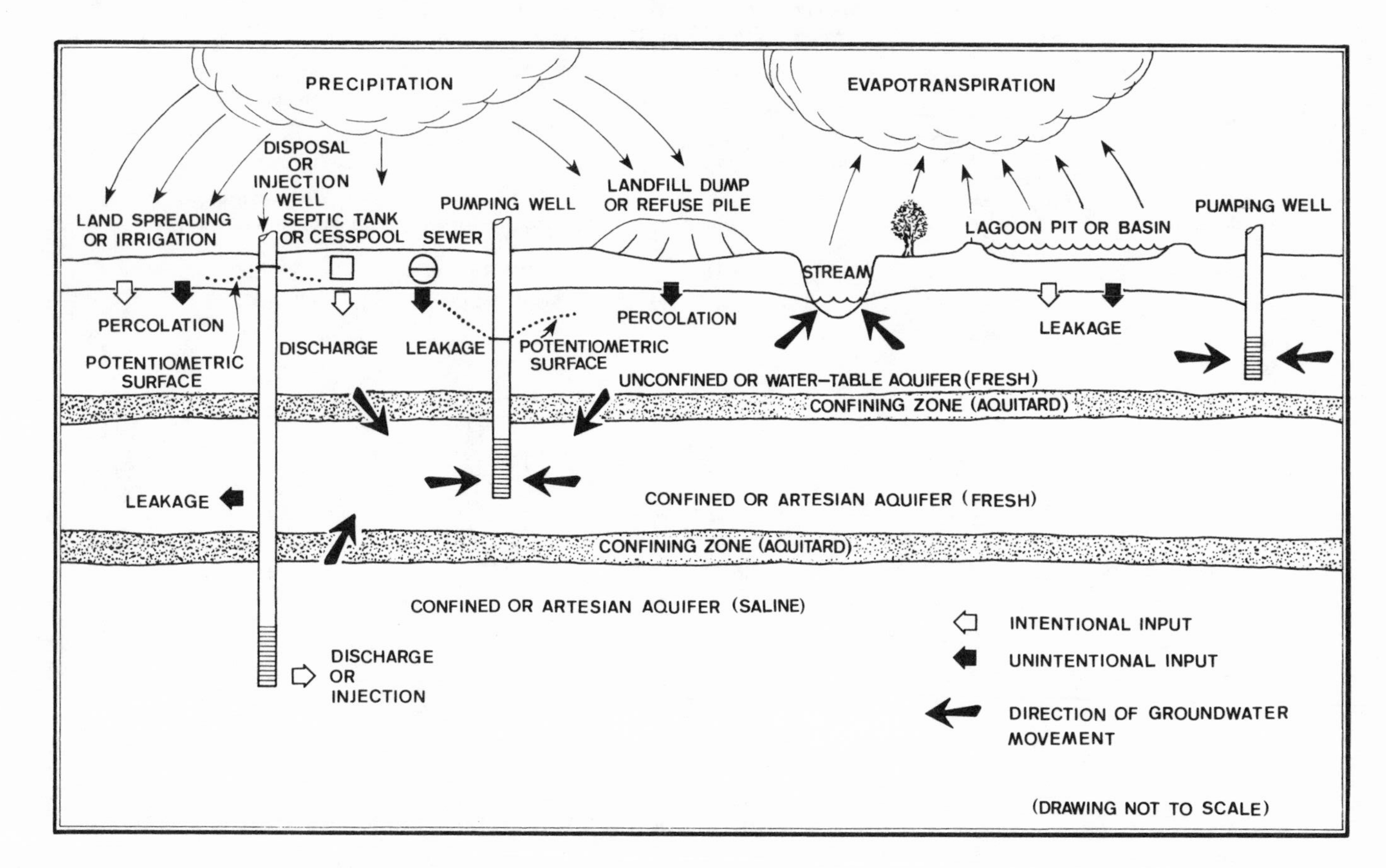

Figure 4–5. Density of Housing Units Using On-Site Domestic Waste-Disposal Systems, by County
Source: U.S. EPA, 1977.

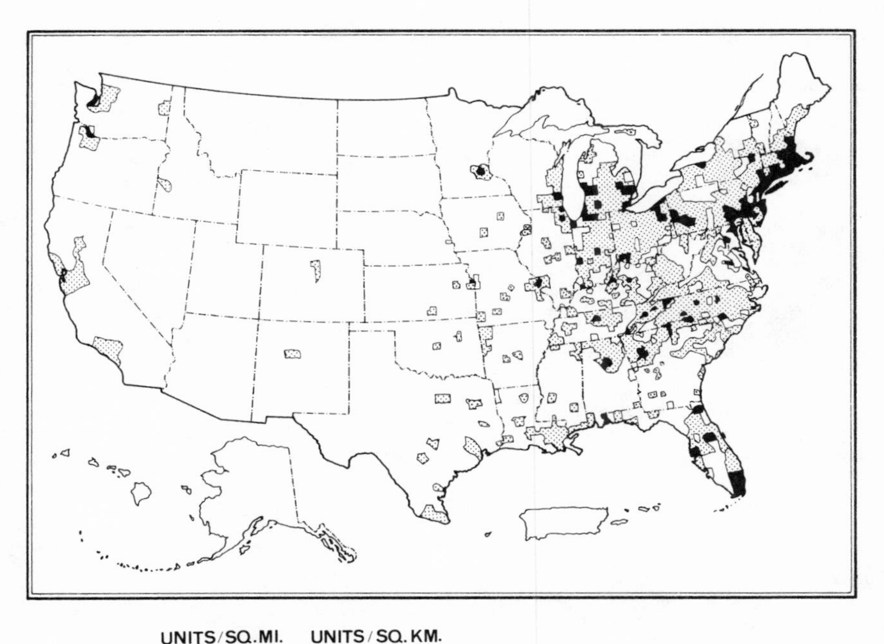

	UNITS/SQ.MI.	UNITS/SQ.KM.
□	< 10	< 3.8
▒	10 - 40	3.8-15.4
■	>40	>15.4

Figure 4–6. Density of Population Served by Municipal Sewage Treatment Facilities Discharging Effluent to Land, by County
Source: U.S. EPA, 1977.

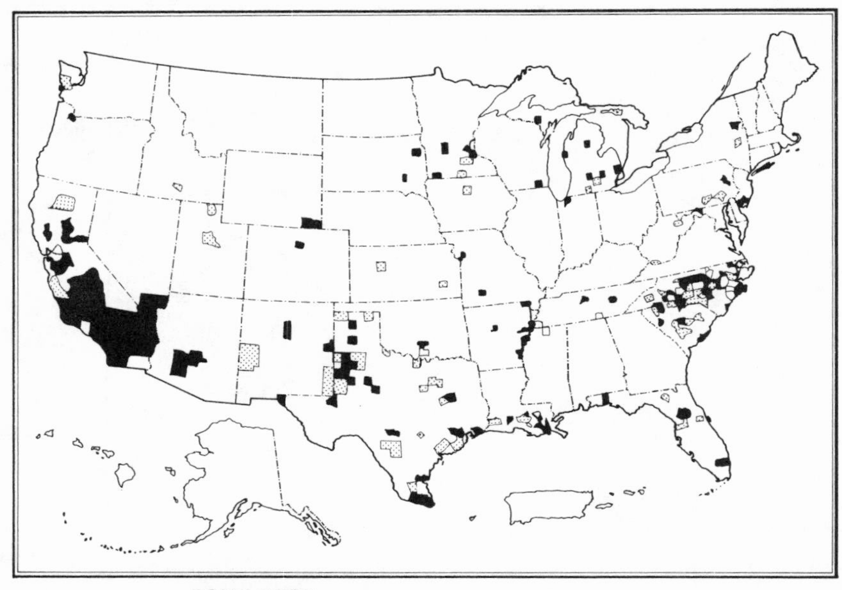

POPULATION

	SQ. MI.	SQ. KM.
(blank)	< 6	<2.3
(stippled)	6 – 10	2.3 – 3.8
(solid)	>10	>3.8

Figure 4–7. Coal Fields of the Conterminous United States

Source: NAS, 1981b.

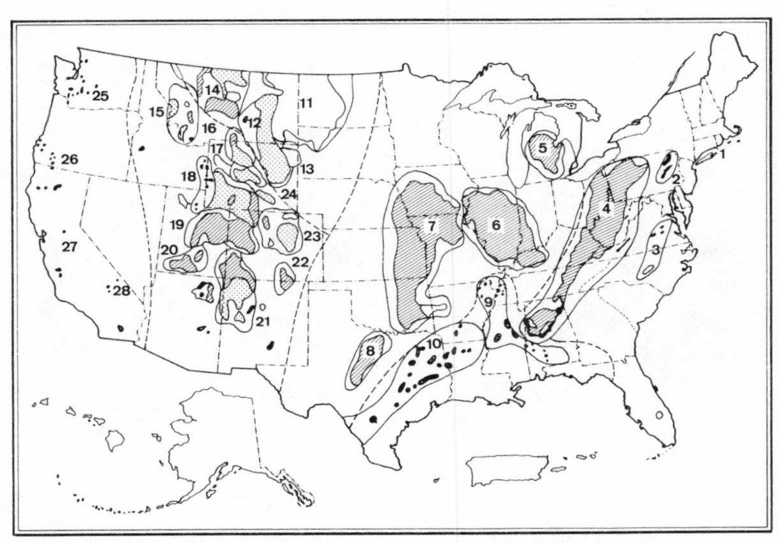

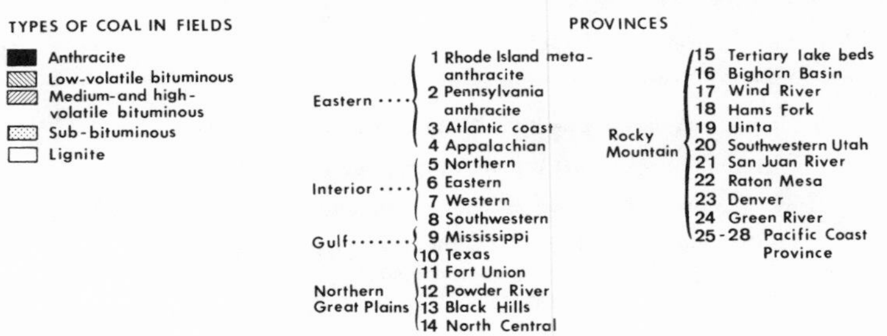

Figure 4–8. States in Which Significant Volumes of Wastewater Are Discharged from Mining and Ore Processing Operations, Excluding Coal and Petroleum, 1972

Source: U.S. EPA, 1977.

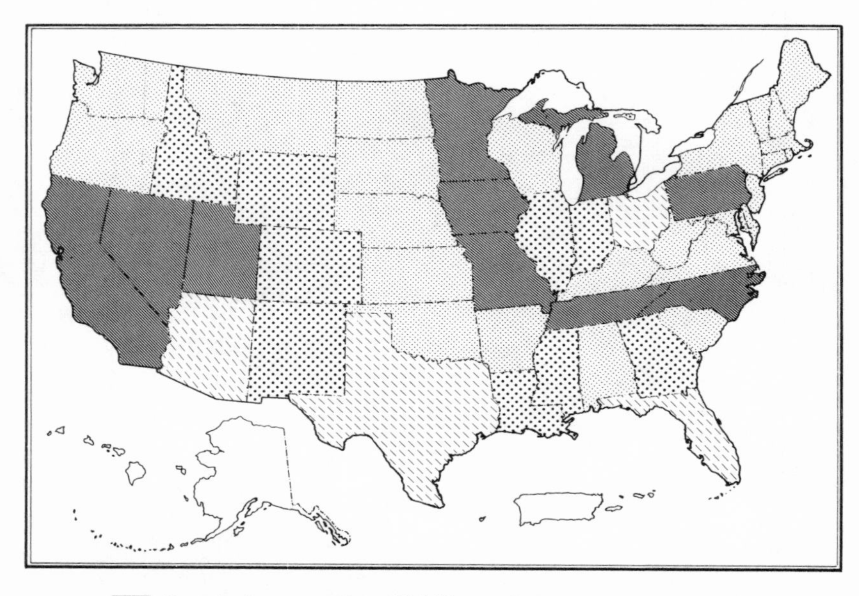

Reported as more than 20 billion gallons per year

Reported as 5-20 billion gallons per year

Volume undisclosed but assumed large

Reported as less than 5 billion gallons per year or undisclosed but assumed small

Figure 4–9. States in Which Significant Volumes of Wastewater Are Discharged from Coal Mining and Processing Operations, 1972

Source: U.S. EPA, 1977.

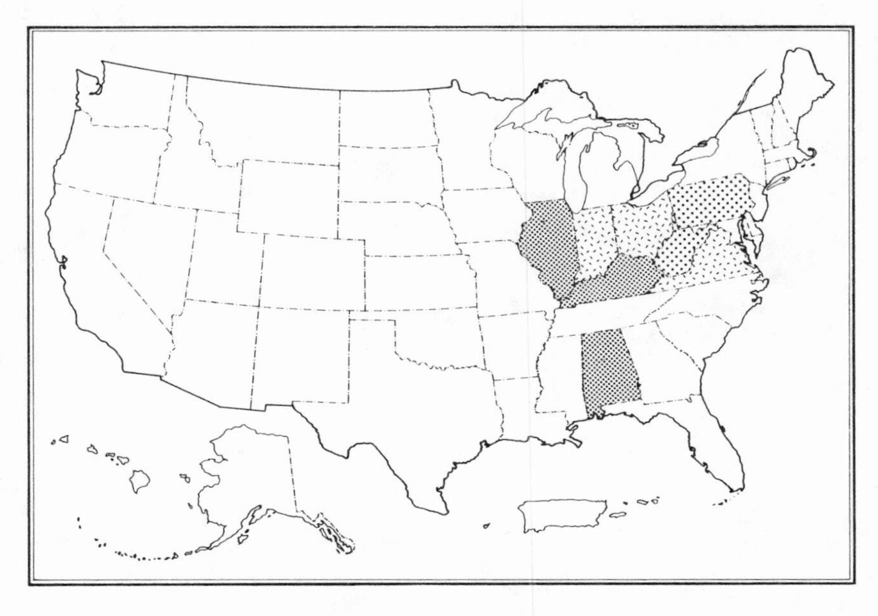

- Reported as more than 20 billion gallons per year
- Reported as 5-10 billion gallons per year
- Volume undisclosed but assumed large
- Reported as less than 5 billion gallons per year or undisclosed, but assumed small

Figure 4–10. Distribution of Cattle Feeding Operations, by County
Source: U.S. EPA, 1977.

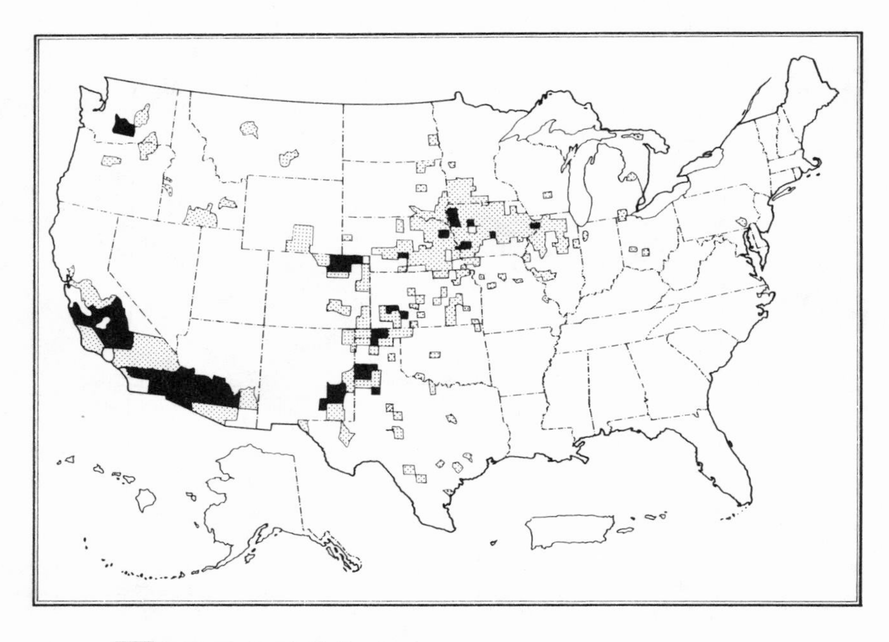

20,000 - 100,000 Head

>100,000 Head

Five

The Severity of Groundwater Contamination

- Methods for assessing severity are varied. They include consideration of whether numerical quality standards for certain specific uses such as drinking water have been exceeded; calculating the number of people affected by well closings; estimating the percentage of usable aquifers that have been contaminated; determining the degree of hazard posed by contaminants; and the ease and cost of finding an alternative source of water.
- Estimates for the percentage of total contaminated groundwater have been made but vary and are inexact.

The question of the severity of groundwater contamination is a troublesome one in determining the overall magnitude of the national problem. The definition of severity can be approached in several ways.

1. If the contaminants in the groundwater exceed the interim standards set for drinking water (see Tables 5–1 and 5–2), then the problem could be said to be severe if the intended use is for drinking-water supplies. The interim standards do not include the many synthetic organic chemicals now found in water. A proposed rule-making for volatile synthetic organic chemicals was published in the Federal Register, 4 March 1982. Consideration should be given to whether contamination renders the water unfit for its intended use, which could include industrial, agricultural, drinking, and other purposes.
2. The number of persons affected by the contamination might be taken into account. Thus, the contamination of an aquifer in the vicinity of a municipal well-field that provides drinking water would be of

Table 5–1. National Interim Primary Drinking-Water Regulations* (Maximum Contaminant Levels—MCL)

Contaminant	MCL
Inorganic chemicals	
Arsenic	0.05 (mg/liter)
Barium	1
Cadmium	0.010
Chromium	0.05
Lead	0.05
Mercury	0.002
Nitrate (as N)	10
Selenium	0.01
Silver	0.05
Fluoride	1.4–2.4
Organic chemicals	
Chlorinated hydrocarbons	
Endrin	0.0002
Lindane	0.004
Methoxychlor	0.1
Toxaphene	0.005
Chlorophenoxys	
2,4-D	0.1
2,4,5-T, Silvex	0.01
Turbidity	1 unit
Microbiologic contaminants	1 coliform bacterium per 100 ml as the arithmetic mean of all samples per month
Radioactivity	
Combined radium-226 and radium-228	5 pCi/liter
Gross alpha particle activity (including radium-226 but excluding radon and uranium)	15 pCi/liter
Average annual concentration of beta particle and photon radioactivity not to produce annual dose equivalent greater than	4 millirem per year
Tritium	20,000 pCi/liter
Strontium-90	8 pCi/liter

*Environmental Protection Agency, 1976.

Table 5–2. National Secondary Drinking-Water Regulations (Secondary Maximum Contaminant Levels)

Contaminant	MCL
Chloride	250 mg/liter
Color	15 color units
Copper	1 mg/liter
Corrosivity	Noncorrosive
Foaming agents	0.5 mg/liter
Hydrogen sulfide	0.5 mg/liter
Iron	0.3 mg/liter
Manganese	0.05 mg/liter
Odor	3 threshold odor number
pH	6.5–8.5
Sulfate	250 mg/liter
TDS	500 mg/liter
Zinc	5 mg/liter

Source: J. M. Last, *Maxcy-Rosen and Public Health and Preventive Medicine*. 11th ed. (Norwalk, Conn.: Appleton-Century-Crofts, 1980), p. 976. Reprinted by permission of the publisher.

more concern than contamination occurring in an isolated, sparsely populated area.

3. In the case of a single aquifer, severity of contamination may be related to the percentage of aquifer that has been contaminated.
4. Nationwide, the severity of the problem may be indicated by the percentage of the aquifers affected.
5. A different measure of severity might be obtained if the volume of known and suspected contaminated plumes is expressed as a percentage of the known groundwater reserves nationwide.
6. The degree of hazard posed by the contaminants varies according to the volume discharged and the toxicity and concentration of the contaminant. Toxicity may be defined as the degree of hazard and also depend on how contaminants move in the aquifer.

Thus, severity could depend on one or a combination of the following parameters: concentration and toxicity of the contaminants, the number of people affected if the contaminated aquifer is a source of drinking water, and the percentage of the available groundwater both locally and regionally affected by such contamination. Interwoven with each of these parameters is the economic cost of finding an alternate water source if the contamination renders the groundwater unfit for its prior or future uses or if treating the water before use is not possible.

Many of the numbers required for these various methods of assessing the severity of the contamination of groundwater in quantitative terms simply are not available. There have been no nationwide systematic surveys of the occurrence of groundwater contamination, although numerous reports and studies show that incidents of groundwater contamination have occurred in every state. EPA (1980c), in the Appendices to the planning workshops to develop recommendations for a groundwater protection strategy, accurately summarized the sort of information that is available from existing reports and studies as follows:

- documentation of a large number of contamination incidents
- identification of the most important sources of contamination
- determination of the mechanisms of contamination
- in-depth studies of some contamination incidents
- surveys of the number of some types of potential contamination sources nationwide.

EPA (1980c) suggests two possible approaches to estimate the extent of groundwater contamination. The first is to conduct a systematic nationwide survey at randomly selected sites to obtain an estimate of the extent of contamination. If the sample is large enough, EPA states this method could provide a good estimate of both the extent and nature of the problem but not of the causes nor what could be done to control contamination. Since the cost of the drilling required by such a project would be substantial, and the time to accomplish it lengthy, EPA ruled out this possibility, while recognizing its potential usefulness.

The second approach suggested in the Appendices (U.S. EPA, 1980c) is to estimate the number of sources of contamination and the amount of contamination per source, and from these to estimate the order of magnitude of the problem. Recognizing that the information available for this method is less precise, EPA points out that it can make use of existing information, both qualitative and quantitative. EPA used this method to develop a preliminary assessment, for which it was necessary to estimate both the sources of contamination that are the most important from a national perspective and the area of groundwater contaminated by these sources. This would be achieved by estimating the number of sites in each contaminating category, the area contaminating each site, calculating the total area estimated to be contaminated in each source category, and producing a final estimate of contamination from all categories of sources. In addition to these estimates, EPA (1980c) states that the probable extent of contamination from sources that could not be quantitatively measured should be discussed. A preliminary assessment of the problem nationwide would be based on a comparison of the area contaminated with the total area of usable aquifers. Naturally such a string of estimates is an irritant to the fastidious scientific mind, even though the object of the exercise, to achieve a preliminary assessment

Table 5–3. Relative Importance of Different Waste-Disposal Sources of Groundwater Contamination

	National	Northeast	Southeast	South Central	Southwest	Northwest
Industrial impoundments	I	I	I	III	III	I
Land disposal sites	I	I	I	II	II	II
Septic tanks & cesspools	I	I	I	III	III	I
Municipal waste water	II	II	III	II	III	I
Petroleum exploration	II	III	III	I	I	I
Mining	II	II	II	II	III	II
Other important contamination sources, including non-disposal sources		Spills, leaks, road salt: storage tanks	Spills, leaks, storage tanks, agricultural activities	Natural leaching, irrigation return: abandoned wells	Natural leaching, irrigation return: sea-water encroachment	Irrigation return: abandoned wells

NOTE: Relative importance is based on the typical health hazard of the contaminants, the typical size of the area affected, and the distribution of the waste-disposal practice across the U.S. A waste-disposal practice may be a serious problem in certain areas, but if the number of such areas is relatively small, then the practice would not be given a high national rating. A very widespread practice which does not create serious problems even where sources of contamination are concentrated would also be given a low rating with regard to national importance. The ratings in the table are defined as follows: I—high, II—moderate, III—low.

Source: U.S. EPA, 1980c.

of the order of magnitude of the problem nationwide—a ball-park figure—is doubtless achieved. Such assessments do serve a useful purpose, but only when their inherent flaws are kept in mind.

Table 5–3 gives EPA's summary of the relative importance of different waste-disposal sources of groundwater contamination for various regions of the country, based upon the five EPA reports completed in the 1970s and described on page 112 of this report. Unfortunately, the relative importance of non-disposal sources was not assessed.

Estimates of the Percentage of Groundwater That Is Contaminated

The methods EPA used to estimate the area of contamination from impoundments and landfills are outlined in the Appendices (U.S. EPA, 1980c), but few details are given. For example, EPA estimated that the 25,000 active industrial impoundments identified in the 1978 Surface Impoundment Assessment are unlined and therefore could contaminate unconfined aquifers. Half the impoundments are known to be sited over usable aquifers on very permeable soil; thus 8,400 industrial impoundments may leak into usable aquifers. The extent of the plume of contamination caused by leaking impoundments is estimated from the volume and type of waste, the length of time the leakage occurs, and the hydrogeology of the area. EPA assumes that an impoundment is 10 acres and has been in operation for 10 years. Such an impoundment on permeable soil will produce 60 acres of contamination. If it is further assumed that none of the plumes overlaps or is intercepted by surface water, 790 square miles of contamination will be produced in total. Considering that the last two assumptions may not hold, EPA used a range from 400 to 800 square miles as the preliminary assessment of groundwater contamination due to surface impoundments.

Using a similar analysis to assess the contamination attributable to landfills, EPA came up with a figure of from 1,300 to 8,400 square miles. It should be pointed out, however, that no national survey of the number of landfill sites has been conducted, that leachate production is dependent on rainfall, which may be seasonal, and that the number of illegal dump sites is unknown.

The EPA combined estimate of contamination due to surface impoundments and landfills was thus from 1,700 to 9,200 square miles. The next stage was to assume that 60% of the 3.5 million square miles of U.S. land surface is underlain by usable aquifers; thus from 0.1% to 0.4% of the usable aquifers near the land surface are contaminated by industrial impoundments and landfill sites. EPA (1980c) cautions that the relatively small area of contamination should be viewed in relation to the fact that these two types of waste-disposal sites are usually found in areas of significant industrial and domestic water use and that the problem could be exacerbated by the area's dependence on groundwater. Since groundwater pumping creates a zone of influence that affects plumes, the area over which water is rendered unusable may be larger than the area of the plumes.

EPA considered impoundments and landfills the most significant sources of contamination but also evaluated secondary sources, such as subsurface disposal systems and exploration and mining for petroleum. These sources were estimated to have contaminated less than 1% and 0.1%, respectively, of the nation's usable aquifers. Thus EPA (1980c) concluded that by area up to 1% of the usable aquifers near the land surface in the United States may be contaminated at present by waste-disposal practices and by petroleum exploration and mining and that the areas of contamination will increase with time. EPA did not include an estimate of the percentage of available groundwater contaminated by non-disposal related activities.

Another independent assessment has recently been completed by Lehr (1982). Lehr assumes that there is a total of 200,000 point sources, including septic tanks, landfills, pits, ponds and lagoons, and the like, twice the range of from 75,000 to 100,000 industrial sites often taken as a baseline. Lehr further assumes that each site creates a plume of pollution that is 1,000 feet wide and 100 feet thick, that it advances at the rate of 125 feet per year, and has been traveling for 40 years. Both the rate of travel and the distance traveled are faster and longer than most other assessments assume, thus Lehr's is a worst-case estimate. Thus, each of the 200,000 plumes has moved a mile from its source and is polluting aquifers that are 25% porous. Assuming that each is a discrete plume, Lehr arrives at a figure of approximately 200 trillion gallons of polluted groundwater. Lehr assumes a conservative figure of 40% of all the available groundwater is found within one-third mile of the land's surface, and he arrives at a figure of 100 quadrillion gallons of available groundwater. Two hundred trillion gallons of polluted groundwater thus represents 0.2% of the available groundwater in the top one-third mile of the earth's crust in the United States. If one assumes a specific yield of groundwater closer to 5% than 10%, a larger plume (1,500 feet wide, 1.5 miles long, 150 feet thick, then over 1% of the groundwater would be polluted. If there were 300,000 plumes, pollution would reach 2%. Lehr concludes that no matter how liberal or conservative the estimate, the fraction of groundwater polluted is very small.

Lehr (1982) outlines other calculations. He takes the EPA estimate of leakage of known pollution sources of 1.5 trillion gallons per year, doubles it to account for unknown sources, assumes a leakage time of

33.33 years to arrive at a figure of 100 trillion gallons of polluted groundwater, half that of his estimate outlined above. If the U.S. Geological Survey (USGS) estimate of groundwater availability (200 quadrillion gallons) is used, the estimated percentage of polluted groundwater is even lower. Lehr concedes that in certain areas of the country (New York, New Jersey, and New England industrial areas) much more than 1% of the groundwater has been polluted, but there is still a considerable amount available which is not contaminated. Lehr predicts that the initiation of new sources of pollution could be eliminated in 10 years, and by then 98% of our available groundwater will have remained unpolluted. The problem, he concludes, is serious, but not the crisis some groups would have us believe.

The Population Affected by Groundwater Contamination

Unfortunately, very little information is readily available concerning the population affected by well closings due to groundwater contamination. In 1978 the New Jersey township of South Brunswick was obliged to close down public supply Well 11 due to contamination by 1, 1, 1-trichloroethane, an organic chemical often used as a degreasing agent and for cleaning septic tanks. The level of contamination of the pumped well water was usually in the 150 to 500 parts per billion (ppb) range but did, at times, exceed 1,000 ppb. Other contaminants subsequently found in the water from Well 11 or adjacent domestic and industrial wells include 1, 1-dichloroethane, trichloroethylene, tetrachloroethylene, benzene, toluene, zinc, and arsenic. All contaminated domestic wells in the vicinity of Well 11 were taken out of service. Since 1978 the township has been dependent on Wells 12 and 13, which remain uncontaminated and are tested regularly (Geraghty and Miller, Inc., 1979). New Castle County in Delaware recognized that the groundwater was being contaminated mainly due to solid-waste disposal, primarily at the Llangollen landfill. The estimated groundwater availability in New Castle County totals 52 million gallons per day (mgd) (Frick and Shaffer, n.d.), and the groundwater use in 1974 was 27.9 mgd, nearly 54% of that available. The total daily demand for both surface and groundwater in 1974 was 78 mgd and is projected to rise to 89 mgd in 1985, and to 105 mgd in 1995. In 1974 the population of New Castle County was 393,600, and this was projected to rise to 474,200 by 1995. It is estimated that in 1995 the amount of water resources that are rendered unusable because of pollution will be 6.7 mgd.

In Nassau and Suffolk Counties on Long Island, New York, the population of nearly 3 million is almost entirely dependent on groundwater as the only source of drinking water. More than 36 community wells have been closed due to contamination by tetrachloroethylene, trichloroethane, trichloroethylene, and other volatile synthetic organic compounds. The Council on Environmental Quality (CEQ, 1981a) estimates that more than two million people were affected by such closings. CEQ (1981a) lists other such instances. In 1980, 39 public wells in San Gabriel Valley, California, were closed due to contamination from trichloroethylene. The wells supplied water to more than 400,000 persons in 13 cities. In Bedford, Massachusetts, four municipal wells supplying 80% of the drinking water for the town were closed due to contamination by trichloroethylene and dioxane. Water had to be purchased from neighboring towns, one of which subsequently had to close its main well due to similar contamination. Although these examples give an indication of the number of persons affected by well closings because of groundwater contamination, there are no national surveys on the number of persons thus affected by well closings or exposed to contaminants.

The volume and toxicity of wastes that may contaminate groundwater also affect our own perception of the severity of contamination. As Keeley (1977) points out, septic tanks are considered a major problem in some areas because of their numbers and distribution, but industrial lagoons, although less numerous, often contain a more hazardous waste from the point of view of toxicity.

Six

The Effects of Groundwater Contamination on Public Health

- The effects of groundwater contamination on public health may fall into one of three categories: (1) acute waterborne disease due to pathogenic organisms, (2) poisoning or other acute responses due to chemical contaminants, (3) chronic long-term effects.
- The impact of groundwater contamination on human health is difficult to quantify accurately.
- Pathogenic contaminants have caused outbreaks of disease.
- Chemical contaminants have caused acute public health effects such as poisoning.
- The correlation between cardiovascular disease and high mineralization of groundwater is uncertain.
- High concentrations of minerals in groundwater may be linked with various forms of cancer, but studies are not conclusive. It is important that these implications be defined.
- It is impossible to assess, in quantitative terms, the national risk of drinking contaminated groundwater due to the lack of comprehensive national surveys on the extent of groundwater contamination and the paucity of testing of groundwater contaminants for carcinogenicity.

The effects of groundwater contamination on public health may fall into one of three categories: acute waterborne disease due to a variety of pathogenic organisms, poisoning or other acute responses to chemical contaminants, and chronic long-term disease. These effects are due to two distinct forms of groundwater contamination, namely, microbial and chemical contamination.

Table 6–1. Economic Costs of Environmental Health Hazards

Category of Hazard	Annual Health Costs 1972 Estimates (Billions of Dollars)
A. Health Costs Due to Environmental Hazards	
I. Direct Environmental Hazards	
Air Pollution	8.6
Water Pollution	4.4
Infectious Diseases	
Hepatitis	0.73
Salmonellosis	0.0004
Influenza	4.9
Syphilis	0.007
Tuberculosis	0.7
Occupational Hazards	4.4
Unsafe Products	6.3
Motor Vehicle Accidents	10.1
Total All Direct (Total I)	40.1
II. Costs Resulting from Environmentally Induced Behavior	
Alcohol Abuse	24.2
Drug Abuse—Heroin	3.7
Tobacco Use	7.6
Total All Costs of Environmental Hazards (I and II)	75.6
B. Costs of All Illnesses	188.

Source: S. E. Bunch and P. Jacobs, *Journal of Environmental Health* vol. 41, no. 5 (1979), p. 268. Reprinted by permission of the National Environmental Health Association, Denver, Colorado.

Every incidence of illness given in this chapter is attributable to contaminated groundwater. Some of the chemical causes of illness due to drinking water have been investigated for surface waters only, however, as groundwater may also contain some of these chemicals, the findings for surface waters are discussed where deemed appropriate. Bunch and Jacobs (1979) estimated that in 1972 health hazards due to water pollution accounted for $4.4 billion of the total $188 billion estimated costs of all health hazards, but did not subdivide this total into separate costs attributable to groundwater and surface-water contamination (Table 6–1). These figures are somewhat out of date, but more recent ones are not available. Human health can be affected by the consumption of fresh foods irrigated by contaminated water or by the consumption of foods processed with contaminated groundwater, as well as by the more direct route of water consumption (Hubert and Canter, 1980a).

The Incidence of Disease

Information concerning the effects of contaminated water on public health may be obtained from two main sources, the Centers for Disease Control (CDC) in Atlanta and the EPA laboratory in Cincinnati. The Centers for Disease Control publish annual summaries of water-related outbreaks of disease. An outbreak is constituted by two or more persons' experiencing illness after the consumption of water intended for drinking. In cases of chemical poisoning a single case may constitute an outbreak. Causes of outbreaks are subdivided by system deficiencies, namely untreated surface water or untreated groundwater, treatment deficiencies, and distribution-system deficiencies. Waterborne-disease outbreaks are reported to CDC by state health departments on a standard reporting form. CDC believes that only a fraction of the outbreaks that actually occur are reported. The efficiency of reporting outbreaks to the health authorities varies tremendously from region to region. Once reported, the interest, diligence, and resources of the state or local health authority determine the quality of the investigation. Thus, the CDC reports cannot be considered a definitive record of the incidence of disease and etiology, a fact recognized by that agency. States with good reporting systems and a staff member interested in waterborne disease might appear to have a much higher incidence of disease than states with an equal or greater actual incidence but a poor reporting system. Similarly, an apparent increase in the number of outbreaks in recent years is probably due to more complete reporting (CDC, 1979). The pinpointing of the etiologic agent may also prove to be difficult. Table 6–2 lists some of the disease-causing pathogens and chemicals that are known to be responsible for outbreaks in the United States, and the clinical symptoms and laboratory or epidemiological criteria required for their confirmation.

The Health Effects Research Laboratory of the Environmental Protection Agency (EPA) asks all state water-supply agencies each year for information about the outbreaks of waterborne disease. These data are included in the annual CDC report. In addition, computer printouts detailing all outbreaks of disease attributable to groundwater contamination from 1945–1980 are available from this EPA laboratory in Cincinnati, Ohio. The printout lists outbreaks by state and gives the month and year of their occurrence, the number of persons affected by the illness, the etiologic agent

Table 6–2. Guidelines for Confirmation of Waterborne Disease Outbreaks Associated with Both Surface Water and Groundwater Sources

Etiologic Agent	Clinical Syndrome	Laboratory and/or Epidemiologic Criteria
1. *Escherichia coli*	a) Incubation period 6–36 hours b) Gastrointestinal syndrome—majority of cases with diarrhea	a) Demonstration of organisms of some serotype in epidemiologically incriminated water and stool of ill individuals and not in stool of controls —OR— b) Isolation from stool of most ill individuals, organisms of the same serotype which have been shown to be enterotoxigenic or invasive by special laboratory techniques
2. *Salmonella*	a) Incubation period 6–48 hours b) Gastrointestinal syndrome—majority of cases with diarrhea	a) Isolation of *Salmonella* organism from epidemiologically implicated water —OR— b) Isolation of *Salmonella* organism from stools or tissues of ill individuals
3. *Shigella*	a) Incubation period 12–48 hours b) Gastrointestinal syndrome—majority of cases with diarrhea	a) Isolation of *Shigella* organism from epidemiologically implicated water —OR— b) Isolation of *Shigella* organism from stools of ill individuals. The recovery of *Shigella* is difficult and therefore non-isolation of the organism does not prove its absence (Kawata, personal communication).
4. *Vibrio cholerae*	*a)* Incubation period 24–72 hours b) Gastrointestinal syndrome—majority of cases with diarrhea and without fever	a) Isolation of *V. cholerae* from epidemiologically incriminated water —OR— b) Isolation of organisms from stools or vomitus of ill individuals —OR—

Table 6–2 (continued)

Etiologic Agent	Clinical Syndrome	Laboratory and/or Epidemiologic Criteria
		c) Significant rise in vibriocidal, bacterial agglutinating, or antitoxin antibodies in acute and early convalescent sera, or significant fall in vibriocidal antibodies in early and late convalescent sera in persons not recently immunized
5. *Campylobacter fetus* ssp. *jejuni*	a) Incubation period not known b) Gastrointestinal syndrome—majority of cases with diarrhea	a) Isolation of *Campylobacter* organisms from epidemiologically implicated water —OR— b) Isolation of *Campylobacter* organisms from stools of ill individuals
6. *Yersinia enterocolitica*	a) Incubation period 3–7 days b) Gastrointestinal syndrome—majority of cases with diarrhea	a) Isolation of *Yersinia* organisms from epidemiologically implicated water b) Isolation of *Yersinia* organisms from stools of ill individuals c) Significant rise in bacterial agglutinating antibodies in acute and early convalescent sera
7. *Leptospira*	a) Incubation period 4–19 days b) Protean group of diseases—headache, conjunctivitis, rash, meningitis, etc.	a) Isolation of leptospires from epidemiologically implicated water b) Isolation of leptospires from blood of ill individuals c) Significant rise in bacterial agglutinating or complement fixing antibodies in acute and early convalescent sera
8. Others	Clinical data appraised in individual circumstances	Laboratory data appraised in individual circumstances
CHEMICAL		
1. *Heavy metals Antimony	a) Incubation period 5 min. to 8 hours (usually less	Demonstration of high concentration of metallic ion

*The chronic effects of heavy metals are summarized on pages 99–103.

Table 6–2 (continued)

Etiologic Agent	Clinical Syndrome	Laboratory and/or Epidemiologic Criteria
Cadmium Copper Iron Tin Zinc, etc.	than 1 hour b) Clinical syndrome compatible with heavy metal poisoning—usually gastrointestinal syndrome and often metallic taste	in epidemiologically incriminated water
2. Fluoride	a) Incubation period usually less than 1 hour b) Gastrointestinal illness—usually nausea, vomiting, and abdominal pain	Demonstration of high concentration of fluoride ion in epidemiologically incriminated water
3. Other chemicals	Clinical data appraised in individual circumstances	Laboratory data appraised in individual circumstances
PARASITIC		
1. *Giardia lamblia*	a) Incubation period: Variable; 1–4 weeks b) Gastrointestinal syndrome—chronic diarrhea, cramps, fatigue and weight loss	a) Demonstration of *Giardia* trophs in epidemiologically incriminated water —OR— b) Demonstration of *Giardia* trophs in stools or duodenal aspirates of ill individuals
2. *Entamoeba histolytica*	a) Incubation period: Variable; usually 2–4 weeks b) Variable gastrointestinal syndrome from acute fulminating dysentery with fever, chills, and bloody stools to mild abdominal discomfort with diarrhea	a) Demonstration of *Entamoeba histolytica* in epidemiologically implicated water —OR— b) Demonstration of *Entamoeba histolytica* in stools of affected individuals
3. Others	Clinical and laboratory data appraised in individual circumstances	
VIRAL		
1. Hepatitis A	a) Incubation period 15–28 days b) Clinical syndrome compatible with hepatitis—usually including jaundice, GI symptoms, dark urine	Liver function tests compatible with hepatitis in affected persons who consumed the epidemiologically incriminated food
2. Parvovirus-like Agents (Norwalk, Hawaii, Miami)	a) Incubation period 16–72 hours b) Gastrointestinal syn-	a) Demonstration of virus particles in stool of ill individuals by immune

Table 6–2 (continued)

Etiologic Agent	Clinical Syndrome	Laboratory and/or Epidemiologic Criteria
	drome—vomiting, watery diarrhea, abdominal cramps	electron microscopy —OR— b) Significant rise in antiviral antibody in acute and convalescent sera
3. Rotavirus	a) Inducation period 24–72 hours b) Gastrointestinal syndrome—vomiting, watery diarrhea, abdominal cramps	a) Demonstration of the virus in the stool of ill individual
4. Enterovirus	a) Incubation period: Variable b) Syndrome: Variable; poliomyelitis, aseptic meningitis, herpangina, etc.	a) Isolation of virus from epidemiologically implicated water —OR— b) Isolation of virus from ill individuals
5. Others	Clinical evidence appraised in individual circumstances	Laboratory evidence appraised in individual circumstances

Source: CDC, 1980.

if known, the type of water system involved and its location, the deficiency in the system that led to the outbreak, and the type of water source involved, i.e., well or spring. Prior to 1938 the national public-health records are incomplete, and diagnostic techniques were not adequate.

In the period 1971–77 there were 192 reported outbreaks of acute waterborne disease caused by all types of agents and affecting nearly 37,000 persons. Of these, 49% of the outbreaks and 42% of the illnesses were caused by the use of untreated or inadequately treated groundwater (Craun, 1979). Craun also states that a large number of outbreaks were seasonal, affecting travelers, campers, visitors to recreational areas, and restaurant patrons in the summer months, and involved non-municipal systems dependent primarily on groundwater. Of the 95 outbreaks attributable to groundwater systems, contamination by overflow or seepage of sewage, mainly from septic tanks and cesspools, was responsible for the greatest number of outbreaks and the majority of the illnesses (Table 6–3). Thirty-eight outbreaks and nearly 11,000 cases of illness due to treatment deficiencies in groundwater systems, such as inadequate or interrupted disinfection, were reported for the same time period (Craun, 1979). It should be remembered, however, that the reported outbreaks represent a fraction of the unknown total of actual occurrence.

A recent report by Hubert and Canter (1980a) reviews the available literature on the adverse effects on human health of exposure to groundwater contaminants. It examines the routes of transport and the fate of causative agents as well as the means of preventing such contamination, and explores an interaction matrix to be used in the assessment of illness due to groundwater contamination.

Acute Illness Due to Pathogenic Contaminants

Five categories of pathogens are found in water: bacteria, viruses, protozoa, worms, and fungi. The most significant waterborne diseases worldwide are still typhoid and cholera, which were a scourge in the industrialized nations, including the United States, up to the late nineteenth century (Okun, 1980). Gastrointestinal illnesses constitute the major category of illnesses resulting from groundwater contamination (Hubert and Canter, 1980a).

Bacteria

Of the more than 400 types of bacteria present in human and animal feces, *Escherichia coli,* an organism which is not usually pathogenic and is always found in the gastrointestinal tracts of humans and other warm-blooded animals, has been used for most of this century as a monitor of the safety of water for human consumption (NAS, 1977). The potential for human infection by pathogenic bacteria depends upon the bacterial survival rate and the contamination potential which, in turn, is affected by the type of soil, the rate and duration of bacterial loading, the groundwater flow, and the integrity of the media surrounding the aquifer (Hubert and Canter, 1980a). Survival times may vary from less than one day for

Table 6–3. Waterborne Disease in the U.S. Due to Source Contamination of Untreated Groundwater Systems, 1971–77

	Outbreaks	Cases of Illness
Flooding	1	88
Contamination through limestone or fissured rock	4	138
Chemical contamination	6	102
Contamination by surface runoff	5	231
Overflow or seepage of sewage	20	3,100
Data insufficient to classify	21	880
	57	4,539

Source: G. F. Craun, *Groundwater* vol. 17, no. 2 (1979), pp. 183–191. Reprinted with permission of Water Well Journal Publishing Company, Worthington, Ohio.

Salmonella typhi, Vibrio cholerae, and *Entamoeba histolytica* cysts on vegetables to several months for *Salmonellae* in soil and *Shigellae* in water containing humus (Burge and Marsh, 1978). The viability of bacteria in porous media under favorable conditions in the tropics may be five years, although 60 to 100 days might be the maximum in temperate regions (Romero, 1972). Bacteria in water flowing through porous media are removed by filtration, die-off, and adsorption (Freeze and Cherry, 1979). In medium-grained sand and finer materials, pathogenic coliform organisms only penetrate a few yards (Krone et al., 1958), whereas in sand or gravel aquifers such transport may be in the order of hundreds of yards (Krone et al., 1957). Transport in fractured rock, where relatively high groundwater velocities occur (upwards of several feet per day), permits transport in the order of miles for a microorganism whose viability may range from days to months (Freeze and Cherry, 1979).

EPA-approved testing for bacterial contamination is standardized throughout the United States (Hubert and Canter, 1980a) and consists of three phases, a presumptive test, a confirmed test, and a completed test. These procedures are summarized by NAS (1977).

The information provided by the EPA laboratory in Cincinnati shows that between 1945 and 1980 there were 94 groundwater-related outbreaks of disease nationwide that were proved to be of bacterial origin, causing 26,041 cases of illness.

Viruses

More than 100 different enteric viruses have been identified in human fecal material (WHO, 1979), and these may survive for several months in wastewater, tapwater, soil, and shellfish. In addition, the normal practice of wastewater chlorination may not be sufficiently effective to inactivate viruses. The diseases caused by enteric viruses range from rashes, diarrhea, and fever to meningitis, paralysis, encephalitis and, myocarditis (WHO, 1979) and are summarized in Table 6–4. The sources of infection include contaminated water and food pathways. The minimum infective dose of ingested viruses depends on the type of virus involved, the route of entry, and the susceptibility of the host. Doses as low as a single infectious unit may cause disease in man. The 1979 WHO report concludes that current epidemiological techniques are not sensitive enough to detect low-level transmission of viral diseases through water for two reasons. The symptoms of enteric-virus disease are too varied to be attributed to a single etiological agent or may cause inapparent infections that are difficult to recognize as being waterborne. Nearly 60% of the recently reported cases of waterborne disease in the United States were caused by unknown or unrecognized agents (WHO, 1979). Infectious hepatitis can often be attributed to the waterborne category, and 84 outbreaks

Table 6–4. Human Enteric Viruses That May Be Present in Water

Virus group	No. of types	Disease caused
Enteroviruses:		
Poliovirus	3	Paralysis, meningitis, fever
Echovirus	34	Meningitis, respiratory disease, rash, diarrhoea, fever
Coxsackievirus A	24	Herpangina, respiratory disease, meningitis, fever
Coxsackievirus B	6	Myocarditis, congenital heart anomalies, rash, fever, meningitis, respiratory disease, pleurodynia
New enteroviruses	4	Meningitis, encephalitis, respiratory disease, acute haemorrhagic conjunctivitis, fever
Hepatitis type A (probably an enterovirus)	1	Infectious hepatitis
Gastroenteritis virus (Norwalk type agents)	2	Epidemic vomiting and diarrhoea, fever
Rotavirus (Reoviridae family)	?	Epidemic vomiting and diarrhoea, chiefly of children
Reovirus	3	Not clearly established
Adenovirus	>30	Respiratory disease, eye infections
Parvovirus (adeno-associated virus)	3	Associated with respiratory disease in children, but etiology not clearly established

Note: Other viruses which because of their stability, might contaminate water are the following

(1) SV40-like papovaviruses, which appear in the urine. The JC subtype is associated with progressive multifocal leukoenceaphalopathy.

(2) Creutzfeld-Jakob (CJ) disease virus. Like scrapie virus, the CJ virus resists heat and formaldehyde; it causes a spongiform encephalopathy, characterized by severe progressive dementia and ataxia.

Source: WHO, 1979.

between 1946 and 1977 were documented in the United States (Hubert and Canter, 1980a).

Land application of wastewater for irrigation and for disposal may lead to viral contamination of the groundwater. The movement of viruses in the soil depends upon the rate of application, the composition and structure of the soil, its pH, organic content, and strength of the effluent (WHO, 1979). Viruses are readily absorbed onto clays under suitable conditions and are also removed by sandy loams and soils with a high organic content. Fractured rock permits the viruses to travel great distances unimpeded.

Current methods of monitoring viral contamination are summarized in Table 6–5 and require special facilities, thus they are not routinely performed on drinking-water samples (Hubert and Canter 1980a). Sewage-treatment processes are not likely to remove all viruses present. Sedimentation may remove 50%, the activated sludge process, 60–99%, trickling filters and stabilization ponds, 80–95%. Chemical coagulation with

Table 6–5. Methods for the Detection of Virus in Different Types of Water and Sludges

Method	Type of Sample
Direct inoculation without concentration	Wastewater, sludge
Swab sampling	Wastewater samples (method sensitive but not quantitative)
Filter adsorption/elution methods Adsorption and precipitation methods employing polyvalent cation salts Use of preformed alum, aluminum hydroxide, iron (III) oxide (50), iron (III) chloride, or lime flocs Flocculation by added salts Hydroextraction and aqueous polymer two-phase separation techniques Soluble alginate Precipitation by low pH	0.2–5.0-liter samples where more than 1 infectious unit of virus per litre is expected
Flat membranes, hollow fibre Flow-through filter adsorption of acidified samples followed by elution at high pH Single or multistage procedures	Large-volume samples, of 5–400 liters or more. In general, single-stage procedures may be used for samples of up to 20 liters—i.e. for samples containing relatively large amounts of virus such as are likely to occur in sewage, treated sewage effluents, and polluted surface water
Filtration through pleated filters followed by elution Organic flocculation followed by elution Filtration through adsorptive filters with positive charge followed by elution Adsorption to glasspowder followed by elution	Groundwaters, less polluted surface waters, and highly treated wastewater (multistage procedures)

Source: WHO, 1979.

lime achieves a 90–99% reduction (WHO, 1979). The principal sources of viral contamination of groundwater contain human and animal fecal material. They include sewage effluent disposed of in injection wells, land-waste disposal, animal feedlots and dairies, septic tanks, and cesspools (Hubert and Canter, 1980a).

Information from the EPA laboratory in Cincinnati shows that between 1945 and 1980 there were 55 outbreaks of disease due to viruses in the United States that were groundwater related, and these resulted in 3,291 cases of illness. The majority of the outbreaks were due to the hepatitis virus, but the total includes 6 outbreaks of Norwalk-type agents affecting 670 persons, 3 outbreaks due to parvovirus affecting 937 people, and one outbreak of polio affecting 16 persons.

Parasites

This category covers protozoa, worms, and fungi. Hubert and Canter (1980a) report no recorded incidents of the outbreak of disease attributable to the contamination of groundwater by parasitic organism. Outbreaks due to *Giardia, Entamoeba histolytica,* and *Ascaris lumbricoides* were reported due to the contamination of surface water, and Hubert and Canter concluded that the absence of outbreaks due to the contamination of groundwater is probably due to the size of the organisms involved. The EPA, however, in a printout of the incidence of disease due to groundwater contamination from 1945–1978, lists nine outbreaks of protozoan parasitic disease between 1953 and 1980. These outbreaks were responsible for 2,018 cases of illness due to *Giardia* in Arizona, Colorado, and Pennsylvania and 75 cases of illness due to *Entamoeba histolytica* in Arizona, Indiana, Missouri, Oklahoma, and South Carolina.

A conference on the Microbial Health Considerations of Soil Disposal of Domestic Wastewaters was held by the National Center for Ground Water Research (NCGWR) in 1981, and sponsored by the EPA. The aim of the conference was to identify important health-related research needs associated with the deposit of domestic wastes on land via septic tanks, cesspools, and land-application systems (NCGWR, 1981). The papers included reviews of the current practices of disposal, the transport and fate of various classes of pathogens, outbreaks of waterborne disease, risk evaluations, and possible control measures. Pathogen removal by soils in the land application of wastes can be improved by changing the infiltration rate (Lance, 1981). Increased pollution is often traced to the contaminated recharge water from partially treated wastes which comes in contact with groundwater (Hagedorn, 1981). Sobsey (1981) concludes that the information on the transport and fate of viruses is inadequate, especially on the mechanisms of microbially mediated antiviral activity in soils. Gerba (1981) states that the current body of information concerning viruses in groundwater is not sufficient to develop guidelines for estimating safe distances between waste sources and drinking-water wells and proposes that this gap be filled by further field studies. Cabelli (1981) describes the criticism levelled at the microbial-indicator systems most frequently used to monitor drinking water in the United States, the total-coliforms and the standard-plate count. It is thought that coliform organisms do not survive environmental stress, including disinfection or residence in wastewaters, as well as do some of the viral enteric pathogens. He suggests that alternative indicators, such as enterococci, *Clostridium perfringens* spores, acid-fast bacilli, yeasts, and coliphage, would better reflect the survival characteristics of viral pathogens and noted that two of these are used along with *E. coli* as indicators in Europe. Deficiencies in the indicator system could mean that the risk of disease is understated. An evaluation of the risk to public health of various methods of disposing of wastewater explored by Cooper and Olivieri (1981) uses a probability-matrix technique which requires data from two groups of experts. The first group delineates the health problems associated with a given process and estimates the probability of their occurence, and the second group judges the severity of the problems delineated by the first group. Boyle (1981) describes the major causes of subsurface-disposal failure leading to contamination and suggests technical and managerial remedies particularly for septic-tank failures. Despite its aim, the conference does not appear to have produced a list, in order of priority, of the health-related research needs.

When groundwater is used for drinking water by municipal suppliers, pretreatment, such as chlorination, minimizes the possibility of outbreaks of disease caused by pathogens. Deficiencies in treatment cause problems. In domestic wells with no pretreatment of the water, prevention of contamination is of paramount importance.

Acute Illness Due to the Chemical Content of Water

Acute illness due to chemical poisoning is reported in the EPA computer printout of the incidence of illness attributable to the ingestion of contaminated groundwater. Hubert and Canter (1980a) listed both the known cases of chemical contamination affecting public health and their accompanying symptoms. The EPA printout lists thirteen other reported outbreaks of disease attributable to groundwater contamination between 1959 and 1980, excluding those cases caused by toxic organic chemicals. The contaminants were selenium, copper, fluoride, nitrate, arsenic, and sodium hydroxide, and together they resulted in a total of 303 cases of illness. Reported outbreaks between 1945 and 1980 due to toxic organic chemicals totalled 6 and caused 52 cases of illness. The chemicals involved were oil wastes, phenols, pesticides, and others. The chronic effects of chemical contamination are dealt with on page 98. Weimar (1980) noted that approximately 1,000 new chemicals enter the environment each year in addition to an estimated 30,000 that already exist there. Estimates range as high as 55,000 (CEQ 1980c), but not all of these chemicals would find their way into landfills or impoundments, nor would all of them prove harmful to human health. Toxicological testing falls into two main categories, *in vivo* and *in vitro* methods. *In vivo* testing involves the use of animals and can be of long or short duration and tests for chronic or acute health effects. *In vitro* testing involves the use of isolated cells or microorganisms, usually in a culture, and the testing is usually of short duration. Epidemiological studies are of three kinds and include the collection and evaluation of data resulting from observations on human populations followed over time, or prospective studies, the comparison of death certificates of a control population, or retrospective studies, and the study of the past history of patients, or case-control studies. Hubert and Canter (1980a) note that epidemiological studies often produce inconclusive results because of the complexity of environmental factors that may be involved but not included in the studies. Although the chemical contamination of some aquifers has been established, related incidents of the effects on human health have often been established. Between 1946 and 1970 twelve chemically induced outbreaks of disease affecting 60 persons out of a total of 358 outbreaks of waterborne disease were reported, and a further 9 out of 99 outbreaks occurred from 1971 to 1974, involving 474 persons (Craun and McCabe, 1973; Craun et al., 1976), although other incidents may have gone unreported.

Many of the chemicals recently found in groundwater originate from industrial waste. A common contaminant, nitrate, however, comes mainly from natural sources—sewage disposal, animal feedlots, and the use of agricultural fertilizer. High levels of nitrate may cause methemoglobinemia in infants, indicated by cyanosis, respiratory distress, and gastrointestinal disturbances. Death may occur from the ingestion of water containing 50–100 mg/l NO_3 (Hubert and Canter, 1980a). The incidence of methemoglobinemia in the United States is not known as it is not on the list of diseases that must be reported to public-health authorities. Another, albeit chronic, health hazard associated with the ingestion of large concentrations of nitrate is the possible formation of carcinogenic nitrosamines (NAS, 1977, 1981c).

Locally occurring deposits may contaminate groundwater with arsenic, selenium, and other naturally occurring toxic compounds, rendering it unfit for human consumption. Selenium and other chemicals, although toxic in high concentrations and carcinogenic, are also a required nutrient for humans in trace amounts. Mining operations may produce unacceptable levels of trace metals (Van der Leeden et al., 1975).

Recent investigations have shown widespread contamination of groundwater by toxic synthetic organic chemicals (for a review, see CEQ, 1981a). Although little is as yet known about the potential long-term effects of these compounds when ingested in low concentrations, their acute effects via inhalation and skin absorption, but not by ingestion, have been summarized and may differ somewhat from the effects caused by their ingestion.

In conclusion it may be said that only a few cases of acute effects on public health have been documented in response to chemical contamination.

Chronic Effects of Contaminated Groundwater on Public Health

Chronic illnesses are defined as those which persist, either because the injury is persistent or progressive, or because the exposure is prolonged and the rate of new injury exceeds the rate of repair (NAS 1977). Incidents suggestive of the chronic effects on public health of groundwater contamination have been reported for cancer, malformations, miscarriage, central nervous system disorders, and cardiovascular disease, although there have been few carefully controlled epidemiologic investigations which confirm these associations (Harris, 1982). The controversy surrounding the question of whether contamination can have one or a variety of long-term effects may be divided into two parts, namely the effects associated with the mineral characteristics of the water supply and those that may be associated with its organic chemical contamination. Each will be dealt with in turn.

Chronic Disease Due to the Mineral Content of Groundwater

The maximum contaminant levels shown in Tables 5–1 and 5–2 were set taking into account the human environmental exposure over a lifetime. Standards for other chemicals that may be of concern have not been set due to a lack of data. The debate over whether or not there is a threshold below which no adverse response occurs further complicates the task of setting standards for drinking water (Okun, 1980).

Early studies of the relation between the mineral content of water and apoplexy in Japan and cardiovascular disease in the United States raised the possibility that a so-called water factor was involved (Neri et al., 1974; Sharrett, 1979; Comstock, 1979). Hubert and Canter (1980a) believe that this controversy will continue even though the American Medical Association has stated that adverse effects on health are probably due to life-style rather than to environmental factors. Comstock (1979) states that while there may be a water factor associated with the development of cardiovascular disease, its existence has not been proven. Numerous exceptions to the negative association of the hardness of water due to its calcium and magnesium content with cardiovascular disease, as well as the biological implausibility of such a theory, led Comstock to reject the notion that the elusive water factor is hardness *per se*. Similar associations between water hardness and other diseases and conditions cast doubt on the existence of even an indirect causal association between water hardness and cardiovascular disease. Comstock (1979) does agree, however, that it is possible that the high magnesium content of some hard waters may be an etiological mechanism which would prevent magnesium deficiency in some persons, thus reducing their risk of sudden cardiac death.

Sharrett (1979) considered the relation between the presence of certain minerals in drinking water—calcium and magnesium, chromium, copper, zinc, cadmium, and lead—and cardiovascular disease, and concluded that the geographic studies available do not provide consistent evidence to support such an association. None of the metals showed statistically significant correlations with mortality rates, consistent in sign, from one country or region to another. Sharrett also notes that sudden cardiac death was associated with low levels of magnesium in the tissue of persons who usually drank soft water. The concentration of lead in drinking water is correlated with levels of lead in the blood, but it is not thought to be related to cardiovascular disease.

Hubert and Canter (1980a) give an extensive summary of all the literature available on the relation between the hardness of water and coronary disease, arteriosclerosis, ischemic heart disease, hypertension, and stroke. In addition they review the inherent weaknesses of the studies to date. They point out, for example, that the correlation coefficients used in these studies are affected by chance variation and give no measure of the magnitude of the effect of drinking hard water on a person's health. They also believe that the use of standardized rather than adjusted mortality rates can lead to false assumptions. Comstock (1979) pointed out that the amount of unsoftened tap water consumed in all the studies reported to date was unknown. Neri et al. (1974), Comstock (1979), and Sharrett (1979) have questioned the statistical correlation between water hardness and cardiovascular disease and mortality rates and recommend that future studies should take into account both environmental and life-style factors.

Hubert and Canter (1980a), in reviewing the correlation between water hardness and arteriosclerotic disease, state that many studies show a negative correlation, but that this was often not significant. In the case of ischemic disease, the evidence for its association with water hardness is contradictory and inconclusive. Hypertension may be caused, among other things, by the elements sodium and cadmium, the latter's occurrence in water generally being due to anthropogenic sources (Hubert and Canter, 1980a). It has been suggested that cadmium may be leached from water pipes in soft-water areas, thus accounting for a reduction in hypertension following a change to hard-water usage (Schroeder, 1969). Indeed, other authors have suggested that water hardness may provide, together with certain trace elements such as selenium, a measure of protection against hypertension.

Hubert and Canter (1980a) summarize the conclusions to be drawn from the available literature as follows:

- The relation between water hardness and cardiovascular disease and mortality is uncertain.
- Cardiovascular disease and mortality is known to be greatly influenced by factors varying from diet to stress, and the situation is further complicated by the mineral content of potable groundwater.
- Although many studies show a statistical correlation between water hardness and cardiovascular disease, the responsible element or compound in water has not been conclusively identified.

Because of the uncertainty surrounding the water factor, Hubert and Canter (1980a) conclude that it is impossible to design a water treatment for potable groundwater to remove allegedly harmful constituents related to cardiovascular disease.

The effects on health of inorganic solutes, organic solutes, and radioactive substances in drinking water have been admirably summarized in the study on drinking water and health carried out by the National Research Council of the National Academy of Sciences (NAS, 1977; 1981a). In a later continuation of this study the epidemiological studies of water hardness and cardiovascular disease were also assessed (NAS, 1980 a and b). The panel noted that current knowledge is derived mainly from ecological epidemiological studies, those in which individual exposures and risk factors were not considered. A prior study, the Geochemistry of Water in Relation to Cardiovascular Disease (NAS, 1979), came to the following conclusions:

- Studies encompassing large geographical areas generally showed a correlation between hard water and low cardiovascular-disease rates. This correlation breaks down for smaller study areas or if the population studies are grouped by altitude or by proximity to a seacoast. The association of some noncardiovascular illnesses with soft-water areas raises the possibility that soft water may be a concomitant of some more basic risk factor.

- Most studies reported correlation coefficients rather than risk estimates as a function of exposure. Upper estimates of risk ratios for soft compared to hard water, from those studies with sufficient data to be useful in such an assessment, average approximately 1–25 for cardiovascular disease and 1–2 for arteriosclerotic, stroke, and hypertensive disease.
- Autopsy studies have reported low magnesium levels in the tissue of the heart, diaphragm, and pectoral muscle of persons who die from myocardial infarction as compared to those who die from accidental causes. Similar deficits were observed in persons living in soft-water areas as compared to hard-water areas. These findings are in line with those of Sharrett (1979), Comstock (1979), and Hubert and Canter (1980a). Wolman (in press) states that recent studies have failed to demonstrate a causal relation between water hardness and heart disease.

Berg and Burbank (1972) investigated correlations between carcinogenic trace metals in water supplies and cancer mortality. It is recognized that while certain trace metals are essential to human nutrition, higher concentrations may be harmful (Wolman, in press). Trace metals may be introduced into groundwater due to the natural local occurrence of specific minerals in the aquifer or from disposal of certain types of industrial waste. Berg and Burbank (1972) point out that present-day occurrences of cancer should be correlated with trace-metal levels of 20 to 30 years ago, but such data are not available. They compared mortalities for 34 types of cancer with the incidence of 8 metals in surface water in the United States. The positive correlations of 28 were double the number expected. No significant correlations were found for iron, cobalt, or chromium. The correlations for lead were positive for kidney cancer, all lymphoma and leukemia, and intestinal cancer mortalities, which correspond to the known biological activities of lead. Beryllium was significantly correlated with all cancers, and this, the authors considered, also reflected its biological activity. Arsenic and nickel are thought to be human carcinogens. It should be mentioned that arsenic compounds have not been reliably demonstrated to produce tumors in laboratory animals, but epidemiological studies show that the incidence of certain cancers and precancerous conditions increases in humans who are chronically exposed to arsenic compounds by oral or respiratory routes (NAS, 1981a). The results are shown in Table 6–6. Cadmium showed the strongest correlations with the most types of cancer, and although cause and effect are by no means proven, the authors suggested further studies.

Table 6–6. Statistically Significant Positive Correlations Between Metal Concentrations and Cancer Death-Rates

Metal	Cancer (ICD)	Probability of Positive Association
Arsenic	Larynx (161)	0.024
	Eye (192)	0.009
	Myeloid leukemia (204.1)	0.042
Beryllium	Breast (women) (170)	0.040
	Uterine cervix (171)	0.016
	Other uterus (172–174)	0.006
	Bone (196)	0.024
	All cancers (140/205)	0.016
Cadmium	Mouth and pharynx (140/149)	0.003
	Esophagus (150)	0.00004
	Large intestine (153/154)	0.00001
	Larynx (161)	0.004
	Lung (162/163)	0.001
	Breast (women) (170)	0.003
	Bladder (181)	0.009
	Myeloma (203)	0.008
	All lymphomas (200/203, 205)	0.016
	All cancers (140/205)	0.0005
Chromium	None	
Cobalt	None	
Iron	None	
Lead	Stomach (151)	0.0026
	Small intestine (152)	0.038
	Large intestine (153/154)	0.009
	Ovary (175)	0.02
	Kidney (180)	0.008
	Myeloma (203)	0.042
	All lymphomas (200/203, 205)	0.0005
	All leukemia (204)	0.006
Nickel	Mouth and pharynx	0.044
	Large bowel	0.031

Source: J. W. Berg and F. Burbank, *Annals of the New York Academy of Sciences* 199 (1972), p. 252. Reprinted by permission of New York Academy of Sciences.

Some evidence indicates that low levels of certain metals may have a protective effect against cancer. Pories et al. (1972), stating that iodine is the best known inhibitor of experimental neoplastic growth, also found such inhibitory properties were shown by arsenite, copper, platinum, selenium, and zinc. Inclusion in the diet of arsenite decreased the incidence of all tumors in animals and also stunted carcass growth. Copper is known to potentiate the biological activity of certain anti-cancer agents. This could be due to the fact it is a potent free radical inhibitor or because it shields specific sites on liver protein molecules. It is known that there is a high frequency of pre-existing goiter, a condition caused by iodine deficiency, in patients with thyroid cancer. Platinum is known to halt cell division, and although its neoplastic inhibitory mechanism is unknown, it may be due to a platinum-induced release of viral genomes initiating an antibody reaction against the tumor. Dietary selenium of 1 ppm reduced the incidence of animal tumors. It is known that cancer death rates are higher in areas with low selenium levels. Zinc deficiency decreases tumor growth in animals, but its role in human cancer is not well understood, and the data are contradictory.

Thus, although trace minerals are necessary to health, higher concentrations may be harmful. Excessive concentrations of certain minerals have been implicated in the various chronic forms of cardiovascular disease and cancer, but the studies to date are not conclusive. It is possible that water containing certain heavy metals may also protect against a broad spectrum of human tumors. Although the evidence is fragmentary, it deserves further investigation (Pories et al., 1972).

Chronic Disease Due to Contamination by Toxic Organic Chemicals

Burmaster's comprehensive report, *Contamination of Ground Water by Toxic Organic Chemicals,* was published by the Council on Environmental Quality (CEQ, 1981a). He reviewed the sources of toxic organic contamination, methods of prevention, incidents involving drinking-water contamination, and estimates of the health risks due to toxic organic chemicals. The Safe Drinking Water Committee of the National Academy of Sciences has also reviewed the effects of organic solutes on human health (NAS, 1977) and the toxicity of selected organic contaminants (NAS, 1981a).

Many toxic organic chemicals are colorless, tasteless, and odorless in the concentrations at which they occur in drinking water. CEQ (1981a) found that hundreds of drinking-water wells which had provided domestic water for millions of persons had been closed over a period of three years due to contamination by synthetic organic chemicals and that the concentrations of these chemicals were often orders of magnitude higher than those found in surface water. This would be a reflection of the lack of mixing and the minimal dispersion that occurs in contaminated plumes of groundwater in comparison with surface water.

Table 6–7. Probabilities of Detecting Toxics in New Jersey Groundwater and Surface Water

	probability detectable in groundwater	probability detectable in surface water	significantly different at 0.05 level
fluoroform	0.03	0.08	yes
methyl chloride	0.01[a]	0.04	yes
vinyl chloride	0.01[a]	0.03	yes
methylene chloride	0.23	0.45	yes
chloroform	0.64	0.64	no
1,2-dichloroethane	0.10	0.12	no
1,1,1-trichloroethane	0.78	0.79	no
carbon tetrachloride	0.64	0.68	no
1,1,2-trichloroethylene	0.58	0.56	no
dichlorobromoethane	0.34	0.43	yes
1,1,2-trichloroethane	0.07	0.09	no
dibromochloromethane	0.14	0.18	yes
1,2-dibromoethane	0.08	0.06	no
1,1,2,2-tetrachloroethylene	0.43	0.88	yes
bromoform	0.22	0.33	yes
1,1,2,2-tetrachloroethane	0.06	0.11	yes
diiodomethane	0.06	0.02	yes
total dichlorobenzene	0.03	0.07	yes
m-dichlorobenzene	0.02	0.04	yes
p-dichlorobenzene	0.03	0.06	yes
o-dichlorobenzene	0.03	0.03	no
aroclor 1242	0.11	0.08	no
aroclor 1248	0.06	0.14	yes
aroclor 1254	0.03	0.14	yes
gem-dichloroethylene	0.44	0.65	yes
dibromomethane	0.12	0.28	yes
trans-dichloroethylene	0.51	0.63	yes
bromodichloroethane	0.18	0.06	no
BHC-alpha	0.16	0.39	yes
lindane	0.21	0.34	yes
BHC-beta	0.50	0.60	yes
heptachlor	0.21	0.21	no
aldrin	0.26	0.24	no
heptachlor epoxide	0.26	0.40	yes
chlordane	0.40	0.56	yes

Table 6–7. (continued)

	probability detectable in groundwater	probability detectable in surface water	significantly different at 0.05 level
o,p'-DDE	0.19	0.44	yes
dieldrin	0.17	0.39	yes
endrin	0.11	0.14	no
o,p'-DDT	0.09	0.18	yes
p,p'-DDD	0.10	0.27	yes
p,p'-DDT	0.08	0.17	yes
arsenic	1	1	no
beryllium	1	1	no
cadmium	1	1	no
copper	1	1	no
chromium	1	1	no
nickel	1	1	no
lead	1	1	no
selenium	1	1	no
zinc	1	1	no

[a]Probability is less than 0.01.

Source: G. W. Page, *Environmental Science and Technology* vol. 15, no. 12, (1981), p. 1425. Reprinted by permission of the American Chemical Society.

Page (1981), using data collected by the New Jersey Department of Environmental Protection, compared groundwater and surface water for patterns and levels of contamination by toxic substances. Samples from 1,000 wells and 600 surface-water supplies in New Jersey were analyzed for 56 toxic substances: 27 light chlorinated hydrocarbons, 20 heavy chlorinated hydrocarbons, and 9 heavy metals. The probabilities of detecting them are shown in Table 6–7. For 64% of the toxics, the highest concentration was found in groundwater, and Page considered that this may pose a significant threat to some persons consuming groundwater. Similarly high concentrations of contaminants in groundwater were also found in other states and reported to CEQ (1981a). These are shown in Table 6–8. Page (1981) states that in New Jersey, since groundwater is at least as contaminated as surface water and the patterns of contamination are similar for the two, an emphasis should be given to the control of toxic chemicals in groundwater equal to that given to their control in surface water.

Greenberg et al. (1981), also using data collected by the New Jersey Department of Environmental Protection, examined population exposure

Table 6–8. Toxic Organic Chemicals Found in Drinking-Water Wells

Chemical	Concentration (ppb)	State	Highest surface water concentration reported (ppb)
Trichloroethylene (TCE)	27,300	Pennsylvania	
	14,000	Pennsylvania	
	3,800	New York	160
	3,200	Pennsylvania	
	1,530	New Jersey	
	900	Massachusetts	
Toluene	6,400	New Jersey	
	260	New Jersey	6.1
	55	New Jersey	
1,1,1-Trichloroethane	5,440	Maine	
	5,100	New York	5.1
	1,600	Connecticut	
	965	New Jersey	
Acetone	3,000	New Jersey	NI
Methylene chloride	3,000	New Jersey	
	47	New York	13
Dioxane	2,100	Massachusetts	NI
Ethyl benzene	2,000	New Jersey	NI
Tetrachloroethylene	1,500	New Jersey	
	740	Connecticut	21
	717	New York	
Cyclohexane	540	New York	NI
Chloroform	490	New York	
	420	New Jersey	700
	67	New York	
Di-n-butyl phthlate	470	New York	NI
Carbon tetrachloride	400	New Jersey	30
	135	New York	
Benzene	330	New Jersey	
	230	New Jersey	4.4
	70	Connecticut	
	30	New York	
1,2-Dichloroethylene	323	Massachusetts	

Table 6–8. (continued)

Chemical	Concentration (ppb)	State	Highest surface water concentration reported (ppb)
	294	Massachusetts	9.8
	91	New York	
Ethylene dibromide (EDB)	300	Hawaii	
	100	Hawaii	NI
	35	California	
Xylene	300	New Jersey	
	69	New York	24
Isopropyl benzene	290	New York	NI
1,1-Dichloroethylene	280	New Jersey	
	118	Massachusetts	
	70	Maine	0.5
1,2-Dichloroethane	250	New Jersey	4.8
Bis (2-ethylhexyl) phthalate	170	New York	NI
DBCR (Dibromochloropropane)			
	137	Arizona	
	95	California	NI
	68	California	
Trifluorotrichloroethane	135	New York	NI
	35	New York	
Dibromochloromethane	55	New York	317
	20	Delaware	
Vinyl chloride	50	New York	9.8
Chloromethane	44	Massachusetts	12
Butyl benzyl phthlate	38	New York	NI
gamma-BHC (Lindane)	22	California	NI
1,1,2-Trichloroethane	20	New York	NI
Bromoform	20	Delaware	280
1,1-Dichloroethane	7	Maine	0.2
alpha-BHC	6	California	NI
Parathion	4.6	California	0.2
delta-BHC	3.8	California	NI

NI = Not Investigated
Source: CEQ, 1981a.

to toxic substances in New Jersey. The State of New Jersey organized a research program in response to the news that its residents showed the highest white male cancer rate in the United States (Mason and McKay, 1974). Non-white male and female and white female rates were also among the highest in the country. These findings have been criticized for lack of proper controls for critical variables (Demopoulos and Gutman, 1980). Analyses for forty-five substances were carried out on 408 groundwater samples, representing a cross section of locations and land and water uses. The results showed that pesticide contamination tends to occur in agricultural and forest areas, and light chlorinated hydrocarbon pollution in urban areas.

The contamination of groundwater by synthetic organic chemicals has come to light relatively recently, mainly because they are not routinely monitored. The regional offices of EPA report serious contamination of drinking-water wells in 34 states and say that this estimate may rise to 40. Over 33 toxic chemicals which have been found in wells are listed in Table 6–8 (CEQ, 1981a).

Synthetic organic chemicals, including most chlorinated hydrocarbons, can cause health problems ranging from acute effects from high doses, such as nausea, dizziness, tremors, and blindness to skin eruptions and central-nervous-system impairment at lower concentrations. CEQ (1981a) suggested that ingestion of low concentrations of synthetic organic chemicals over an extended period of years may prove fatal. Studies of occupational medicine, cancer studies using laboratory animals, and epidemiological studies were reviewed by CEQ to determine the possible long-term effects of such exposure. Most of the epidemiological evidence linking drinking-water contaminants with cancer was based on surface-water sources, as were the studies on cardiovascular disease and water hardness. Although the risk assessment of the ingestion of surface water cannot be directly applied to the ingestion of groundwater because the two sources may contain quite different compounds, it nevertheless provides useful insights into the cancer risks associated with some chemicals or classes of chemicals common to both. Absolute risks are very difficult to measure,. usually apply only to the specific population for which they are determined, and are influenced by all the other pertinent characteristics of the specific population. Relative risks, however, are more likely to apply to other populations, although they, too, are influenced by the characteristics of the population exposed. The effects of chlorination are likely to be limited to the use of surface waters, however, because groundwater generally has a low humic-acid content, and it is these acids that react with chlorine during the chlorination process to produce trihalogenated methanes. Furthermore, groundwater from domestic wells, as opposed to municipal wells, usually does not undergo chlorination prior to use (G. W. Comstock, Johns Hopkins University, personal communication). The ecological epidemiological studies of surface-water ingestion suggest an association between either chlorination or the presence of trihalogenated methanes and cancer mortality in several areas of the United States. In five case studies in New York, Illinois, Wisconsin, Louisiana, North Carolina, the risk of rectal cancer was found to be higher for populations supplied by chlorinated water than for those supplied by unchlorinated water. Colon cancer risks were statistically significantly raised in three of the studies, New York, Wisconsin, and North Carolina, and bladder cancer risks in two, New York and North Carolina. No clear trend was evident to determine whether cancer risks increased with increasing exposure to organic contaminants (CEQ, 1981a). The associations of certain types of cancer with the ingestion of chlorinated water are thought by many investigators to be non-specific and probably associated with something else beside water exposures (G. W. Comstock, Johns Hopkins University, personal communication). Surface-water sources are more likely to be chlorinated than groundwater sources of drinking water. Studies of occupational exposure have shown that some chemicals have adverse effects on human reproductive, central nervous, and other systems, but there is no direct human evidence to indicate whether exposure to such chemicals, at the highest concentrations found in groundwater, would represent a significant threat to human reproduction (CEQ, 1981a).

Evidence from animal studies of carcinogenicity has been reviewed for 31 of the 33 compounds listed in Table 6–8 and is summarized in Table 6–9. Two are known to be human carcinogens, 10 are confirmed animal carcinogens, 2 are suggested animal carcinogens, 1 (1, 1, 1-Trichloroethane) showed negative evidence of being an animal carcinogen in animal bioassays, but 15 had yet to be tested as animal carcinogens.

A problem exists on how maximum contaminant levels (MCLs) for water-borne contaminants should be established to best protect the public health. Page (in press) notes that estimates for the cost of establishing carcinogenicity in one compound can range between $500,000 to $1.25 million and the procedure is time-consuming. Very few of the contaminants in water supplies have been so tested. Conolly (1980) testified at the EPA oversight hearings on groundwater contamination that the metabolism for dichloroethylene and dichloroethane has been studied, and that it is known that they pass through reactive intermediate stages in which they have a potential for damaging living tissue. The actual damage depends on the particular chemical, the rate of metabolism, and the ability of the organism to tolerate the presence of reactive intermediates. Conolly defines two types of carcinogens. The first are the genetic carcinogens, those which cause genetic changes and may well cause

Table 6–9. Selected Synthetic Organic Chemicals Detected in Drinking-Water Wells

Chemical	Evidence for Carcinogenicity
Benzene	H
alpha-BHC	CA
beta-BHC	NTA
gamma-BHC (lindane)	CA
Bis (2-ethylhexyl) phthalate	NTA
Fromoform	NTA
Butyl benzyl pthlate	NTA
Carbon tetrachloride	CA
Chloroform	CA
Chloromethane	NTA
Cyclohexane	NTA
Dibromochloropropane	CA
(DBCP)	NTA
Dibromochloromethane	SA
1,1-Dichloroethane	CA
1,2-Dichloroethane	NTA
1,1-Dichloroethylene	NTA
1,2-Dichloroethylene	NTA
Di-n-butyl phthlate	CA
Dioxane	CA
Ethylene dibromide (EDB)	NTA
Isopropyl benzene	NTA
Methylene chloride	SA
Parathion	CA
Tetrachloroethylene	NTA
Toluene	NA
1,1,1-Trichloroethane	CA
1,1,2-Trichloroethane	CA
Trichloroethylene (TCE)	NTA
Triflurotrichloroethane	H, CA
Vinyl chloride	NTA
Xylene	

H—Confirmed human carcinogen
CA—Confirmed animal carcinogen
SA—Suggested animal carcinogen
NA—Negative evidence of carcinogenicity from animal biossay
NTA—Not tested in animal bioassay

The evidence for benzene and vinyl chloride was from epidemiological studies.

Source: CEQ, 1981a.

cancer at low concentrations. The second type are the epigenetic carcinogens, those whose effects are primarily acute toxicity and the chronic irritation of tissues which may lead to cancer at high concentrations. Conolly said that synergism of contaminants is a new area of study in which very little is known. As the contamination of groundwater is usually from a group of chemicals, synergistic effects could be very important and should be taken into account when MCLs are set.

Until MCLs are established there are two possibilities for action that have been suggested. Either all potential carcinogens and toxic substances could be eliminated from the water supply in case they cause future harm, or such action could be delayed until its potential benefits are better elucidated. The long time lag between exposure to a carcinogen and the appearance of malignancy is yet another complicating issue. As it could take up to 30 years to establish MCLs for contaminants on the priority pollutant list, some prudent interim measure could be adopted if deemed necessary.

The lack of comprehensive nationwide surveys of the extent and severity of groundwater contamination and the paucity of groundwater contaminants that have actually been tested for carcinogenicity make it impossible to assess the national risk of drinking groundwater (CEQ, 1981a; Hubert and Canter, 1980a). We do know, however, that in their pure form, at least some of the chemical contaminants are carcinogenic, that at high concentrations and in pure form some cause reproductive problems or affect the central nervous system or the cardiovascular system, and that in high concentrations some compounds cause poisoning and other problems such as skin rashes and diarrhea. The pathogens probably cause more outbreaks of disease than are actually reported (Hubert and Canter, 1980a). Thus, adverse effects on human health have resulted from exposure to contaminated groundwater, but more research is required on the actual incidence and causal agents of disease and a more rigorous inventorying of outbreaks of water-related disease would be very useful. Long-term monitoring of well water and the health of the population dependent on it might elucidate the cancer and cardiovascular risks and should be undertaken in the near future.

Seven

The Geographical Extent of Groundwater Contamination

- The U.S. EPA commissioned five regional assessment reports summarizing geology, major aquifers, natural groundwater quality, and major pollution problems for the southwest, south-central, southeast, northeast, and northwest regions of the United States.
- The Environmental Assessment Council compiled anecdotal data of case histories of contamination for ten states in different regions of the country: Arizona, California, Connecticut, Florida, Idaho, Illinois, Nebraska, New Jersey, New Mexico, and South Carolina.
- Contamination in each region or state reflects the hydrogeology, climatic conditions, population density, and degree of industrial and/or agricultural activity.
- Major types of contamination across the country based on these studies are chlorides, nitrates, heavy metals, and hydrocarbons.
- New studies might well reveal new sources of contamination.

Regional Assessments of Groundwater Contamination in the United States Conducted by EPA

EPA commissioned five regional assessments of groundwater in the United States in the 1970s. An additional three reports that were to have covered Alaska and Hawaii, the Great Lakes area, and the north-central region were not completed. The reports summarize the geology, major aquifers, natural groundwater quality, and major pollution problems of each area. The regions dealt with were: Arizona, California, Nevada, and Utah (Fuhriman and Barton, 1971); the Northeast (Miller et al., 1974); the south-central states (Scalf et al., 1973); the northwest United States (Van der Leeden et al., 1975), and the southeast United States (Miller et al., 1977). The findings for all the principal sources of contamination are shown in Table 7–1. The priority listing of contaminants reflects the hydrogeology, climatic conditions, population density and, degree of industrial or agricultural activity for each of these regions. The perception of the relative significance of the sources of contamination may have changed recently due to a greater knowledge of the occurrence of toxic organic chemicals. Natural pollution is considered to be the most important source of contamination in the arid south-central and southwestern states. The extensive agricultural irrigation that has transformed parts of the Southwest into a major crop-producing area causes problems from irrigation return-flow. The slow rate of recharge of many of the confined and unconfined aquifers in this area, coupled with extensive withdrawals, has led to an overdraft of groundwater and concomitant changes in its quality. The south-central region, being the major area of petroleum production, has a major problem with oil-field brines. The main cause for concern in the Northeast, Northwest, and Southeast was considered to be individual septic-tank systems because of their

Table 7–1. Sources of Groundwater Pollution Throughout the United States and Their Importance for Each Region

	North-east	North-west	South-east	South-central	South-west
Natural Pollution					
Mineralization from Soluble Aquifers				1	1
Water from Fault zones, Volcanic Origin					2
Evapotranspiration of Native Vegetation				2	2
Aquifer Interchange					3
Groundwater Development					
Connate Water Withdrawal					3
Overpumping/Land Subsidence				1	4
Underground Storage of Water/ Artificial Recharge	4		1	4	

Table 7–1. (continued)

	North-east	North-west	South-east	South-central	South-west
Water Wells	4				
Saltwater Encroachment	3	4	3		1
Agricultural Activities					
Dryland Farming		1			
Animal Wastes, Feedlots		4		3	
Crop Residues, Dead Animals		4			4
Pesticide Residues	4	3	2		4
Irrigation Return Flow		1		2	1
Fertilization of Agricultural Land	4	3	2		2
Mining Activities	2	2	2		3
Waste Disposal					
Septic Tanks/Cesspools	1	1	2	2	1
Land Disposal, Municipal and Industrial Wastes			3	2	2
Landfills	1	3	1		
Surface Impoundments		2	1	3	
Radioactive Waste Disposal		3			
Injection Wells for Waste Disposal		2		4	2
Disposal of Oil Field Brines				1	1
Miscellaneous/Other					
Accidental Spills	2	3	1	3	2
Urban Runoff					3
Highway Deicing Salts	1	4	4		
Seepage of Polluted Surface Waters	3		4		3
Buried Pipelines and Storage Tanks		1			
Abandoned Oil and Test Wells	1				
Petroleum Exploration and Development	3		4		

Numbers indicate orders of priority of contamination:
1 = high 3 = medium low
2 = medium high 4 = low

Sources: Adapted from tables used in Fuhriman and Barton, 1971; Miller et al., 1974; Scalf et al., 1973; van der Leeden et al., 1975; Miller et al., 1977.

sheer numbers and density. The Northeast and Southeast both have problems associated with industrial development, namely buried pipelines and storage tanks and landfills and impoundments. It should be noted that the assessment for the Northeast was completed in 1974, before the publicity attendant on Love Canal and the Valley of the Drums had made public the potential threat of such dump sites and spurred additional investigations. All the regional reports were completed before the 1978 Surface Impoundment Assessment made the number of potential sites of contamination available.

Keeley (1976) points out that some problems found to be indigenous to one area may not occur in another, but several sources of groundwater contamination occur at a higher or moderate degree of severity in each area investigated. He notes that the four pollutants most commonly reported in the five regional investigations are chlorides, nitrates, heavy metals, and hydrocarbons, but that this may merely be a reflection of the monitoring practices in effect. Sampling for organic chemicals, of which there are thousands associated with municipal and industrial wastes, is not routine and is also expensive. Keeley (1976) also makes the important point that the priorities among the problems in the five regions were not established on the basis of hard statistical information, as such information was not and is not available. The priorities were established empirically on the basis of the experience of the authorities and individuals who have worked in the five regions studied.

State Summaries Compiled in 1981–82 by the Environmental Assessment Council for This Report

Recent federally mandated surveys under the Safe Drinking Water Act (SDWA) have produced more information concerning the number of potential sites where groundwater contamination might occur (U.S. EPA, 1978b). In addition, many individual states have recently undertaken inventories of case histories of their groundwater contamination. No systematic national sampling survey has yet been carried out. The data presented here are from known incidents of contamination. They give an indication of the most commonly reported groundwater-contamination problems in the states studied. They should not be generalized on a nationwide basis. For an accurate nationwide assessment, a systematic survey is indispensable. For the purpose of this report, each state was asked to provide such information if it was available. The information received varied in its usefulness to this study. Some states have completed their inventories, while others have only just started or are still in the process of documentation. One or two states report that, for them, groundwater contamination is not a major problem. We have taken a sample of the states to investigate further whether the additional information available over the last few years could cast more light on the severity and patterns of occurrence of groundwater problems. The states discussed in this report were chosen mainly because they had the most extensive case histories of groundwater contamination, but they also serve as examples of differing levels of industrialization, agricultural activity, population density, dependence on groundwater, and climatic conditions. These characteristics are summarized in Tables 7–2 and 7–3. The states we have chosen to look at in more detail are Arizona, California, Connecticut, Florida, Idaho, Illinois, Nebraska, New Jersey, New Mexico, and South Carolina. For each of these, summaries of the groundwater usage, the major aquifers and their characteristics, the natural groundwater quality and major sources of contamination are given.

The format for the charts reporting contamination is a modification of that used by Lindorff and Cartwright (1977). An explanation of the categories follows:

- The contaminants are divided by source rather than constituents as the latter are not always specified.
- Industrial and manufacturing products and wastes may be liquid or solid. Wood processing plants were included in this category. Where the wastes were specified as petroleum or its derivatives the case histories were included under that category.
- Landfill leachate is derived from solid, semisolid, or liquid waste of either municipal or industrial origin.
- Petroleum products include, among many others, home-heating oil and aircraft fuel.
- Chlorides usually are designated as originating from highway deicing salts, agricultural return-flow, oil-field brines or saltwater intrusion.
- Organic wastes are those derived from plant, animal, or human wastes and include those from feedlots, dairy barns, fruit and vegetable processing plants, and sewage.
- The category "Others" or "Miscellaneous" contains such examples as residue from water softeners and outbreaks of disease due to pathogens.

In order to give an idea of the severity of contamination, it is noted whether the incident threatened or actually affected a drinking-water supply, either municipal or domestic, where the information was available. In addition, threats of fire, explosion, and outbreaks of disease are listed where known. Although many case histories do not detail how the contamination was detected, some do, and these are given in the "Means of Detection" section. The discovery of groundwater contamination is not an end in itself, and there are many remedial actions that can be taken to alleviate or reduce the problem, even though these are often costly. Where such actions

(Text continues on p. 121)

Table 7–2. General Land-Use Profiles for States Appearing in the "State Summaries" and "Aquifer Classification" Sections

Groundwater as % of total water use, 1975	ARIZONA 61%	CALIFORNIA 38	CONNECTICUT 5	FLORIDA 18	IDAHO 31	ILLINOIS 15	MAINE 4
Population, 1980	2,718,425	23,667,565	3,107,576	9,746,342	944,038	11,426,596	1,125,027
% Change in population from 1970	53.1%	18.5	2.5	43.5	32.4	2.8	13.2
% of population that is rural, 1980*	16.2%	8.7	21.2	15.7	46.0	16.7	52.5
Total land area (millions of acres)	72.96	101.57	3.21	37.54	53.48	36.06	21.29
Rank in size	6	3	48	22	13	24	39
% of total acreage used for cropland, 1978	2.2%	1.2	7.8	12.0	12.4	70.3	3.2
% of cropland that is harvested farmland, 1978	70.7%	75.9	71.4	61.4	73.5	90.0	70.8
% of cropland that is pastureland, 1978	9.1%	13.9	22.2	28.9	11.5	6.0	14.2
% of cropland that is used for cover crops, 1978**	0.2%	0.7	2.3	1.4	1.2	1.4	4.7
# of manufacturing establishments, 1977	2,892	45,289	6,485	12,399	1,495	19,517	2,157
Value added by manufacture, 1977 (millions of dollars)	$3,333	54,862	10,934	9,255	1,430	40,279	2,343

Table 7–2. (continued)

Groundwater as % of total water use, 1975	MASSACHUSETTS 4%	NEBRASKA 68	NEW HAMPSHIRE 6	NEW JERSEY 11	NEW MEXICO 50	NEW YORK 4	NORTH CAROLINA 9	SOUTH CAROLINA 3	WYOMING 6
Population,1980	5,737,037	1,569,825	920,610	7,364,823	1,302,981	17,558,072	5,881,813	3,121,833	469,557
% Change in population from 1970*	0.8%	5.7	24.8	2.7	28.1	−3.7	15.7	20.5	41.3
% of population that is rural, 1980	16.2%	37.1	47.8	11.0	27.9	15.4	52.0	45.9	37.3
Total land area (millions of acres)	5.30	49.51	5.94	4.98	77.82	31.43	33.71	19.91	62.60
Rank in size	45	15	44	46	5	30	28	40	9
% of total acreage used for cropland, 1978	5.9%	45.2	3.3	15.1	3.0	19.7	18.5	17.5	4.4
% of cropland that is harvested farmland, 1978	68.7%	73.4	69.0	82.0	53.0	72.5	73.2	73.9	65.5
% of cropland that is pastureland, 1978	24.9%	10.5	23.5	11.1	20.9	19.3	15.9	18.0	18.3
% of cropland that is used for cover crops, 1978**	1.4%	1.5	0.8	1.9	3.0	1.4	2.4	1.1	1.1

Table 7–2. (continued)

Groundwater as % of total water use, 1975	MASSACHUSETTS 4%	NEBRASKA 68	NEW HAMPSHIRE 6	NEW JERSEY 11	NEW MEXICO 50	NEW YORK 4	NORTH CAROLINA 9	SOUTH CAROLINA 3	WYOMING 6
# of manufacturing establishments, 1977	11,133	1,965	1,825	15,696	1,323	36,578	9,954	4,229	505
Value added by manufacture, 1977 (millions of dollars)	$16,349	2,867	2,175	22,853	734	44,290	18,231	8,186	382

*Rural areas are those with less than 1,000 people/sq. mile; also, areas with less than 2,500 people.

**Cover crops are those planted to protect the land from freezing or erosion and are not harvested.

Sources: U.S. Dept. of Commerce, 1981; U.S. Dept. of Commerce, 1980; U.S. Dept. of Commerce, 1978.

Table 7–3. Economic Activities That Could Contribute to Groundwater Contamination

ARIZONA	*manufacturing*—electrical, communications, aeronautical equipment; produces over half the nation's copper.
CALIFORNIA	*manufacture* of transportation equipment, machinery, electronic equipment; principal *natural resources*—petroleum, cement, nat. gas.
CONNECTICUT	*manufacturing*—weapons, sewing machines, jet engines, helicopters, motors, hardware, tools, cutlery, clocks, ballbearings, submarines. *agriculture*—grows, per acre, the nation's most valuable tobacco crop.
FLORIDA	*agriculture*—oranges and grapefruits; also, sugarcane, tomatoes, beans, celery, potatoes, field corn, watermelons, limes, mangos. *natural resources*—produces 80% of nation's phosphate.
IDAHO	*mining*—produces more than ⅓ of all silver mined in U.S.; also, antimony, lead, garnet, cobalt, phosphate rock, vanadium, zinc, mercury. *agriculture*—produces ¼ of nation's potatoes.
ILLINOIS	*agriculture*—nation's biggest exporter of agricultural products. *livestock*—second largest producer of hogs. *manufacturing*—iron and steel production in Chicago area.
MAINE	*agriculture*—produces 9.4% of the national potato crop and 95% of nation's low-bush blueberry crop. 90% of land is forested. *manufacturing*—fifth largest producer of boots and shoes.
MASSACHUSETTS	*manufacturing*—electronics and communications equipment industries. *agriculture*—nation's largest cranberry crop.
NEBRASKA	*agriculture*—leading grain producer; bumper crops of rye, corn, wheat. Omaha—nation's largest meatpacking center; second largest cattle market in world.
NEW HAMPSHIRE	*manufacturing*—leather goods, electrical and other machinery, textiles, pulp and paper products. *agriculture*—small farming in fruits, vegetables, poultry, dairy.
NEW JERSEY	*industry*—chemicals; also, pharmaceuticals, instruments, machinery, electrical goods, apparel; one of world's foremost research centers. *agriculture*—garden vegetables, poultry farming, dairying.
NEW MEXICO	*mining*—leader in output of uranium, potassium salts; also, petroleum, natural gas, copper, gold, silver, zinc, lead, molybdenum. *industry*—leader in energy research and development—nuclear, geothermal.
NEW YORK	*manufacturing*—second largest manufacturing center in country—apparel, printing, publishing. *agriculture*—leading wine producer; also, dairying, poultry.

Table 7–3. (continued)

NORTH CAROLINA	*manufacturing*—largest producer of furniture, brick, textiles; also, metalworking, chemicals, paper. *mining*—leading producer of mica and lithium. *agriculture*—largest producer of tobacco.
SOUTH CAROLINA	*manufacturing*—asbestos, wood, pulp, steel products, chemicals, machinery, apparel. *agriculture*—second largest grower of peaches; fourth in tobacco.
WYOMING	*mining*—most important industry; oil and natural gas; leads nation in production of sodium carbonate and bentonite; second in production of uranium. *agriculture*—wheat, oats, sugar beets, corn, potatoes, barley, alfalfa; second largest producer of wool.

Source: Dolmatch, 1982.

have been taken, they are listed in the appropriate section of the charts. A discussion of possible remedial actions and their cost is given in Chapter 9 of this report.

Finally, it should be emphasized again that the case histories listed here are not part of a national, random-sampling survey but rather so-called anecdotal data based on reported individual cases of groundwater contamination. As such, they only indicate the potential magnitude of the problem rather than document its actual magnitude. Because of the nature of the charts, the information contained therein provides an indication of the range and importance of some point sources, but not of all non-point sources. Where the latter are of importance, for example, in Nebraska, a separate analysis of the importance of such sources is given where information is available.

Arizona

Arizona uses 4,800 million gallons per day (mgd) of groundwater, representing 61% of its total water use (Fuhriman and Barton, 1971). The state is divided into five groundwater basins: the Upper and Lower Santa Cruz, White Mountain, Salt River Valley, and Upper Salt River Basins (Arizona Division of Health Services, 1979). The Upper and Lower Santa Cruz Basins and the Salt River Valley comprise an area known as the Basin and Range Lowlands Province, where the two major population centers of Arizona are located—Tucson and Phoenix. This area uses the most groundwater in the state and has the highest potential for contamination. Greater than 95% of all groundwater pumped in Arizona is consumed in this province. Sixty percent of the water consumed here is groundwater. The Upper Santa Cruz Basin is 100% dependent on groundwater. Eighty-five percent of all industrial activity and 60% of all mining activity occurs in the Basin and

Range area. A majority of its aquifers are highly permeable, unconsolidated alluvial material which produces high well yields. The northeastern part of the state has very limited groundwater potential (Fuhriman and Barton, 1971). Groundwater withdrawals exceed recharge throughout most of the state.

Very few cases of groundwater contamination are known to have occurred, as a total of only 23 incidents have been reported (Table 7–4). All of them threatened or affected the water supplies. The most common source of contamination was industrial wastes at 30%, or 7 cases, closely followed by landfill leachate at 26%, or 6 cases, and human and animal wastes at 26%, or 6 cases. Each of the incidents involving human and animal wastes led to outbreaks of disease. The incidents were discovered, for the most part, by investigation, and in only 26% of the cases was some sort of remedial action taken. It should be noted that, although only 2 incidents of natural pollution were reported, Arizona is considered to have areas of hard water (see Figure 3–7), and natural leaching of the soil by percolating waters causes natural accumulations of minerals which may limit the uses to which the groundwater may be put (Fuhriman and Barton, 1971). The presence of phreatophytes also increases the mineral content of the water and Fuhriman and Barton (1971) consider natural pollution to be significant in Arizona.

California

California uses more groundwater than any other state in the nation—approximately 13.39 bgd (California Department of Water Resources, 1975). Groundwater supplies about 40% of the state's water needs. The largest groundwater reservoir underlies the Central Valley Region, which occupies 10% of California's land area and includes the San Joaquin Valley (Thomas and Phoenix, 1976).

Most of California's groundwater occurs in alluvial sediments in the valleys and plains flanking mountain ranges. These sediments have mainly been deposited by existing streams. Groundwater basins underlie approximately 40% of the state's land area (Figure 7–1) and have a total storage capacity for water of about 424 trillion gallons (California Department of Water Resources, 1975). The usable portion of this total, that is, "the reservoir capacity that can be shown to be economically capable of being dewatered during periods of deficient surface supply and capable of being resaturated, either naturally or artificially, during periods of excess surface supply" (Fuhriman and Barton 1971), is estimated to be 47 trillion gallons (California Department of Water Resources, 1975). The proportion of usable storage that is actually occupied varies from region to region. In northern California, the annual draft on groundwater is replenished by recharge. Central and southern California, on the other hand, experience serious

Table 7–4. Arizona: Summary of Information from Documented Case Histories

Contaminant	Total	Cases Affecting or Threatening Water Supplies		Cases Causing or Threatening Fire or Explosion	Effects on Public Health	
		Afftd.[1]	Threat.		Documented	Potential
Industrial Wastes[2]	7(30%)	3	4			
Landfill Leachate	6(26%)		6			
Petroleum Products						
Chlorides (road salt and oil field brine)						
Organic Wastes	6(26%)	6			6	
Pesticides[3]	1					
Radioactive Wastes						
Mine Wastes[4]	1	1				
Natural Contamination						
—Lead	1		1			
—Hexavalent Chromium	1		1			
Totals	23	11(48%)	12(52%)		6	
Means of Detection						
Well Contamination	7			Not Mentioned	5	
Investigation	11			Fumes in Basement		
Stream Contamination				Fumes in Ground		
Spill on Ground				Fumes in Sewer Line		
Leak Discovered				Animal Deaths		

Table 7–4. (continued)

Remedial Action

Direct		Indirect	
Ground Water Pumped and Treated		Extent of Ground-Water Contamination Determined	2
Contaminated Soil Removed		—Leading to Remedial Action	1
Trench Installed		—No further Action	1
Artificial Recharge Employed		New Water Supply Provided	
Nutrients Added		Action Being Considered	
Source of Contamination Eliminated		Monitoring Begun	
Surface Water Collected and Treated		Damages Awarded	
Landfill Site Closed	2	Charcoal Filters Installed	
Site Regraded		None Mentioned	16(69%)
		Well Abandoned	3

1. Afftd. = affected; Threat. = threatened
2. Industrial Wastes—Trichloroethylene (TCE) contamination in Tucson area from Hughes Aircraft dumping during WW II. Counted as one case.
3. Pesticides—Dibromochloropropane (DBCP), pesticide for nematodes, is a major contaminant of wells in Yuma County. 33 wells out of 76 wells sampled are contaminated. Counted as one case.
4. Mine Wastes—Tailings ponds from copper mining are a major contaminant in the Globe-Miami area. Counted as one case.

Sources: Arizona Division of Health Services, 1979; Fuhriman and Barton, 1971; Hadeed, 1979; Lemmon, 1980; Robertson, 1975; Schmidt, 1972; Schmidt, 1973; U.S. EPA, 1981a.

overdrafts of groundwater due to low-precipitation and high-evaporation rates. Precipitation falling on valley floors in the southern half of the state generally remains within the depth of the soil penetrated by plants (California Department of Water Resources, 1975). Only in years with exceptionally heavy precipitation is there enough moisture to penetrate below the root zone. Annual groundwater pumping exceeds recharge in several basins, resulting in an overdraft of 717 billion gallons annually. In 1972 about 489 billion gallons of this annual overdraft was in the San Joaquin Valley. The California Water Plan of 1957 was designed to answer overdraft problems by proposing facilities for the storage and transport of surface water from places of surplus in order to satisfy water demands in the areas of overdraft. Today California has an elaborate aqueduct system to recharge needy aquifers artificially (Figure 7–2).

Overall groundwater quality in the state is considered to be good and beneficial for all uses (California Department of Water Resources 1975). There is no readily accessible complete inventory of case histories of groundwater contamination in California available, but some information on general and persistent contamination problems in the state will be summarized. As the data often do not refer to specific cases of contamination but to generalized occurrences, it has not been possible to compile a chart similar to those of the other states.

The California State Water Resources Control Board identified six general statewide groundwater problems of present or potential concern (California State Water Resources Control Board, 1980):

1. Nitrate concentrations from various sources are increasing, causing a current problem in some areas, a potential problem in other areas. Animal wastes are one potential source of nitrate contamination. In 1968 beef and dairy cattle numbered almost 1,900,000 head, most being fed on the open range (Fuhriman and Barton, 1971). Poultry numbered 260 million, and the hog population was at 150,000 head.

Estimated Wastes Generated per Year	
Solid Wastes	23,000,000 tons/yr.
BOD	810,000 tons/yr.
Nitrogen	220,000 tons/yr.
Phosphorus	44,000 tons/yr.

2. The overdraft of groundwater has resulted in seawater intrusion of the 262 coastal groundwater basins (Fuhriman and Barton, 1971), mineralization due to recirculation or percolation of used water, and induced connate water migration. The most serious seawater intrusion has occurred in the following areas (Fuhriman and Barton, 1971):

- The West Coast of Los Angeles County

- East coastal plain pressure area of Orange County
- Petaluma Valley in Sonoma County
- Napa-Sonoma Valley in Napa and Sonoma Counties
- Santa Clara Valley in the San Francisco Bay area
- Pajaro Valley in Monterey and Santa Cruz Counties
- Salinas Valley area in Monterey County
- Oxnard Plain Basin in Ventura County
- Mission Basin in San Diego County

In the Los Angeles area, three barriers have been constructed against seawater encroachment. Overdrafting has also resulted in land subsidence which has been most severe in the San Joaquin Valley, where subsidence in excess of 20 feet has occurred in some areas (Fuhriman and Barton, 1971). Land subsidence may be responsible for cases of arsenic contamination in this region. It is thought that arsenic adheres to clay particles and, as the pressure is increased in the soil due to the subsidence of the land, the arsenic goes into solution.

3. In the absence of officially designated hazardous-waste dumpsites, there has been a significant amount of illegal dumping. Many rubbish sites do not conform to regulation. Fuhriman and Barton (1971) identified 207 legal sites which had inadequate control of surface drainage.
4. Percolation ponds for handling industrial and military wastes are often inadequate for the types of wastes being disposed. Oil-field brines and brines from water-softener regeneration plants are particularly troublesome (California Department of Water Resources, 1975).
5. Crop-dusting has introduced numerous pesticides which have the potential to reach groundwater.
6. The design of proper monitoring wells may be the biggest roadblock to the process of establishing waste-discharge requirements.

Contamination problems have also been identified on a more regional basis. The U. S. Geological Survey (USGS) has divided California into nine hydrologic regions (Figure 7–1), and each has a Regional Board.

Region One, North Coast. This consists of areas of remote wilderness and redwood stands (California State Water Resources Control Board, 1980). Tourism and timber-harvesting are important to the economy. Water quality is generally good to excellent. Potential contamination problems include the disposal of wood-processing wastes into unlined ponds along the Russian River, producing arsenic, chromic compounds, and phenols, and the build-up of nitrates where percolation ponds overlie recharge areas along rivers and coastal terraces (California State Water Resources Control Board, 1981).

Region Two, San Francisco Bay This region is highly urbanized. Agriculture is the major activity in Napa, Petaluma, Sonoma, and lower Santa Clara Valleys, and in eastern Contra Costa County (California State Water Resources Control Board, 1980). Contamination sources of major concern (California State Water Resources Control Board, 1981) include the poultry ranches in the Petaluma area, which have increased the level of nitrates in local groundwaters. Elevated levels of trace metals from unknown sources have been discovered in Santa Clara Valley. Monitoring is continuous in these areas. There is a widespread use of individual waste-disposal systems, which have the potential to cause serious problems in the future.

Region Three, Central Coast Santa Cruz and Monterey Peninsula are the major urban areas, and agriculture and food processing are the major industries. The economy is also supported by oil production, tourism, and manufacturing. Water quality is generally good to excellent. Contamination problems of major concern include seawater intrusion into coastal aquifers and increases in nitrate concentration in many areas. Waste discharges to land and certain agricultural practices have also increased the salinity of the groundwater. Salt limits have been placed on municipal waste discharges. There are also serious overdrafts within the Paso Robles groundwater basin. Chemical and pesticide use are actively monitored and controlled to insure the protection of the groundwater.

Region Four, Los Angeles Half the water supply in this region is imported, the other half comes from local groundwater supplies. The southern part of this region is densely populated and industrial. There is intensive urban development in the coastal plain, San Fernando Valley, San Gabriel Valley, and the adjoining foothills. The northern Ventura–Santa Clara basin is rugged and mountainous, with large undeveloped areas. Contamination problems of major concern include elevated levels of trace metals in Santa Clara Valley, a lack of hazardous-waste disposal sites, and high nitrate concentrations in San Gabriel Valley. Fifty-four wells in San Gabriel Valley and Los Angeles County were found to be contaminated with trichloroethylene (TCE). Cleanup operations are proceeding.

Region Five, Central Valley This area contains 40% of the state lands and the majority of its streams. Rainfall averages over 100 inches per year in the north and less than 5 inches per year in Kern County. The Sacramento and San Joaquin Rivers dominate the stream system. Stream water is used for irrigation and municipal water supply. Contamination problems of major concern for groundwater include the improper disposal of oil-field brines and cut water. Brines are known to have percolated into the groundwater around Tulare Lake in 1980. There is also concern for disposal and industrial wastes, about which very little information is available. The pesticides dibromochloropropane (DBCP) and methyl bromide are toxic substances which are commonly a problem in groundwaters. Nitrate problems from many sources occur in the developed foothills of the Sacramento and San Joaquin Valleys. Industrial and military discharges and illegal dumping of contaminants have been found at Aerojet-General, Occidental, and Mather and McClellan. Aerojet-General, one of the nation's largest producers of liquid- and solid-propellant rocket engines, created a major groundwater contamination problem when groundwater beneath the corporation's land became polluted with inorganic chemicals, a herbicide, arsenic, phenols, perchlorate, trichloroethylene, and several other suspected carcinogens. A cleanup project began in mid-1981. Leaching of wood-processing wastes into groundwater is a problem in the Upper Sacramento Valley and other foothill areas.

Region Six, Lahontan This region is divided into northern and southern sub-basins. Agriculture and cattle grazing dominate the economy in the north. Lake Tahoe and the Truckee River are the major tourist highlights of the north basin. The southern basin is primarily desert. Agriculture and military and space installations support the economy. Groundwater-contamination problems of major concern include nitrate contamination from septic tanks along the Truckee River and in Sierra Valley. Another potential problem is the disposal of toxic substances at Edwards Air Force Base. Municipal and industrial wastewater discharges 20 to 50 years ago also created a plume of poor quality groundwater in Barstow, known as the "Barstow Slug." Proposals are being made for cleanup.

Region Seven, Colorado River Basin This region includes the irrigated agricultural lands of the Coachella, Imperial (valued for winter crops), Palo Verde, and Bard Valleys. Excellent quality groundwater is available for domestic use. Colorado River water is imported for irrigation and groundwater recharge. The contamination problems of major concern include elevated concentrations of nitrates in most groundwater basins from sewage systems and agricultural operations and a serious overdraft, particularly in the upper Coachella Valley. More imported water is needed for recharge. Existing disposal sites in Imperial Valley need to be relocated since they are subject to washout or flooding. The reinjection of geothermal brines into groundwater zones other than the geothermal-production zone has degraded usable groundwaters. The build-up of pesticides in soils is also a potential problem.

Region Eight, Santa Ana This area includes 2,800 square miles of valley floor and mountains. Valleys overlie extensive groundwater basins divided into upper and lower Santa Ana and the San Jacinto River watershed. Upper basin groundwaters are somewhat overdrawn but of good quality. The lower Santa Ana River watershed is highy urbanized and covers most of

Orange County. Groundwater in Orange County has been severely overdrawn. In the mid-1950s seawater intruded four miles inland because of overdraft (Toups, 1974). Several million acre-feet of Colorado River water have been imported to recharge groundwater basins so as to prevent seawater intrusion. Other contamination problems of major concern include high concentrations of nitrates, particularly in the Redlands, Upper Santa Ana River, and Chino basin areas, salt imbalance leading to increased mineralization in the San Jacinto Valley, and the abandoned Stringfellow Class I Hazardous-Waste Site, which threatens a groundwater basin downstream. About 32 million gallons of hazardous wastes were deposited at this Riverside County site between 1956 and 1972. Wastes escaped from disposal ponds on several occasions. Cleanup is ongoing.

Region Nine, San Diego Along this 85 miles of fully urbanized coastline, the contamination problems of major concern include a serious overdraft which is responsible for the high salinity of groundwater from saltwater encroachment and degradation from agricultural and other nonpoint sources. There is a serious lack of data for this region.

Connecticut

Connecticut uses very little groundwater to meet its freshwater needs—116 mgd, representing 8.2% of its total water use (Handman et al., 1979). Nearly one-third of the groundwater used, or 34.2 mgd, goes for public supply; the domestic supply comes entirely from groundwater, about 49.0 mgd; 30.8 mgd is used by industry. The remaining 1.19 mgd is used for livestock, irrigation, and miscellaneous activities.

Connecticut has two major types of aquifers—unconsolidated and bedrock—which produce water with a natural quality that is good to excellent. Calcium and bicarbonate are the principal ions in most samples; sodium, sulphate, chloride, and silica are the other major inorganic constituents. The water is generally soft to moderately hard. Iron and manganese are the most common problem constituents. Groundwater quality varies between aquifers and within relatively short distances of the same aquifer.

Connecticut provided details of 64 cases of groundwater contamination (Table 7–5), 58% or 37 of which affected the water supplies. In addition, Rolston et al. (1979) have mapped 450 wells known to have produced contaminated water and Miller et al. (1974) reported that "several dozen" wells were contaminated by saltwater intrusion in the Long Island Sound area. Due to lack of specific information these were not included in the chart. The most frequently reported or known contamination stems from industrial or manufacturing products and wastes, which account for 44% of the cases. No remedial action was reported for over 70% of the cases.

Table 7–5. Connecticut: Summary of Information from Documented Case Histories

Contaminant	Total	Cases Affecting or Threatening Water Supplies		Cases Causing or Threatening Fire or Explosion	Public Health Effects	
		Afftd.	Threat.		Documented	Potential
Manufacturing & Industrial Wastes	28(44%)	19	1			
Landfill Leachate	5					
Petroleum Products	10	4				
*Chlorides (road salt and saltwater intrusion)	7	4				
Organic Wastes (plant, animal and human)	9	7			5	
Pesticides/Fertilizers	2	1				
Radioactive Wastes						
Mine Wastes						
Others	3	2				
Totals	64	37(58%)	1		5	
Means of Detection						
Well Contamination	31			Not Mentioned	10	
Investigation	6			Fumes in Basement		
Stream Contamination	2			Fumes in Ground		
Spill on Ground	3			Fumes in Sewer Line		
Leak Discovered	7			Fumes in Water	3	
Others	7			Animal Deaths		

Table 7–5. (continued)

Remedial Action

Direct		Indirect		
Ground Water Pumped and Treated	4	Extent of Ground Water Contamination Determined		2
Contaminated Soil Removed		—Leading to Remedial Action	2	
Trench Installed		—No further Action		
Artificial Recharge Employed		New Water Supply Provided		6
Nutrients Added		Action Being Considered		
Source of Contamination Eliminated	2	Monitoring Begun		1
Surface Water Collected and Treated		Damages Awarded		
Landfill Site Closed	1	Charcoal Filters Installed		
Site Regraded	1	None Mentioned		45(70%)
Others	3			

*Miller et al. (1974) stated "several dozen" wells contaminated in the Long Island Sound area—as no specifics given, treated as one case.

Sources: Handman and Bingham, 1980; Handman et al., 1979; Miller et al., 1974; U.S. EPA, 1981a; Lindorff and Cartwright, 1977; U.S. Congressional Research Service, 1980.

Florida

Florida is a major user of groundwater, requiring more than 3,000 mgd in 1975, representing 18% of its total water use. In 1970, 760 mgd of groundwater were used for public water supply, 180 mgd for rural uses, 1300 mgd for irrigation, and 710 mgd for industrial uses (Miller et al., 1977). Rural and public water supplies were most heavily dependent on groundwater, drawing 96% and 86%, respectively, of their fresh water from aquifers. Irrigation was least dependent, using groundwater for only 57% of its water needs.

There are four major types of aquifers in Florida that naturally produce water of good quality—the sandy, chalky limestone Floridian aquifer, the limestone, sandstone Biscayne aquifer, the sand and gravel aquifer, and the shallow sand aquifer (Miller et al., 1977). The Floridian aquifer produces water that is both hard and low in iron and fluoride. The Biscayne aquifer contains very hard water, which is also more mineralized and more alkaline than that of the other aquifers. The sand and gravel aquifer has very soft water, which is acidic and, while high in iron, it is low in other mineral content. It is very vulnerable to nitrate contamination. The shallow aquifer contains alkaline, hard water, with a low iron content, and it is also susceptible to nitrate contamination.

Florida has recently completed an inventory of its known cases of groundwater contamination, and 92 cases were reported. Of these, 63% affected or threatened water supplies (Table 7–6). In fact, 50% of the cases were discovered via the contamination of wells. The most significant sources of groundwater contamination are chlorides from saltwater intrusion and agricultural return-flow and industrial or manufacturing products or wastes, which accounted for a total of 72% of the cases. Of all the cases, only 35% of them have had any kind of remedial action applied.

Idaho

In 1975 Idaho used 5,600 mgd of groundwater, representing 31% of the total water used in that state (Lehr, 1981). Fourteen percent of the total groundwater used goes to irrigation (Van der Leeden et al., 1975). There are five major drainage basins in Idaho. The Snake River Basin, the largest, is the home of 86% of the state's population. One of the world's most productive aquifer systems, the Snake Plain Aquifer, lies here under the Snake Plain, which is a great structural depression covering 10,040 sq. miles. It is filled with a series of basaltic flows alternating with beds of pyroclastic and sedimentary materials. The aquifer supplies over 70% of the water needs of 200 municipal water-supply systems and about 100 industrial plants. Idaho's groundwater is generally of good quality, with localized incidences of a high content of dissolved solids, sodium, and fluoride. The biggest natural groundwater problem is hardness.

There are relatively few documented case histories of groundwater

Table 7–6. Florida: Summary of Information from Documented Case Histories

Contaminant	Total	Cases Affecting or Threatening Water Supplies Afftd.	Threat.	Cases Causing or Threatening Fire or Explosion	Public Health Effects Documented	Potential
Manufacturing & Industrial Wastes	32(35%)	7	4			
Landfill Leachate	4	2	1			
Petroleum Products	1					
Chlorides (agricultural return flow and saltwater intrusion)	34(37%)	33				
Organic Wastes (animal, plant and human)	8	5			2	
Pesticides/Fertilizers	4	1				
Radioactive Wastes	1					
Mine Wastes	2	1				
Others	6	4			4	
Totals	92	53(58%)	5		6	
Means of Detection						
Well Contamination	46(50%)			Not Mentioned	15	
Investigation	19			Fumes in Basement		
Stream Contamination	2			Fumes in Ground		
Spill on Ground	1			Fumes in Sewer Line		
Leak Discovered	3			Animal Deaths		
Others	8					

Table 7–6. (continued)

Remedial Action

Direct		Indirect	
Ground Water Pumped and Treated	1	Extent of Ground Water Contamination Determined	5
Contaminated Soil Removed		—Leading to Remedial Action	
Trench Installed		—No further Action	
Artificial Recharge Employed		New Water Supply Provided	9
Nutrients Added		Action Being Considered	1
Source of Contamination Eliminated	1	Monitoring Begun	3
Surface Water Collected and Treated		Damages Awarded	
Landfill Site Closed		Charcoal Filters Installed	
Site Regraded		None Mentioned	56(61%)
Others	22		

NB. In Florida the documentation phase is still underway.

Sources: Florida Department of Environmental Regulation, 1980, 1981a and b; Miller et al., 1977; U.S. EPA, 1981a.

Table 7–7. Idaho: Summary of Information from Documented Case Histories

Contaminant	Total	Cases Affecting or Threatening Water Supplies		Cases Causing or Threatening Fire or Explosion	Public Health Effects	
		Afftd.	Threat.		Documented	Potential
Industrial Wastes	4(14%)	2	2			
Landfill Leachate	1	1				
Petroleum Products	3	3				
Chlorides (road salt and oil field brine)	1		1			
Organic Wastes	14(48%)	11	2		7	2
Pesticides	1		1			
Radioactive Wastes	3(10%)	1	2			
Mine Wastes	2		2			
Totals	29	18(62%)	10(34%)		7	2
Means of Detection						
Well Contamination	10			Not Mentioned		
Investigation	12			Fumes in Basement		
Stream Contamination				Fumes in Ground		
Spill on Ground				Fumes in Sewer Line		
Leak Discovered				Animal Deaths		
				Outbreaks of Illness	7	

Table 7–7. (continued)

Remedial Action

Direct		Indirect	
Ground Water Pumped and Treated	1	Extent of Ground-Water Contamination Determined	2
Contaminated Soil Removed		—Leading to Remedial Action	
Trench Installed	1	—No further Action	2
Artificial Recharge Employed		New Water Supply Provided	
Nutrients Added		Action Being Considered	1
Source of Contamination Eliminated	1	Monitoring Begun	4
Surface Water Collected and Treated		Damages Awarded	1
Landfill Site Closed		Charcoal Filters Installed	
Site Regarded		None Mentioned	16(55%)
Agricultural Drain Well Capped	2		

Sources: U.S. EPA, 1981a; Van der Leeden et al., 1975; U.S. EPA, 1978b; Lindorff and Cartwright, 1977.

contamination (Table 7–7), but there are several potential sources of contamination to be concerned about. The National Reactor Testing Station is located in the eastern part of the Snake River Plain. The disposal of liquid-wastes is constantly monitored and, as of 1975, strontium-90 was the only contaminant to exceed the maximum standard for drinking water (Van der Leeden, 1975). The majority of radionuclides disposed of here have short half-lives and are of no consequence. Mining is another potential source of contamination. There is mining on a large-scale for silver, lead, zinc, sand, gravel, and stone. Many abandoned mines are potential hazards. There are 11 abandoned coal mines, 1,749 abandoned metal mines, and 208 abandoned non-metal mines. The extensive agricultural industry in Idaho presents several potential contamination hazards. Fertilizers and pesticides are used in large quantities. Dieldrin, now banned but once used heavily for the control of Weiss worm in potatoes, still persists in the soil. In 1973 there were 563 feedlots, mostly located along the Snake River. There are at least 5,000 domestic and agricultural waste-disposal wells located in the Snake River Plain. A few cases of serious contamination have resulted due to the high permeability of the aquifer. Of the 29 known incidents, the majority, 14 or 48%, are due to contamination from human and animal organic wastes. Industrial and radioactive wastes combined account for 24% of the cases. Of the incidents, 62% actually affected the water supplies, and 34% threatened them. Thirty-one percent of the contamination incidents resulted in, or posed the threat of, outbreaks of disease. The means of detection was usually by well contamination or by investigation. In 55% of the cases no mention was made of any applied remedial action.

Illinois

In Illinois, groundwater is the source of fresh water for approximately 1,600 public water-supply systems and the principal source for industry, agriculture, and almost all private water-supply systems in the state (Gibb and O'Hearne, 1980). The state was using about 1,000 mgd of groundwater in 1978, which accounted for about 8% of its total freshwater use. In 1970, 38% of the entire state population and 82% of the rural population was dependent on groundwater as a drinking source (Piskin et al., 1980).

The principal aquifers in Illinois are of three major types—unconsolidated sand and gravel formations, partially cemented sandstone, and consolidated deposits of creviced limestone or dolomite (Walker, 1969). The shallow sand and gravel aquifers have a high potential for contamination, as do outcropped areas of creviced limestone found in western and southern Illinois and the shallow dolomite formations of northern Illinois.

Fifty-eight cases of contaminated groundwater have been documented in Illinois. The summary of information from documented case histories is shown in Table 7–8. Of the known incidents of groundwater contamination,

Table 7–8. Illinois: Summary of Information from Documented Case Histories

Contaminant	Total	Cases Affecting or Threatening Water Supplies		Cases Causing or Threatening Fire or Explosion	Public Health Effects	
		Afftd.	Threat.		Documented	Potential
Industrial Wastes	12(21%)	7	5			
Landfill Leachate	16(28%)	2	6			
Petroleum Products	3	1				
Chlorides (road salt and oil field brine)	6	1	1			
Organic Wastes (animal & human)	20(34%)	18	2		15	
Pesticides						
Radioactive Wastes						
Mine Wastes	1	1				
Totals	58(25.9%)	30(52%)	14(24%)		15	
Means of Detection						
Well Contamination	10			Not Mentioned	5	
Investigation	20			Fumes in Basement	1	
Stream Contamination				Fumes in Ground		
Spill on Ground	3			Fumes in Sewer Line		
Leak Discovered	2			Animal Deaths	2	
				Illness	15	

Table 7–8. (continued)

Remedial Action

Direct		Indirect	
Ground Water Pumped and Treated	1	Extent of Ground Water Contamination Determined	
Contaminated Soil Removed		—Leading to Remedial Action	
Trench Installed	2	—No further Action	
Artificial Recharge Employed		New Water Supply Provided	7
Nutrients Added		Action Being Considered	4
Source of Contamination Eliminated	6	Monitoring Begun	4
Surface Water Collected and Treated	1	Damages Awarded	2
Landfill Site Closed	6	Charcoal Filters Installed	
Site Regraded	1	None Mentioned	16
Impoundments Upgraded	1		

Sources: Piskin et al., 1980; Walker, 1969; U.S. EPA, 1981a; Lindorff and Cartwright, 1977; U.S. Congressional Research Service, 1980.

44 of them, or 76%, affected or threatened the water supplies. The prevalent source of contamination is animal and human wastes, of which there are 20 cases, or 34%, followed by industrial waste and landfill leachate at 21% and 28%, respectively. Groundwater from shallow wells often has large concentrations of nitrate. Eighty-one percent of the dug wells, which were less than 50 feet deep, contained more than 10 mg/l nitrate-nitrogen, as opposed to 34% of the deeper, drilled wells in Washington County (NAS, 1977). Every incident of contamination from animal or human wastes affected or threatened the water supplies. The majority of incidents, 45 cases, or 78%, were detected by well contamination, investigation, and the outbreaks of illness. Illinois has a good record for applying remedial actions, as 66% of the incidents have received some sort of action.

There are no documented cases of groundwater contamination from waste-injection wells, but they are potentially hazardous sources of contamination (Ford et al., 1981). In Illinois there are 9 Class I wells (the deepest variety, injecting below the deepest underground source of drinking water), and 17,167 Class II wells, which are related to enhanced recovery of oil and gas, brine-injection, and liquid-hydrocarbon-storage wells. There are no Class III wells in Illinois.

Nebraska

This predominantly agricultural state uses nearly twice as much groundwater as Florida, 5,900 mgd, or 68%, of its total water supply coming from groundwater (Lehr, 1981). Most of this is supplied by the extensive Ogallala Aquifer, which underlies parts of Texas, Kansas, and Nebraska (see page 45). Other aquifers of importance are the Holocene or Pleistocene aquifers that occur in the principal river valleys, and the Pleistocene sands and gravels (Engberg and Spalding, 1978). The natural quality of groundwater is generally good. The mean total dissolved solids count from 1,518 wells was 474 mg/l. (The maximum contamination level for total dissolved solids as established by the National Secondary Drinking Water Regulations is 500 mg/l.) Most crops can tolerate this level.

The cases of groundwater contamination due, for the main part, to point sources are summarized in Table 7–9. Of the 35 incidents, 34% threatened or affected the water supplies. Incidents involving pesticides and fertilizers accounted for 15, or 43%, of the cases, but these compounds are also involved in non-point source contamination (Table 7–10). The second most significant source of contamination is plant, animal, and human wastes, accounting for 11 cases, or 31%. Most of the incidents were discovered following an investigation, and in 74% of the cases no remedial action was reported.

Various surveys in Nebraska sampled 4,350 wells and found that 700, or 16% of all those sampled, contained NO_3–N_2 contamination in excess

Table 7–9. Nebraska: Summary of Information from Documented Case Histories

Contaminant	Total	Cases Affecting or Threatening Water Supplies		Cases Causing or Threatening Fire or Explosion	Public Health Effects	
		Afftd.	Threat.		Documented	Potential
Manufacturing & Industrial Wastes	4	3				
Landfill Leachate						
Petroleum Products						
Chlorides (agricultural return flow & oil field brine)	3	1				
Organic Wastes (plant, animal and human)	11	3	1			
Pesticides/Fertilizers	15	2				
Radioactive Wastes						
Mine Wastes						
Others	2	2			1	
Totals	35	11(31%)	1		1	
Means of Detection						
Well Contamination	4			Not Mentioned	6	
Investigation	17			Fumes in Basement		
Stream Contamination				Fumes in Ground		
Spill on Ground				Fumes in Sewer Line		
Leak Discovered				Fumes in Water	1	
Others	5			Animal Deaths		

Table 7–9. (continued)

Remedial Action

Direct		Indirect	
Ground Water Pumped and Treated	1	Extent of Ground Water Contamination Determined	
Contaminated Soil Removed		—Leading to Remedial Action	
Trench Installed		—No further Action	
Artificial Recharge Employed		New Water Supply Provided	1
Nutrients Added		Action Being Considered	1
Source of Contamination Eliminated	3	Monitoring Begun	
Surface Water Collected and Treated		Damages Awarded	
Landfill Site Closed		Charcoal Filters Installed	1
Others	4	None Mentioned	25 (71%)

Depletion of stream flow was found at 20 of 49 stations analyzed due to groundwater reduction. Water table declines of up to 30 feet have occurred in areas of intense groundwater irrigation development.

Table 7–10. Nebraska: Summary of Groundwater Pollution Due to Nitrate—Nitrogen Pollution

Problem area identification will start in December 1981 under the state groundwater protection program.

Nitrate contamination. Samples taken from wells from 1976–80.

Number of Wells Sampled	Number of Wells With Nitrate–Nitrogen Contamination		Non-Point	Point
34	20		19	1
537	118		118	—
557	61		3	58
581	17		—	17
558	45		5	40
566	102		102	—
575	29		29	—
615	55		55	—
53	53		53	—
18	17		17	—
256	183		174	9
Total 4350	700		575	125
% 100	16	As % of NO_3-Nitrogen Contaminated Wells	82	18

Sources: Tables 7–9 and 7–10: Nebraska Department of Environmental Control, 1980a, b and 1981; Engberg and Spalding, 1978; U.S. EPA, 1981a; Spalding and Exner, 1980; Junk et al., 1980; Spalding et al., 1978a, b and 1979; Gormley and Spalding, 1979; Exner and Spalding, 1979; University of Nebraska, 1980.

of the standard of 10 mg/l (Table 7–10). Studies showed that of the contaminated wells, 575, or 82%, were contaminated by non-point sources such as the nitrogen fertilizer contained in irrigation return-flow. Septic tanks, barnyards, and feedlots are point-sources which accounted for the remaining 125, or 18% of the cases reported.

In Figure 7–3 the upper map shows the distribution of pumping wells in Nebraska, and the lower map shows areas where the water table has been lowered and the small area where an elevation has actually taken place. Increases in the level of the water table have been caused primarily by infiltration of surface water that has been diverted for irrigation purposes. Of the 49 stations analyzed, the stream flow was down in 20, indicating a drop in groundwater level. Nebraska designated three control areas in 1977 and 1979 where regulations are being or have been developed to control the rate of groundwater pumpage.

New Jersey

New Jersey, one of the most densely populated regions in the United States, has more than 16,000 potable wells (Tucker, 1981).

Sixteen percent of the drinking water in the state is derived from underground sources. In the southern half of the state, more than 90% of the population receives its drinking supply from groundwater. In 1976 it was estimated that 406 mgd of groundwater went to public supply, 75 mgd to rural supply, 118 mgd to industry, and 53 mgd to irrigation—a total of 652 mgd, or 54% of the total fresh water supply used in New Jersey. The aquifers of the state produce water that is generally of good quality. In the northwestern half of the state, there are several types of consolidated aquifer formations.

The most extensive formation is one composed of shale, slate, and sandstone and produces poor well yields. The Kittatinny Limestone Aquifer is a major one with high well yields, many in excess of 100 gallons per minute (gpm). Sandstone and quartzite formations occur here and are poor aquifers. Gneiss, schist, and granite formations produce well yields in the range of 5–10 gpm. In the southeastern half of the state, unconsolidated aquifers of sand, gravel, clay, silt, and marl are found which produce very high well yields of 500–700 gpm. Water from the northwest is hard to very hard, and water from the southeast is soft to moderately hard. In some areas there are high concentrations of iron and chloride. Some formations on the coastal plain contain saline water below a depth of 1,000 feet.

In 1981 New Jersey completed an extensive sampling of its groundwater aquifers for toxic chemical contamination and in addition compiled a comprehensive inventory of groundwater-contamination cases, 374 incidents in total. The aquifer samples for chemical analysis were collected from a random sampling of wells throughout the state, a sampling that was, however, designed to cover all the different areas. Where problems were found, extra investigations of potential sites of contamination in the same area were conducted. The contamination inventory lists all known groundwater pollution in the state but may not include new cases. Tables 7–11 to 7–15 give information about the known incidents of contamination. Of 166 cases of contamination due to legal industrial, domestic, and municipal dumping (Table 7–11), 73% were due to dumping of industrial wastes, and 44% of these threatened or affected the water supplies. Contamination due to the disposal of animal or human wastes accounted for 11% of the incidents, but 84% of these cases affected the water supply, and 42% resulted in outbreaks of disease. In all but 15 of the cases, or 91%, some form of remedial action or monitoring program has been instituted.

Table 7–12 shows the incidents of contamination attributable to accidental spills. Most, 85%, involved petroleum products and of these, 55% threatened or affected the water supplies. Of the total of 163 incidents, 92, or 57%, affected or threatened water supplies. In all but 10% of the incidents some form of remedial action or monitoring program has been instituted.

Table 7–13 shows 26 cases of groundwater contamination that are

Table 7–11. New Jersey: Summary of Information from Documented Case Histories of Industrial, Domestic, and Municipal Dumping

Contaminant	Total	Cases Affecting or Threatening Water Supplies: Afftd.	Cases Affecting or Threatening Water Supplies: Threat.	Cases Causing or Threatening Fire or Explosion	Public Health Effects: Documented	Public Health Effects: Potential
Industrial Wastes	122(73%)	34(28%)	19(16%)			
Landfill Leachate						
Petroleum Products	11	3				
Chlorides (road salt and oil field brine)	5	4				
Organic Wastes (human and animal)	19(11%)	16(84%)			8(42%)	
Pesticides	4					
Radioactive Wastes						
Mine Wastes	1	1				
Miscellaneous	4					
Totals	166	58(35%)	19(11%)		8(5%)	
Means of Detection						
Well Contamination	34			Not Mentioned	20	
Investigation	76			Fumes in Basement		
Stream Contamination	9			Fumes in Ground		
Spill on Ground	4			Fumes in Sewer Line		
Leak Discovered	1			Animal Deaths		
Soil Contamination	9			Outbreak of Illness	8	
				Septic Overflow	2	

Table 7–11. (continued)

Remedial Action

Direct		Indirect		
Ground Water Pumped and Treated	5	Extent of Ground-Water	5	
Contaminated Soil Removed	1	Contamination Determined		
Trench Installed	1	—Leading to Remedial Action		4
Artificial Recharge Employed		—No further Action		1
Nutrients Added		New Water Supply Provided	4	
Source of Contamination Eliminated	8	Action Being Considered	67	
Surface Water Collected and Treated	1	Monitoring Begun	46	
Landfill Site Closed		Damages Awarded		
Site Regarded		Charcoal Filters Installed		
Treatment Facility Installed	5	None Mentioned	15(9%)	
Pads and Covering for Salt Piles	2	Installation of New Sewers	2	

Sources: New Jersey department of Environmental Protection, 1981a; U.S. EPA, 1981a.

Table 7–12. New Jersey: Summary of Information from Documented Case Histories—Accidental Spills

Contaminant	Total	Cases Affecting or Threatening Water Supplies		Cases Causing or Threatening Fire or Explosion	Public Health Effects	
		Afftd.	Threat.		Documented	Potential
Industrial Wastes	6	8	3			
Landfill Leachate						
Petroleum Products	138(85%)	31(22%)	42(30%)	4		
Chlorides (road salt and oil field brine)	1	1				
Organic Wastes (human and animal)	9	1				
Pesticides	2	1	1			
Radioactive Wastes						
Mine Wastes						
Miscellaneous	7	3	1			
Totals	163	45(28%)	47(29%)	4		
Means of Detection						
Well Contamination	41			Not Mentioned	4	
Investigation	2			Fumes in Basement	9	
Surface Water Contamination	14			Fumes in Ground		
Spill on Ground	19			Fumes in Sewer Line	7	
Leak Discovered	55			Animal Deaths		
				Explosion	2	
				Other	11	

Table 7–12. (continued)

Remedial Action

Direct		Indirect		
Ground Water Pumped and Treated	8	Extent of Ground-Water	13	
Contaminated Soil Removed	6	Contamination Determined		
Trench Installed	12	—Leading to Remedial Action		4
Artificial Recharge Employed	1	—No further Action		9
Nutrients Added		New Water Supply Provided	9	
Source of Contamination Eliminated	60	Action Being Considered	24	
Surface Water Collected and Treated		Monitoring Begun	28	
Landfill Site Closed		Damages Awarded		
Site Regraded		Charcoal Filters Installed		
		None Mentioned	16(10%)	

Source: New Jersey Department of Environmental Protection, 1981a.

Table 7–13. New Jersey: Summary of Information from Documented Case Histories—Sanitary Landfills

Contaminant	Total	Cases Affecting or Threatening Water Supplies		Cases Causing or Threatening Fire or Explosion	Public Health Effects	
		Afftd.	Threat.		Documented	Potential
Industrial Wastes						
Landfill Leachate	26	5	6			
Petroleum Products						
Chlorides (road salt and oil field brine)						
Organic Wastes						
Pesticides						
Radioactive Wastes						
Mine Wastes						
Totals	26	5	6			
Means of Detection						
Well Contamination	2			Not Mentioned		
Investigation	25			Fumes in Basement		
Stream Contamination				Fumes in Ground		
Spill on Ground				Fumes in Sewer Line		
Leak Discovered				Animal Deaths		

Table 7–13. (continued)

Remedial Action			
Direct		**Indirect**	
Ground Water Pumped and Treated		Extent of Ground Water Contamination Determined	
Contaminated Soil Removed		—Leading to Remedial Action	
Trench Installed		—No further Action	
Artificial Recharge Employed		New Water Supply Provided	
Nutrients Added		Action Being Considered	4
Source of Contamination Eliminated		Monitoring Begun	7
Surface Water Collected and Treated		Damages Awarded	
Landfill Site Closed	11	Charcoal Filters Installed	
Site Regraded		None Mentioned	4

Source: New Jersey Department of Environmental Protection, 1981a.

Table 7–14. New Jersey: Summary of Information from Documented Case Histories—Illegal Dumping

Contaminant	Total	Cases Affecting or Threatening Water Supplies		Cases Causing or Threatening Fire or Explosion	Public Health Effects	
		Afftd.	Threat.		Documented	Potential
Industrial Wastes	24	2	1	1		
Landfill Leachate						
Petroleum Products						
Chlorides (road salt and oil field brine)						
Organic Wastes						
Pesticides						
Radioactive Wastes						
Mine Wastes						
Totals	24	2	1	1		
Means of Detection						
Well Contamination	3			Not Mentioned	2	
Investigation	16			Fumes in Basement		
Stream Contamination	3			Fumes in Ground		
Spill on Ground				Fumes in Sewer Line		
Leak Discovered				Animal Deaths		

Table 7–14. (continued)

Remedial Action

Direct		Indirect	
Ground Water Pumped and Treated		Extent of Ground-Water Contamination Determined	2
Contaminated Soil Removed	4	—Leading to Remedial Action	1
Trench Installed		—No further Action	1
Artificial Recharge Employed		New Water Supply Provided	
Nutrients Added		Action Being Considered	6
Source of Contamination Eliminated	3	Monitoring Begun	4
Surface Water Collected and Treated		Damages Awarded	
Landfill Site Closed		Charcoal Filters Installed	
Site Regraded		None Mentioned	5

Source: New Jersey Department of Environmental Protection. 1981a.

Table 7–15. New Jersey: Summary of Information from Documented Case Histories—Totals

Contaminant	Total	Cases Affecting or Threatening Water Supplies		Cases Causing or Threatening Fire or Explosion	Public Health Effects	
		Afftd.	Threat.		Documented	Potential
Industrial Wastes	152(40%)	44(30%)	29(19%)	1		
Landfill Leachate	26	5	6			
Petroleum Products	149(39%)	34(23%)	42(28%)	4		
Chlorides (road salt and oil field brine)	6	5				
Organic Wastes (animal and human)	28	17(61%)			8(29%)	
Pesticides	6	1	1			
Radioactive Wastes						
Mine Wastes	1	1				
Miscellaneous	11	8				
Totals	379	115(30%)	78(20%)	5	8	
Means of Detection						
Well Contamination	80			Illness	8	
Investigation	120			Not Mentioned	26	
Surface Water Contamination	26			Fumes in Basement	9	
Spill on Ground	23			Fumes in Ground		
Leak Discovered	56			Fumes in Sewer Line	7	
Soil Contamination	9			Animal Deaths		
Septic Overflow	2			Explosion	2	
				Other	11	

Table 7–15. (continued)

Remedial Action

Direct		Indirect	
Ground Water Pumped and/or Treated	13	Extent of Ground Water Contamination Determined	20
Contaminated Soil Removed	11	—Leading to Remedial Action	9
Trench Installed	13	—No further Action	11
Artificial Recharge Employed	1	New Water Supply Provided	13
Nutrients Added		Action Being Considered	101
Source of Contamination Eliminated	71	Monitoring Begun	82
Surface Water Collected and Treated	1	Damages Awarded	
Landfill Site Closed	11	Charcoal filters Installed	
Site Regraded		None Mentioned	40(11%)
Others	9		

Sources: New Jersey Department of Environmental Protection, 1981a and U.S. EPA, 1981a.

known to have resulted from landfill leachate, and 43% of these incidents threatened or affected the water supply. Only 4 cases, or 15%, had no remedial action taken or monitoring program started by June 1981.

Table 7–14 summarizes information on 24 known cases of illegal dumping, all of which involved industrial wastes. Only 3, or 12%, posed any problems for the water supply, and one posed a fire threat. In 19 of the cases, or 79%, remedial action had been taken or was under consideration, or monitoring programs had been started.

Table 7–15 gives information on the contamination incidents in New Jersey from all sources. The most numerous incidents are those involving industrial wastes and petroleum products, accounting for 40% and 39% of the cases, respectively. Pesticides account for very few of the cases, considering that New Jersey is both an industrial and an agricultural state. In 41% of the cases some form of remedial action has been taken; in a further 48%, remedial action is being considered or a monitoring program has been started.

New Mexico

Groundwater provided 49% of New Mexico's water in 1970, and 85% of that groundwater was used for irrigation (Scalf et al., 1973). In 1975 groundwater usage increased slightly, accounting for 50% of the total water usage, or 1600 mgd. The general natural condition of groundwater in New Mexico is fair to good. Mineralization is the most widespread and common problem of quality. Nearly all the groundwater is derived from infiltration of precipitation and seepage from streams and is at least slightly mineralized because of its contact with soil and rock. Over 60% of New Mexico's groundwater is saline, having a total content of dissolved solids greater than 1,000 mg/l. Hardness is also a problem in many areas, as are fluorides, nitrates, and occasionally arsenic. The best quality water in New Mexico comes from the High Plains and the Ogallala Aquifer. The Rio Grande Valley has the largest supply of freshwater in the state, but it is of only fair quality.

Groundwater quality is threatened by overpumping in the eastern part of the state; by mining for uranium, copper, molybdenum, and potash in various areas throughout the state; and by oil production in the northeastern and southwestern parts of the state.

There have been 105 reported incidents of groundwater contamination in New Mexico (Table 7–16). Most are cases of chloride contamination from oil-field brines, with 40 cases, or 38% of the total, and of these cases, 36 affected water supplies. Animal and human wastes accounted for 31 cases, or 30% of the total, and 28 of these incidents resulted in contaminated drinking-water supplies. Mine wastes also caused a significant number of incidents, 14, or 13%, but only 6% of those incidents caused adverse

Table 7–16. New Mexico: Summary of Information from Documented Case Histories

Contaminant	Total	Cases Affecting or Threatening Water Supplies Afftd.	Cases Causing or Threatening Fire or Explosion	Public Health Effects	
				Documented	Potential
Industrial Wastes	6	4		2	
Landfill Leachate	1	1			
Petroleum Products	13	12			
Chlorides (road salt and oil field brine)	40(38%)	36(34%)			
Organic Wastes	31(30%)	28(27%)		4	
Pesticides					
Radioactive Wastes					
Mine Wastes	14(13%)	6		—	
Totals	105	87(83%)		6	
Means of Detection					
Well Contamination	79(75%)		Not Mentioned	13	
Investigation	8		Fumes in Basement		
Stream Contamination			Fumes in Ground		
Spill on Ground			Fumes in Sewer Line		
Leak Discovered			Animal Deaths		
			Outbreaks of Illness	5	

Table 7–16. (continued)

Remedial Action

Direct		Indirect	
Ground Water Pumped and Treated		Extent of Ground Water Contamination Determined	1
Contaminated Soil Removed		—Leading to Remedial Action	1
Trench Installed		—No further Action	
Artificial Recharge Employed		New Water Supply Provided	4
Nutrients Added		Action Being Considered	11
Source of Contamination Eliminated	3	Monitoring Begun	1
Surface Water Collected and Treated	4	Damages Awarded	
Landfill Site Closed		Charcoal Filters Installed	
Site Regraded		None Mentioned	75(71%)
New Sewage System Installed	1		
Evaporation Ponds Lined	2		

Sources: New Mexico Environmental Improvement Division, 1980; U.S. EPA, 1981a.

effects on public health. The majority of incidents were discovered by contamination of well water. In fewer than 30% of the cases of groundwater contamination was it mentioned that any remedial action had taken place.

South Carolina

In 1970, 61% of the total population of South Carolina relied upon groundwater for their drinking-water supply (Scalf et al., 1973), and groundwater accounted for 23% of the total water usage from all sources. Lehr (1975), however, shows that in 1975 only 3% of the total water use was attributable to groundwater. Total groundwater usage in 1975 was 200 mgd. There are several types of aquifers in South Carolina. In the Piedmont–Blue Ridge region, the aquifers are composed of granite, schist, gneiss, slate, and phyllite. The groundwater is stored mainly in open fractures, and most wells are low-yielding. Along the coastal plain in the southeastern half of the state, the aquifers consist of sand, gravel, and limestone. In the extreme south, the Ocala limestone aquifer is the principal artesian one, and it is a continuation of the principal artesian aquifer of Georgia and the Floridian aquifer of Florida. The Tuscaloosa Formation aquifer underlies nearly the entire coastal plain. The Peedee and Black Formations comprise one aquifer in the central and eastern part of the southern coastal plain. The Black Mingo Formation is a major aquifer in the central coastal area, and the Santee Limestone Formation is used from the central coastal area for a distance 60 miles further inland (Scalf et al., 1973). The naturally good quality of the groundwater in South Carolina makes it suitable for most purposes. High iron concentration, low pH, high fluoride, excessive hardness, and high chloride are the main problems, but alternate sources of better-quality water are locally available from other aquifers (Scalf et al., 1977). Table 7–17 summarizes the cause of contamination, means of detection, and remedial actions applied, if any, in the 89 known cases of groundwater contamination. Petroleum products are involved in the majority of the incidents, accounting for 43 cases, or 48%, of which 88% affected the water supply. Contamination by industrial wastes accounted for 28 of the incidents, or 31%, of which 50% threatened or affected the water supply. More than half the cases were detected by well contamination. For the majority of incidents, 80 or 89%, remedial action was under consideration, monitoring had been started, or no remedial action was mentioned.

Bearing in mind that these summaries apply only to known incidents of contamination, and that if undertaken, a comprehensive national survey might well uncover other important sources of contamination or different frequencies of the same sources, they show that the problems encountered to date vary from one region of the country to another. Table

Table 7–17. South Carolina: Summary of Information from Documented Case Histories

		Cases Affecting or Threatening Water Supplies		Cases Causing or Threatening	Public Health Effects	
Contaminant	Total	Afftd.	Threat.	Fire or Explosion	Documented	Potential
Industrial Wastes	28(31%)	7	7			
Landfill Leachate	1		1			
Petroleum Products	43(48%)	38(88%)				
Chlorides (road salt, oil field brine & saltwater intrusion)	1		1			
Organic Wastes (animal and human)	7	6(86%)			3(43%)	
Pesticides/Fertilizer	4	2				
Radioactive Wastes	1					
Mine Wastes						
Miscellaneous	4	3	1			
Totals	89	56(63%)	10(11%)		3	
Means of Detection						
Well Contamination	49			Not Mentioned	2	
Investigation	24			Fumes in Basement		
Surface Water Contam.*	6			Fumes in Ground	1	
Spill on Ground	3			Fumes in Sewer Line		
Leak Discovered	1			Animal Deaths	1	
				Other	6	

Table 7–17. (continued)

Remedial Action

Direct		Indirect		
Ground Water Pumped and/or Treated	3	Extent of Ground Water Contamination Determined	1	
Contaminated Soil Removed		—Leading to Remedial Action	1	
Trench Installed		—No further Action		
Artificial Recharge Employed		New Water Supply Provided	3	
Nutrients Added		Action Being Considered	12	89%
Source of Contamination Eliminated	3	Monitoring Begun	10	
Surface Water Collected and Treated		Damages Awarded		
Landfill Site Closed		Charcoal Filters Installed		
Site Regraded		None Mentioned	58	
French Drain System Installed	2			

*Contam. = contamination

Sources: South Carolina Department of Health and Environmental Control, 1980; South Carolina Department of Health and Environmental Control (Draft), 1981.

Table 7–18. Most Frequently Reported Sources of Groundwater Contamination in the Ten States Reviewed by the Environmental Assessment Council

	Groundwater Use, mgd.	Natural Quality of Groundwater	Most Frequently Reported Sources of Contamination	Total Number of Known Contamination Incidents	% Affecting or Threatening Water Supply	% Where Remedial Actions Have Been Undertaken
Arizona	4800	Generally good. Mineralization problems.	1. Industrial wastes 2. Landfill leachate 3. Human and animal wastes	23	100	26
California	13400–19000	Good	1. Saltwater intrusion 2. Nitrates from agricultural practices 3. Brines and other industrial and military wastes	Not known	Not known	Not known
Connecticut	116	Good to excellent	1. Industrial wastes 2. Petroleum products 3. Human and animal wastes	64	59	30
Florida	3000	Generally good	1. Chlorides from saltwater intrusion and agricultural return flow 2. Industrial wastes 3. Human and animal wastes	92	63	39
Idaho	5600	Good	1. Human and animal wastes 2. Industrial wastes 3. Radioactive wastes	29	97	45
Illinois	1000	Generally good	1. Human and animal wastes 2. Landfill leachate 3. Industrial wastes	58	76	70

Table 7–18 (continued)

	Groundwater Use, mgd	Natural Quality of Groundwater	Most Frequently Reported Sources of Contamination	Total Number of Known Contamination Incidents	% Affecting or Threatening Water Supply	% Where Remedial Actions Have Been Undertaken
Nebraska	5900	Generally good	1. Irrigation and agriculture 2. Human and animal wastes 3. Industrial wastes	35	34	26
New Jersey	790	Generally good	1. Industrial wastes 2. Petroleum products 3. Human and animal wastes	374	50	41
New Mexico	1500	Fair to good. Mineralization problems	1. Oil field brines 2. Human and animal wastes 3. Mine wastes	105	83	29
South Carolina	200	Suitable for most uses	1. Petroleum products 2. Industrial wastes 3. Human and animal wastes	89	74	45

7–18 summarizes the results of the survey of the ten states outlined above. Human and animal wastes were among the three most frequently reported sources of contamination for each of the states except California. California and Florida both report that saltwater intrusion in coastal areas is important. California, Florida, and Nebraska each reported problems arising from agricultural practices. The industrial Northeast predictably had problems from industrial wastes, petroleum products, and landfill leachate. New Mexico and California both reported problems from the disposal of oil-field brines. The significant sources of contamination identified from the state summaries (Table 7–18) differ in the order of importance from those identified by the EPA summaries (Table 7–1), which were more empirical assessments (J. W. Keeley; Kerr Environmental Research Laboratory, personal communication), relying on the experience of professionals who had worked in the regions studied. Neither survey can be considered complete, as neither results from a well-designed, comprehensive national survey. The information contained in the state summaries is a best-case scenario; the situation can only get worse as new cases of contamination are discovered. Aside from these drawbacks, the present assessment of groundwater contamination would be more useful if a method for estimating severity could be agreed upon.

Figure 7–1. California Groundwater Basins
Adapted from figure used in California Department of Water Resources, 1975.

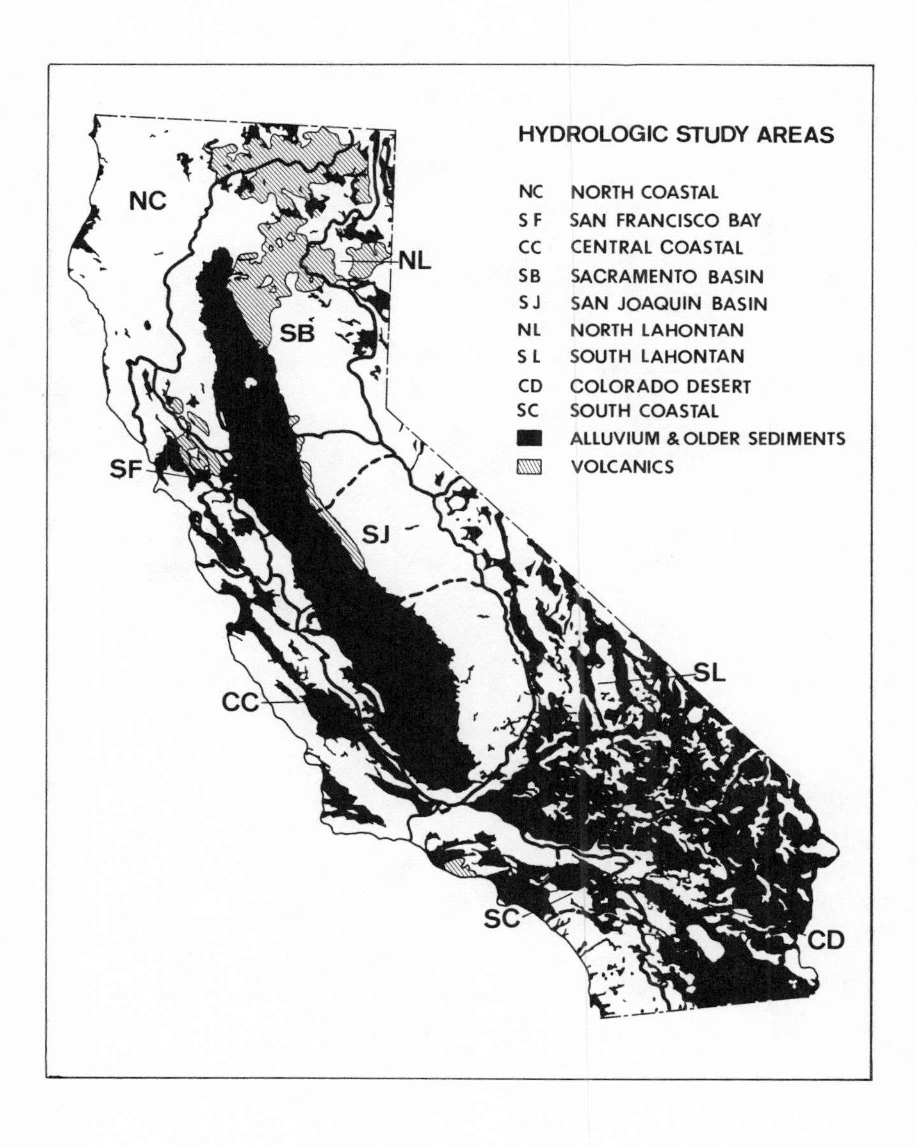

Figure 7–2. Major Aqueducts in California
Adapted from figure used in California Department of Water Resources, 1975.

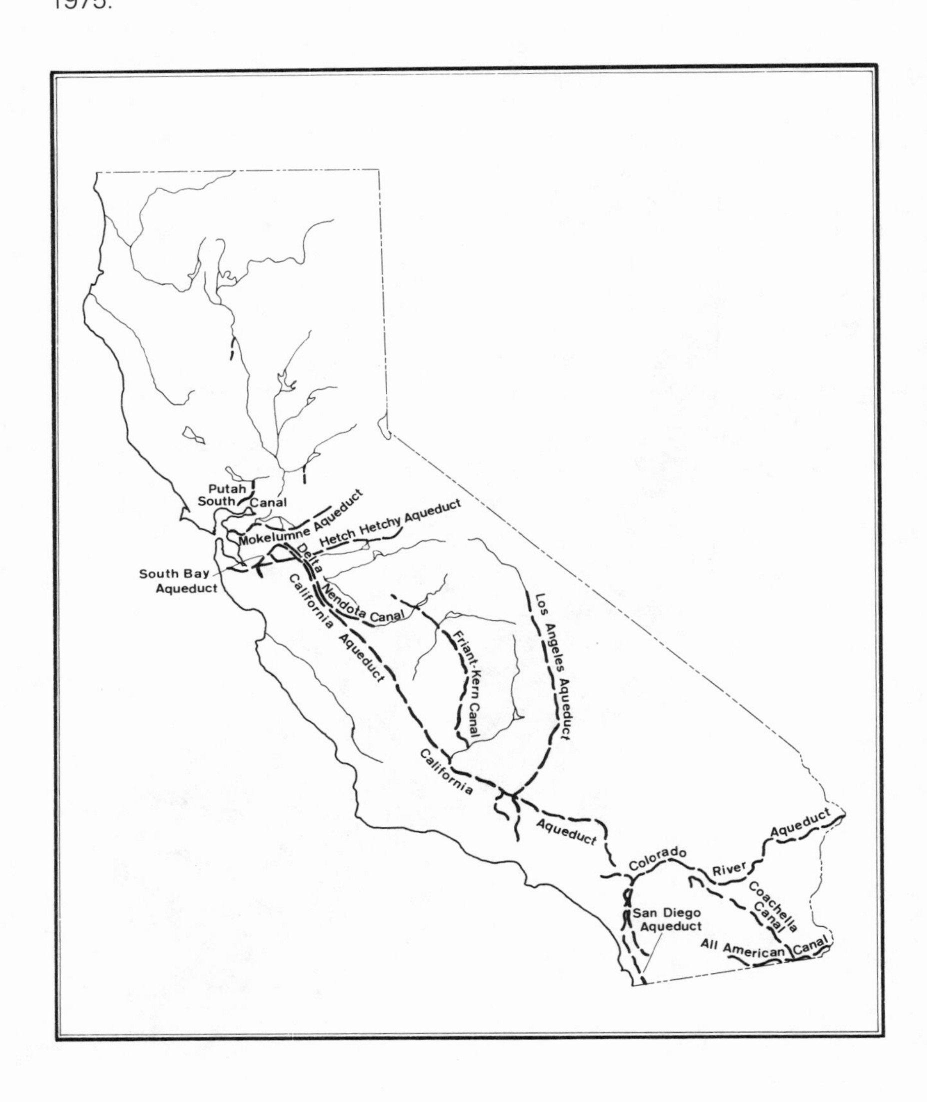

Figure 7–3. Location of Registered Irrigation Wells: Significant Rises and Declines in Nebraska Groundwater Levels from Predevelopment as of Fall 1979

Adapted from figure used in Nebraska Department of Environmental Control, 1980a.

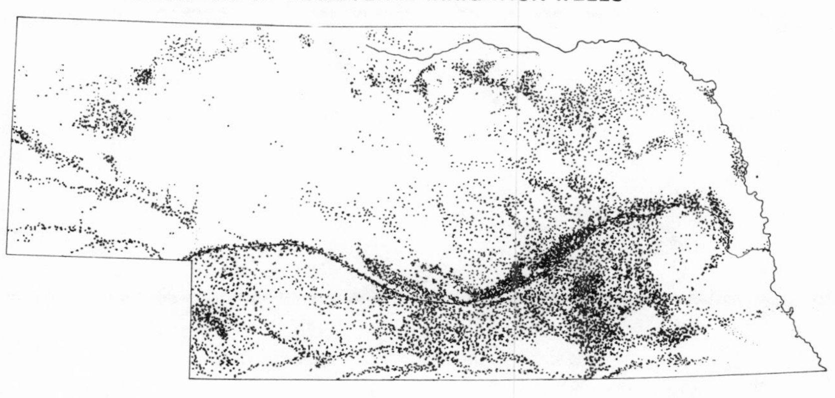

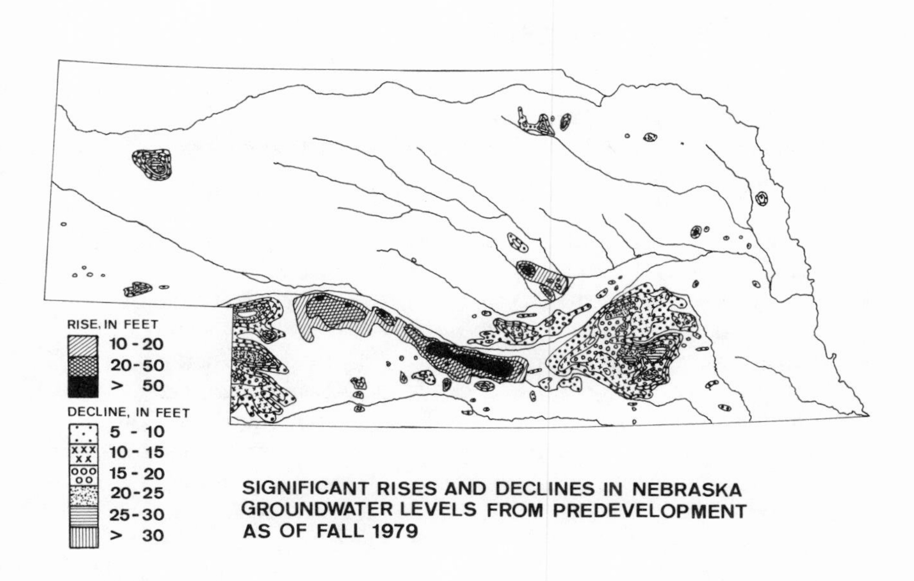

Eight

Monitoring the Quality of Groundwater

- Monitoring the quality of groundwater may help prevent, reduce, and eliminate groundwater pollution.
- The design of monitoring programs vary according to climate, population, hydrology and pollution sources.
- Costs of monitoring programs may vary considerably from case to case. A thorough monitoring program is expensive, but necessary to appraise the problem of contamination.
- The usefulness of monitoring is highly dependent on the quality of the program.

Monitoring the quality of groundwater may help to prevent, reduce, and eliminate groundwater pollution. When poorly designed, monitoring procedures may increase the chance of pollution by providing more openings for contaminants to enter the ground. A recent book by Everett (1980) reviews monitoring methodology, the costs of various methods, data management, and monitoring practices for disposal wells and concludes with illustrative examples. An earlier review, also put out by the General Electric Company (Tinlin, 1976), gives site-specific illustrative examples of monitoring practices for incidents involving oil-field brine, disposal, plating-waste contamination, landfill-leachate contamination, oxidation ponds, and agricultural return-flow. The firm of Geraghty and Miller runs periodic seminars on the Fundamentals of Groundwater Quality Protection in which they deal with monitoring practices in detail (Miller, 1981b and c).

Everett (1980) points out that as factors such as climate, population, hydrology, and pollution sources vary regionally, the design of an appropriate monitoring program will vary accordingly. A single set of guidelines would not suffice unless it were general and flexible. Everett defines monitoring as "a scientifically designed surveillance system of continuing measurements and observations." As of 1980 the U.S. Environmental Protection Agency (EPA), together with the states, was trying to organize a national groundwater-quality monitoring system. EPA defined four main types of monitoring:

- Ambient-trend monitoring measures quality in relation to standards and reflects temporal and spatial trends in a groundwater area.
- Source monitoring measures effluent quality and quantity from pollution sources that could affect groundwater. Present methodology is usually geared towards this type of monitoring (Everett, 1980) and concentrates on the most important sources.
- Case-preparation monitoring is used to accumulate data for enforcement actions.
- Research monitoring is used for studies of groundwater quality and pollution occurrence and movement.

Everett (1980) considers that the value of groundwater resources would be enhanced if they were used in optimal amounts for appropriate purposes, including irrigation, cooling, drinking, and waste disposal. He considers that aquifers should not be exempt from receiving wastes, but that the location and amount of such waste disposal should be properly determined.

The Federal Water Pollution Control Act amendments of 1972 (PL 92–500), the Clean Water Act of 1977, the Safe Drinking Water Act (SDWA) (PL 93–523), and the Resource Conservation and Recovery Act (RCRA) (PL 94–580) each require groundwater-quality monitoring (see page 241). Interstate compacts such as those for the Delaware River Basin and the Susquehanna River Basin have the authority to monitor groundwater quality and to formulate and carry out plans to protect groundwater quality (Everett, 1980). State laws and regulations affecting groundwater vary and are summarized later in this report.

Groundwater-quality monitoring is presently carried out by:

- The United States Geological Survey
- State geologic and water agencies
- Local water districts
- City, county, and state health departments (for water-supply wells)
- All hazardous waste land-disposal facilities that maintain RCRA Interim Status

In addition, data is collected by sanitation districts on the quality of wastewater after treatment and before land disposal, by industries on self-supplied groundwater and treated effluent prior to land disposal, and by consulting firms working in water resources. At the federal level, the EPA, the U.S. Bureau of Reclamation, the U.S. Army Corps of Engineers, and the U.S. Soil Conservation Service also collect groundwater-quality data (Everett, 1980).

Both Tinlin (1976) and Everett (1980) present multistep methodologies for monitoring groundwater contamination from anthropogenic sources. The steps may be summarized as follows:

1. Selection of area to monitor based on administrative, physiographic, and priority considerations
2. Identification of pollution sources, causes, and methods of waste disposal
3. Identification of potential pollutants
4. Definition of groundwater usage in terms of volumes extracted and the location of pumping areas
5. Definition of a hydrogeologic situation, including aquifer characteristics, recharge areas, discharge areas, and groundwater-flow maps and velocities
6. Determination of existing groundwater quality for use as base-line quality data to assess change. Historical quality analyses, if available, are an important source of information (Miller, 1981c).
7. Evaluation of the infiltration potential of wastes on the land surface. Estimation of the volume of polluted liquids that will enter the water table would include estimates of evapotranspiration and consumptive use (i.e., cropping patterns).
8. Evaluation of the mobility of the pollutants from the land surface to the water table would indicate the attenuation potential of the soil. Factors affecting such attenuation are pH, chemical precipitation, oxidation and reduction, volatilization, biological degradation, and assimilation and radioactive decay.
9. Evaluation of the attenuation of pollutants in the saturated zone
10. To ranking sources and causes it is necessary to have information resulting from steps 1–9 in order to accurately rank the sources in order of their importance.
11. Evaluation of existing monitoring programs.
12. Establishment of alternative monitoring approaches when data and information gaps are identified by steps 1–11. This could include waste-load inventories and other non-sampling methods. For liquid wastes, Everett (1980) suggests running fairly complete chemical analyses for calcium, magnesium, sodium, potassium, carbonate, bicarbonate, chloride, sulfate, nitrate, silica, ammonium, fluoride, arsenic, boron, chromium, cadmium,

molybdenum, iron, and manganese. In addition, groundwater should be tested for the presence of the various compounds of sulfur, nitrogen, and phosphorus. Periodic measurements of electrical conductivity can indicate changes in concentrations of ionic groundwater constituents (Miller, 1981b; Everett, 1980). Total dissolved solids (TDS) and pH are also routinely determined. Everett (1980) believes that contamination by toxic organic chemicals will increase in importance in the future but considers that they rarely need to be sampled in wastewaters now—a view not shared by CEQ (1981a). Solid-waste analyses usually concentrate on the content of trace-elements and on radioactivity. Physical analysis of the soil in waste-disposal areas will indicate water movement. Analyses of water in the aquifer are usually similar to those performed for wastewater, but prior screening of wastewater content would reduce the number of analyses that must be performed on the groundwater itself. Table 8–1 shows the constituents in industrial and municipal wastewater that may affect groundwater. Sampling frequencies should be higher for wastewater at the land surface than for groundwater, as wastes have greater fluctuations in composition. The frequency of sampling would vary for all components of the system. Geologic sampling might be done only once, soil sampling several times a year or annually; water in the unsaturated zone monthly or quarterly or in areas of very slow percolation to the water table, every 5 to 10 years. Once seasonal patterns have been established, aquifer water samples from high capacity wells are often collected every six months, although monthly analyses may be indicated where point-source contamination is involved. It is necessary to have more frequent sampling of low capacity wells (Everett, 1980), and to make sure they are not composited as this may dilute the existing concentration.

13. Selection and implementation of the monitoring program involves selecting specific pollutants associated with specific pollution sources, based on cost-effectiveness.
14. Review and interpretation of monitoring results to determine quality trends, new problems, improvement, and effectiveness of remedial actions. Assessment of substandard water occurrences and prediction of future alteration in quality due to population and land-use changes should also be included.
15. Dissemination of the results

    The final step in a well-organized monitoring program is the

Table 8–1. Constituents in Industrial and Municipal Wastewater Having Significant Potential for Groundwater Contamination

MINING		
Metal and Coal Mining Industry		
pH	Zinc	Magnesium
Sulfate	Tin	Silver
Nitrate	Vanadium	Manganese
Chloride	Radium	Calcium
Total dissolved solids	Phenol	Potassium
Phosphate	Selenium	Sodium
Copper	Iron	Aluminum
Nickel	Chromium	Gold
Lead	Cadmium	Fluoride
	Uranium	Cyanide
PAPER AND ALLIED PRODUCTS		
Pulp and Paper Industry		
COD/BOD	Phenols	Nitrogen
TOC	Sulfite	Phosphorus
pH	Color	Total dissolved solids
Ammonia	Heavy metals	Biocides
CHEMICALS AND ALLIED PRODUCTS		
Organic Chemicals Industry		
COD/BOD	Alkalinity	Phenols
pH	TOC	Cyanide
Total dissolved solids	Total phosphorus	Total nitrogen
	Heavy metals	
Inorganic Chemicals, Alkalies, and Chlorine Industry		
Acidity/alkalinity	Chlorinated benzenoids and polynuclear aromatics	Chromium
Total dissolved solids	Phenols	Lead
Chloride	Fluoride	Titanium
Sulfate	Total phosphorus	Iron
COD/BOD	Cyanide	Aluminum
TOC	Mercury	Boron
		Arsenic
Plastic Materials and Synthetics Industry		
COD/BOD	Phosphorus	Ammonia
pH	Nitrate	Cyanide
Phenols	Organic nitrogen	Zinc
Total dissolved solids	Chlorinated benzenoids and polynuclear aromatics	Mercaptans
Sulfate		
Nitrogen Fertilizer Industry		
Ammonia	Sulfate	COD
Chloride	Organic nitrogen compounds	Iron, total
Chromium		pH

Table 8–1. (continued)

Total dissolved solids	Zinc	Phosphate
Nitrate	Calcium	Sodium
Phosphate Fertilizer Industry		
Calcium	Acidity	Mercury
Dissolved solids	Aluminum	Nitrogen
Fluoride	Arsenic	Sulfate
pH	Iron	Uranium
Phosphorus	Cadmium	Vanadium
		Radium
PETROLEUM AND COAL PRODUCTS		
Petroleum Refining Industry		
Ammonia	Chloride	Nitrogen
Chromium	Color	Odor
COD/BOD	Copper	Total phosphorus
pH	Cyanide	Sulfate
Phenols	Iron	TOC
Sulfide	Lead	Turbidity
Total dissolved solids	Mercaptans	Zinc
PRIMARY METALS		
Steel Industry		
pH	Cyanide	Tin
Chloride	Phenols	Chromium
Sulfate	Iron	Zinc
Ammonia	Nickel	
ELECTRIC, GAS, AND SANITARY SERVICES		
Power Generation Industry		
COD/BOD	Copper	Phosphorus
pH	Iron	Free chlorine
Polychlorinated biphenols	Zinc	Organic biocides
Total dissolved solids	Chromium	Sulfur dioxide
Oil and grease	Other corrosion inhibitors	Heat
Municipal Sewage Treatment		
pH	Nitrate	Sulfate
COD/BOD	Ammonia	Copper
TOC	Phosphate	Lead
Alkalinity	Chloride	Tin
Detergents	Sodium	Zinc
Total dissolved solids	Potassium	Various organics

Source: U.S. EPA, 1978b.

dissemination of the results in a readily understandable and usable form.

Depending on several interrelated factors, the costs of a monitoring program may vary considerably from case to case. The two key factors are the type and quality of survey used to locate and identify the contamination and the type and number of monitoring wells. These, in turn, are influenced by site size, geophysical aspects such as depth and type of formations, and often by whether a public agency or the site owner is requesting the program. Surveys of the contaminated site may vary from a preliminary assessment describing whether contamination is present and the general direction of groundwater flow, to a detailed assessment, describing the distribution and quantity of each contaminant and the quantity, rate, and direction of the groundwater flow. The monitoring wells vary in configuration and construction, and both are described later in this chapter. A good monitoring program typically involves two steps. First, only a few wells are drilled, so well installation costs are low, but an initial complete chemical analysis of the water samples from those wells must be done to determine what contaminants are present, which is expensive. Second, after the contaminants have been identified, the costs of routine chemical analysis for those chemicals found to be present will be lower. The number of wells will be expanded, however, so total installation costs rise. Everett (1980) describes capital cost as including well screens and casings, pumps, water samples, pH meters, but states that these costs could be amortized. It has been estimated that 1% of the total capital costs would provide adquate maintenance for the wells. Where a typical monitoring well for a waste-disposal site may cost several thousand dollars, wells monitoring the underground injection of contaminants may cost ten times that much. Monitoring programs for underground injection wells will vary considerably according to formation type, depth, and the location of any hydrologically connected aquifers which also must be monitored. For any monitoring program, costs can only be judged on a case-by-case basis.

Miller (1981c) notes that the use of current and old aerial photographs provides much information concerning the present structure and old use of sites suspected of being sources of groundwater contamination. Other preliminary, non-well drilling procedures include enumeration of of existing resource-sampling points, such as wells, springs, storm sewers, etc., temperature surveys, tracer studies, and vegetative analysis from aerial photographs. The latter is much enhanced by the use of multispectral photography. Bedrock determinations can be made from stereo pairs of aerial photographs. Resistivity equipment, utilizing electromagnetic currents or very low-frequency sound waves can be used to obtain a profile of contamination. Resistivity equipment costs between $3,000 and $7,000 (Miller, 1981b).

Methods of Well Construction

Well drillings are the best exploratory method for investigating groundwater contamination, and there are several methods of well construction that may be used (Miller, 1981b):

- Shallow monitor wells are usually constructed with an auger. The hollow pipe construction permits cores to be taken.
- Wells can be installed by hand by either hammering or vibrating them into the soil. This form of construction is particularly suited to constructing monitoring wells, where geologically feasible, as the groundwater is not further contaminated by well-drilling fluids.
- A cable-tool rig can be used to hammer down a well shaft. It provides good geologic samples but is slow. Air rotary rigs and air hammers are faster, but water and foam may be used during the drilling, and these would contaminate the groundwater. If several wells are to be dug, the equipment must be cleaned and sterilized between each use to avoid cross contamination.

Types of Wells

1. A cluster well gives a three-dimensional picture. The wells can be drilled in one hole or have individual holes for each well. They can be at various depths.
2. A piezometric well consists of a bundle of ⅛-inch tubes, through which water is sampled, which are bound around a rigid 1-inch PVC tube.
3. One well casing can be constructed to have small well screens at different depths along the casing.

When well casings are protected from clogging by gravel packing or the use of a cloth filter, no extraneous substances (such as glue in the case of cloth filters) should be used due to potential contamination of the samples.

Casing Materials and Sampling Procedures

Groundwater is seldom found in equilibrium with atmospheric pressure. Changes in redox potential, pH, and partial pressures of dissolved gases would occur if the water did come into contact with the atmosphere and, to avoid this, samples are generally pumped into a box containing the probes. Preservation of the composition of a water sample necessitates its filtering to remove sediment. The sample containers may be of a variety of materials, depending on the contaminant being monitored. A manual has recently been issued by the National Water Well Association and EPA on groundwater sampling procedure (Scalf et al., 1981).

Braids (1981b) noted that there are two main types of well casings now available, namely steel and plastic, and their use depends upon which contaminants are being monitored and how the wells are set in place. If a well is to be hammered home, then plastic casing is obviously unsuitable. Steel is very surface active and corrodes easily. The corrosion products may contaminate the groundwater samples. The oil finish that is often supplied to steel casing should be removed before a monitoring well is installed.

A more detailed discussion of casing materials and sampling materials is supplied by Everett (1980). Recent costs of chemical determinations are shown in Tables 8–2 and 8–3.

The *EPA Proposed Criteria for Water Quality* (U.S. EPA, 1973b) contains standards designed to protect water quality for public water supplies, agricultural uses, industrial uses, recreation and aesthetics, fresh-water aquatic life and wildlife and, lastly, marine aquatic life and wildlife. Of these, only the first three would be directly affected by groundwater quality, although polluted groundwater discharge would obviously affect all six categories.

Data Management and Information Retrieval

There are several computerized information storage systems suitable for groundwater. The STORET system, developed by the U.S. Public Health Service and now operated by EPA, has a water-quality file and a general point-source file. It was developed to help ensure compliance with the Water Pollution Control Act (PL 92–500). WATSTORE, the National Water Data Storage and Retrieval System, began in 1971 and is operated by the U.S. Geological Survey (USGS). NAWDEX, the National Water Data Exchange, operated by the Water Resources Division of the USGS, is an experimental computerized information index. Details of the capabilities of these three systems are given by Everett (1980).

The National Water Well Association in Worthington, Ohio, has a detailed computerized library for all groundwater literature. They hope to have a similar system for the literature on groundwater contamination but, as yet,

Table 8–2. Cost of Chemical Determinations of Water Samples, 1980

ATOMIC ABSORPTION	Number of Samples 1	Each Additional Sample
A. Analysis		
1. Flame	$ 25	$ 5
2. Furnace (standard addition)	40	30
3. Hydride (As, Se, Sb, Sn)	50	40
4. Mercury—Cold Vapor	40	30
B. Sample Prep		
1. Aqueous Sample	NC	NC
2. Solid Sample	5	5
3. Biological Sample	10	10
4. Preconcentration	15	15

GAS CHROMATOGRAPHY	Number of Samples			
	1	2–10	Each Addtl. Sample	Each Addtl. Analyte
A. Organic Compounds, limited sample prep.	$ 90	$ 75	$ 65	$ 5
B. Petroleum Hydrocarbons	90	75	65	—
C. Oil Spill Identification	125			
D. Pesticide Residues		Request quotation		
E. Active Ingredient Assay	65	50	45	5
F. Development Time (with operator)	65/hr.			

Table 8–2. (continued)

HIGH PERFORMANCE LIQUID CHROMATOGRAPHY	Number of Samples			
	1	2–10	Each Addtl. Sample	Each Addtl. Analyte
A. Monomers/Organics/Phthalates/Plasticizers	$110	$ 90	$ 80	$ 10
B. Biological	110	90	80	5
1. Amino Acids	110	90	80	5
2. Polypeptides	110	90	80	5
3. Sugars	110	90	80	5
C. Development Time (with operator)	75/hr.			

POLYMER CHARACTERIZATION	Cost Per Sample	
	1	Each Additional
Molecular Weight By Gel Permeation Chromatography (GPC)	$ 140	$ 110
Molecular Weight by Laser Light Scattering (LLS) (knowledge of dn/dc required)	300	240
Molecular Weight by GPC/LLS (knowledge of dn/dc required)	600	500
d/n/dc measurement	220	200
Molecular Weight by LLS and dn/dc measurement	390	350
Molecular Weight by GPC/LLS and dn/dc measurement	700	550
Infrared Spectroscopy	40	35

MATERIALS SCIENCE	
A. Scanning Electron Microscopy	$ 85/hr.
B. X-ray Diffraction	

Table 8–2. (continued)

1. Pattern Only	35
2. Camera	50
3. Interpretation	30
4. File Search (computer)	45
C. Optical Microscopy	
1a. Asbestos-Phase Contrast	30
1b. Asbestos-Polarized Light	65
2. Particle Sizing	
a. Optical Microscopy	30
b. Scanning Electron-Microscopy	85/hr.

MASS SPECTROSCOPY	1	2–10	Each Additional Sample
A. Solids Probe	$ 90	$ 75	$ 65
B. Gas Chromatograph, Mass Spectroscopy			
1. Structure Elucidation			
a. First Unknown	210	160	
b. Each Additional Unknown	50	50	
2. Structure Confirmation			
a. Of Prepared Sample	125	90	
b. Each Additional Unknown	35	25	
C. Drug Screening	210	160	
D. Development Time (with operator)	90/hr.		

Table 8–2. (continued)

PRIORITY POLLUTANTS	Number of Samples		
	1	2–10	Each Additional Sample
A. EPA Methods			
601. Purgeable Halocarbons (29)	$220	$180	$170
602. Purgeable aromatics (7)	120	100	90
603. Acrolein/Acrylonitrile	90	75	65
604. Phenols (11)			
a. FID	180	150	140
b. ECD	220	180	140
605. Benzidines (2)	110	90	80
606. Phthalate esters (6)	150	120	110
607. Nitrosamines (3)	110	90	80
608. a. Pesticides (18)	90	75	65
b. PCBs (7)	90	75	65
c. a & b	150	120	110
609. Nitroaromatics and Isophorone (4)	180	150	140
610. Polynuclear Aromatic Hydrocarbons (16)	220	180	170
611. Haloethers (5)	150	120	110
612. Chlorinated hydrocarbons (9)	160	130	120

Table 8–2. (continued)

613. 2,3,7,8—Tetrachlorodibenzodioxin	180	150	140
624. Purgeables—GC MS (30)	280	240	220
625. a. Base Neutrals (47)	300	250	230
b. Acids (11)	220	180	170
c. Pesticides	150	120	110
d. PCBs (7)	120	100	90
e. c & d	220	180	170
f. a, b, c, d, and 624	900	800	750
B. RCRA—EP TOXICITY			
1. Extraction	50	40	35
2. EP Metals (8)	265	135	130
3. Pesticides (4)	90	75	65
4. Herbicides (3)	90	75	65
5. 3 & 4	150	120	110

TITRIMETRY/COLORIMETRY/ELECTROMETRY

	Number of Samples			Number of Samples	
	1	Each Additional Sample		1	Each Additional Sample
Acidity	$ 10	$ 8	Oxygen Demand, Chem	$ 40	$ 30
Alkalinity	10	8	Oxygen,Dissolved	10	10
Boron	30	10	Ozone	20	20
Bromide	30	10	pH	10	6
Carbon Dioxide	10	8	Phosphorus, Hydrolyzable	40	20
Color	10	10	Phosphorus, Organic & Hydrolyzable	50	20

Table 8–2. (continued)

Conductance	10	8	Phosphorus, Reactive	30	10
Cyanide (distillation)	50	40	Reactive Stability	15	15
Cl^-	30	20	Residue, Filterable	15	15
Fluoride (distillation)	50	40	Residue, Nonfilterable	20	20
Hardness	10	8	Residue, Volatile	15	15
Hydrazine	30	10	Settleable Matter	15	12
Chlorine	30	20	Silica	35	20
Iodine	30	20	Sulfate, Sulfide	30	10
Nitrogen, Albuminoid	35	30	Sulfite	10	8
Nitrogen, Ammonia	35	30	Surfactants	35	30
Nitrogen, Nitrate	45	35	Tannin & Lignin	30	10
Nitrogen, Nitrite	30	10	Turbidity	20	20
Oil and Grease	50	40	Volatile Acids	30	30

Note: Terms—Net 30 Days.
Prices effective October 1, 1980
Prices Subject To Change

Source: Reprinted by permission of Cambridge Analytical Associates, Watertown, Mass.

Table 8–3. Cost of Selected Chemical Determinations, June 1981

Samples/Batch	Purgeables	Acid Extractables	Base/Neutrals	Pesticides & PCB's	13 Metals & Total Cyanides	Total
1–3	$240.00	$175.00	$240.00	$175.00	$145.00	$975.00
4–10	230.00	155.00	220.00	155.00	130.00	890.00
>10	200.00	140.00	200.00	140.00	110.00	790.00

Estimated turn-around time 3–4 weeks.

Source: Reprinted by permission from RMC Technical Services, Philadelphia, Pa.

funding for this venture has not been obtained (J. Lehr, American Water Well Association, personal communication).

Possibilities for Improving Monitoring Systems

The parameters which have been monitored historically may not be the best indicators for current groundwater contamination problems. Many of the items measured, such as total suspended solids (TSS) were chosen because they are easy to monitor. TSS represent an index of a contaminant and are not, in themselves, specific contaminants. The important index parameters which are routinely measured in the field are specific electrical conductance, pH, redox potential, and dissolved oxygen. Specific electrical conductance gives a general indication of total dissolved solids (TDS) (Freeze and Cherry, 1979). Recent groundwater monitoring has shown that toxic organic chemicals are a growing problem (CEQ, 1981a), and to date only about 10% of the organic chemicals contaminating drinking water in the United States have been identified (Page, in press). As of 1975 EPA reported finding more than 250 different organic chemicals in drinking waters in the United States (Greenberg et al., 1981). Although it would be possible to establish a water-quality baseline for standard water-quality parameters, there are no guidelines or sample sets of carcinogens (Greenberg et al., 1981). It has recently become possible to measure many substances in concentrations of parts per billion (ppb) by means of gas and liquid chromatography and mass-spectrometry. It has been suggested that the sophistication of the analytical methods has outstripped our sophistication in interpreting exactly what such low-level contaminant concentrations imply for human and environmental health (A. Wolman, Johns Hopkins University, personal communication; Greenberg et al., 1981).

Research Needs

In response to Section 2(a) of the Environmental Research, Development and Demonstration Authorization Act of 1981 (PL 96–569), EPA prepared a *Ground Water Research Plan* (U.S. EPA, 1981b). In this plan, EPA recognizes a need to develop non-contaminating drilling techniques, pumps that accurately sample trace organic compounds from deep groundwater, methods for detecting biological activity which may indicate pollution, and methods for locating possible contamination sources. Geophysical techniques capable of detecting changes in groundwater quality are at present not an adequate replacement for monitoring wells. Efforts to find indicators representative of classes of contaminants should be increased, as should research into non-contaminating tracers. In addition, EPA includes in the plan refinement of advanced detection techniques such as glass fiber and laser optics to reduce monitoring costs and the development of monitoring systems for unsaturated zones for the early detection of pollution.

In addition to research needs for monitoring methods, the plan also includes research programs to:

- Understand the movement, transformation, and fate of contaminants in the subsurface
- Determine changes in behavior, movement, and characteristics of pollutants as they move through the subsurface
- Identify the type and extent of groundwater pollution resulting from specific sources of contamination
- Assess aquifer rehabilitation strategies and cost
- Enhance the availability and accessibility of technical information related to groundwater pollution

Dermer et al. (1980) discuss biochemical indicators of subsurface pollution and point out that techniques that have been optimized for the study of microorganisms in surface water may not be applicable to groundwater. They cite measurement of biological oxygen demand (BOD) as probably being innappropriate for groundwater, and indeed it is not generally used as an indicator of groundwater quality. The organisms found in groundwater are more likely to use sulfate, carbonate, or nitrate as their terminal oxygen acceptor. Many anaerobic organisms may be inhibited or killed by oxygen. Thus BOD would not be a good indicator of groundwater quality. Differing properties of groundwater call for different tests.

Nine

Remedial Action and the Rehabilitation of Aquifers

- Aquifer rehabilitation is difficult, expensive, and time-consuming, with no guarantee of complete success.
- Given the present state of technology, remedial actions may be impossible in many cases.
- Where contamination has occurred there are four possibilities for dealing with the problem ranging from monitoring the plume without attempting cleanup, containment of the plume, and removal of the contaminants.
- The choice of remedial action depends on the physical characteristics of the site, the nature of the contamination, the importance of the aquifer and the resources available.
- Costs of remedial action must be estimated on a case by case basis and may vary from several thousand to several billion dollars.

Upon the discovery that an aquifer is contaminated, a decision must be made as to what kind, if any, of remedial action to take. Several recent reports have reviewed and discussed various methods of remedial action that can be applied to contaminated aquifers (Lindorff and Cartwright, 1977; EPA, 1980; Hajali and Canter, 1980; Geraghty, 1981). All agree that remedial action is complicated, time-consuming, and expensive, and that the best solution to groundwater contamination is prevention. When contamination has occurred, however, the suitability and effectiveness of remedial actions depend on the length of time until discovery, the source and extent of contamination, the type and behavior of contaminants, and the geohydrology of the aquifer. Often when the time period over which contamination has occurred is lengthy, the cost of remedial action is very high. When the source is unknown, a policy of no direct action to remove or halt the contamination may be the most suitable course of action. In both of these cases, a cost-effective solution would be to locate a new source of water (Lindorff and Cartwright, 1977). Shallow contamination plumes in areas of soft geology are easily controlled by excavation and removal, once the problem of safe disposal of the contaminated material is solved. For rehabilitation of contaminated groundwater where remedial action is deemed necessary, as in the case of a sole-source aquifer, a wide range of treatments including detoxification and stabilization alternatives exist. These remedial management alternatives can be classed into two groups (Sills et al., 1980): in-situ alternatives and conventional withdrawal, treatment, and final disposal alternatives.

In-Situ Remedial Alternatives

In-situ techniques of treatment, either through detoxification, stabilization, or immobilization, are still under development and are generally difficult to apply. These various treatment options are based upon a knowledge of the chemistry of the contaminants that are present in either a heterogeneous leachate, the affected groundwater, or bound to the shallow unsaturated soil matrix. Other factors influencing the suitability of these in-situ treatment alternatives include the subsurface mixing regime and reaction kinetics, competing or interfering reactions with the soil matrix or other injected materials, formation of toxic by-products, and environmental conditions such as pH, temperature, and solubility (Sills et al., 1980). The most promising options involve the use of injection wells to introduce biological cultures, chemical reactants, or sealants into the affected soil or groundwater. These actions would detoxify or stabilize a hazardous substance in-situ, form an impervious barrier around a site to prevent lateral migration of contaminated groundwater, enhance a specific contaminant-collection technique, or form an impervious barrier between a contaminated soil matrix and the local groundwater table, with subsequent cleanup of the soils via injection rinsing techniques (Sills et al., 1980). The major drawback to detoxification, stabilization, and immobilization options using injection wells is the high cost of installing enough wells to achieve uniform distribution and mixing of injected substances (Geraghty, 1981).

The two categories of in-situ detoxification are biological degradation and chemical detoxification. Biological degradation involves the addition of mutant strains of microbial organisms capable of utilizing the hazardous substance. Strains of microbial organisms exist which can degrade both simple and complex organics. Emulsifiers may, however, have to be introduced with the microbes to enhance the degradation of insoluble organics. Nutrient supplements may be required for biologically efficient environments. It is important that all metabolites of these processes be analyzed for toxicity. Chemical detoxification may fall into one of three methods:

1. Injection of neutralizing agents for acid or caustic leachates
2. Addition of oxidizing agents such as ozone or chlorine for destruction of organic compounds
3. Introduction of amino acids in order to enhance photo-degradation of ketones, polybrominated biphenyls (PBBs), and polychlorinated biphenyls (PCBs) (Sills et al., 1980)

Stabilization alternatives prevent the plume of contamination from extending. This is usually accomplished by converting contaminants to insoluble forms or by their encapsulation in a highly insoluble matrix. The chemical conversion of contaminants to an insoluble form is limited to inorganic species with insoluble salts and is subject to re-solution with a change in physical or chemical parameters, such as pH. Encapsulation in an insoluble matrix can be achieved by using several commercially available products: silicate, sulfur, or organic polymer-based cementaceous compounds.

In-situ remedial immobilization involves the partial or total containment of the contaminated groundwater either as a singular remedial stabilization technique or to enhance the efficiency of other collection, withdrawal, treatment or detoxification options (Sills et al., 1980). In order partially to contain the contamination, a clay cap can be used to prevent precipitation from leaching contaminants into the groundwater, but it will do nothing to reduce the contamination that existed prior to such capping (Geraghty 1981). Methods of total containment involve impoundment behind physical barriers or the use of injection wells to drain contaminated fluid into a non-potable zone below the contaminated aquifer (Figure 9–3). With the use of this type of injection well (Figure 9–3), there is no need to handle, treat, or dispose of the contaminated fluids at the surface (Geraghty, 1981). Impoundment barriers include slurry walls, grout curtains, sheet steel, and floor seals. Slurry walls, composed of concrete slurry or gels, are emplaced by digging a trench (Figure 9–1) and are, therefore, difficult to use in bedrock or for contamination more than 80–90 feet deep. Grout curtains are formed by injecting a grout of cement, bentonite, epoxy resins, rubber, lime, fly ash, or bitumen under pressure through numerous wells (Figure 9–1). The uncertainty as to whether the injected grout forms an impermeable barrier and the depth limit of 50 to 60 feet are the major drawbacks to the use of grout curtains. Sheet steel can be driven into the soil to form a wall to a depth of about 100 feet, but the formation of impermeable joints between sheets is difficult (Figure 9–1). A horizontal impoundment technique, such as floor seals, may be necessary when the aquifer is deep and the plume of contamination extends only part way through the thickness of the aquifer (Figure 9–2). This procedure is costly, however, and there is little guarantee that a tight seal will result. Geraghty (1981) states that permanently eliminating the potential for movement of a plume is impossible unless all contaminated solids and liquids can be treated or else operators provide perpetual care and maintenance of the containment method.

Conventional Alternatives of Withdrawal, Treatment, and Final Disposal

In contrast to the in-situ remedial actions, the conventional methods of withdrawal, treatment, and final disposal require, as their name suggests, the removal of the contamination, treatment, and disposal to another site. The choice of feasible collection and withdrawal options is usually governed by the size and geohydrology of the site. Important characteristics of the geohydrology include the site surface and groundwater topography, soil hydraulic characteristics, depth to watertable, and depth to impervious layer. The various collection and withdrawal options can be divided among five groups:

1. Collection wells
2. Subsurface gravity collection drains
3. Impervious grout curtains (described above)
4. Cut-off trenches
5. A combination of the above (Sills et al., 1980)

Collection or pump-back or recovery wells are an effective option which is not limited by plume depth. The wells are usually arranged in a line and designed to withdraw from the plume while minimizing inflows of uncontaminated water (Figure 9–4) (Geraghty, 1981). Various sorts of buried drains can be used to intercept the plume, but are not effective in deep aquifers or areas of hard rock (Figure 9–5). Cut-off trenches may intercept the contaminated water, if the plume is not too deep, and drain the water for further treatment or for disposal in a suitable body of surface water.

Treatment Options

Both the feasibility of a treatment option and its performance standards are dependent on the susceptibility of the leachate, contaminated soil, or groundwater to treatment and on the limitations inherent in the options for the final disposal of the effluent. The treatment options are listed and summarized below (Sills et al., 1980):

Reverse Osmosis (RO)

The RO process converts the leachate to fresh water by using pressure in excess of the osmotic pressure of the leachate to force fresh water through a membrane that is permeable to the water molecules but not to the leachate molecules. This process is effective for the removal of most dissolved organics, inorganic salts, heavy metals, and emulsified oils.

Ultrafiltration (UF)

The ultrafiltration (UF) process also uses a pressure-driven method of separation through a membrane, but it operates at lower temperatures and is suitable only for leachates with larger molecules.

Ion Exchange

The ion-exchange process uses a resin bed to remove selected toxic or undesired ions and to replace them with harmless ions. The system is mobile and can be loaded with various types of resins (exchange resins or absorptive resins) to demineralize water which is low in organics and to remove organic or inorganic substances. The resins may then be regenerated using acids, bases, or brine solutions. The suitability of various resins depends largely on their ability to be regenerated.

Wet-Air Oxidation (WAO)

The wet-air oxidation (WAO) process employs an aqueous-phase oxidation of reduced inorganic and organic substances by air carried out at relatively high temperatures.

Combined Ozonation/Ultraviolet Radiation (O_3 /UV)

Combined ozonation/ultraviolet radiation (O_3/UV) is a chemical oxidation process where a hazardous-waste mixture is contacted with ozone and UV radiation simultaneously to destroy many organics, including refractory and toxic chemicals.

Chemical Treatment

These processes precipitate and coagulate dissolved and colloidal particles but are ineffective in removing soluble organic and inorganic substances. Frequently the chemical processes are used in conjunction with other treatment options.

Aerobic Biological Treatment

These processes utilize microorganisms to convert organic matter to organic and inorganic end-products in the presence of dissolved oxygen. Among the processes most favorable for hazardous-waste treatment are: activated sludge, pure oxygen, multi-stage suspended-growth reactors, fixed-media processes, and aerated lagoons.

Activated Carbon (AC)

A wide range of organic and inorganic material can be removed from liquid and aqueous-phased streams by sorption on activated carbon (AC) columns (granular) or in suspension in batch reactors (powdered).

A treatment process may also include more than one of the above options. For example, biological treatment processing may include an activated carbon step in order to cleanse the contaminated leachate of all types of toxic substances.

The feasibility of any treatment depends on the amount of end-product and the method of final disposal. The three primary final disposal options are: discharge to a municipal sewage-treatment plant, discharge to a surface-water body, or land application. Any discharge to a sewage-treatment plant requires pretreatment to remove contaminants that could damage collections sewers, pumping stations, or the plant itself (Sills et al., 1980). In order to discharge to a body of surface water (Figure 9–6), certain planning criteria must be met, such as water-quality standards, federal or state discharge-permit requirements, and overlapping federal and state water-quality laws and regulations. Land-application processes include slow-rate irrigation, overland flow, and rapid infiltration. The feasibility of these techniques depends on data collected about the decomposition/application rates, toxic effects on crop or volunteer vegetation systems, and soil-renovation capabilities (Sills et al., 1980). Often with organics, the method of final disposal is to burn or rebury.

Sills et al. (1980) have suggested a two-phase evaluation procedure for determining the suitable remedial-management alternatives. The first phase, a preliminary screening, determines the most viable management alternatives for a given site. In the second phase, these viable alternatives are evaluated according to technical, economic, and environmental criteria. An iterative screening procedure can compare alternatives as to their effectiveness at treating the contaminants, the establishment of their performance criteria, their cost-effectiveness, and their potential environmental impacts. In determining the cost-effectiveness of each alternative, unit cards obtained from published guides can be applied to each activity in the management alternative. These costs will include short-term costs of capital, labor, and installation and long-term costs of maintenance and monitoring (Paige et al., 1980). Total life-cycle costs of one management alternative can be compared to another by converting all capital, operational, and maintenance costs at the end of the life period to an equitable present-worth cost at the first day which, if invested at a given interest rate, would exactly yield the necessary monies to cover annual costs of the management practice chosen (Sills et al., 1980). Depending on the selected remedial management alternative and the characteristics of the site, the cost of remedial action may vary from several thousand to several billion dollars.

The appropriate response to a groundwater-pollution problem will depend upon the physical characteristics of the site and the nature of the contamination. At times, no remedial action is necessary or, at least, cost-effective, and some indirect action, such as locating a new water source, is the best solution. In other cases, some remedial action is needed to halt the contamination and, possibly, to rehabilitate the aquifer. Two categories of management alternatives for remedial action exist: in-situ detoxification, stabilization,and immobilization and conventional withdrawal treatment and final disposal. Selection of viable management alternatives will depend on the nature and extent of contamination, site-specific feasibility, including cost-effectiveness, and potential environmental impacts. In any groundwater-pollution problem, prevention would have been the best solution. The many prevention methods, such as leak prevention in tanks and pipelines, sealing of storage sites, and careful siting of any waste facility, prove to be a cost-effective alternative to the very expensive remedial-action options.

Figure 9–1. Cross Section of Cutoff Wall (Slurry Trench, Sheet Piling, Grout Curtain)
Note: Some kind of pumped system (well drains) needed to prevent overflow of contaminated water from inside the cutoff wall.
Geraghty & Miller, Inc., *Seminar Proceedings of the Fundamentals of Groundwater Quality Protection* (1981), p. 10. Reprinted by permission of James J. Geraghty.

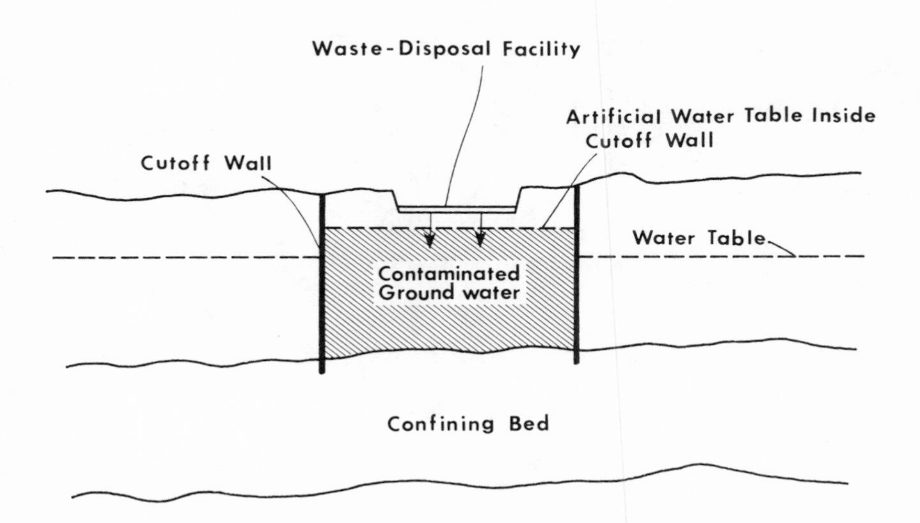

Figure 9–2. Cross Section of Cutoff Wall with Injected Bottom-Seal Grout

Geraghty & Miller, Inc., *Seminar Proceedings of the Fundamentals of Groundwater Quality Protection* (1981), p. 11. Reprinted by permission of James J. Geraghty.

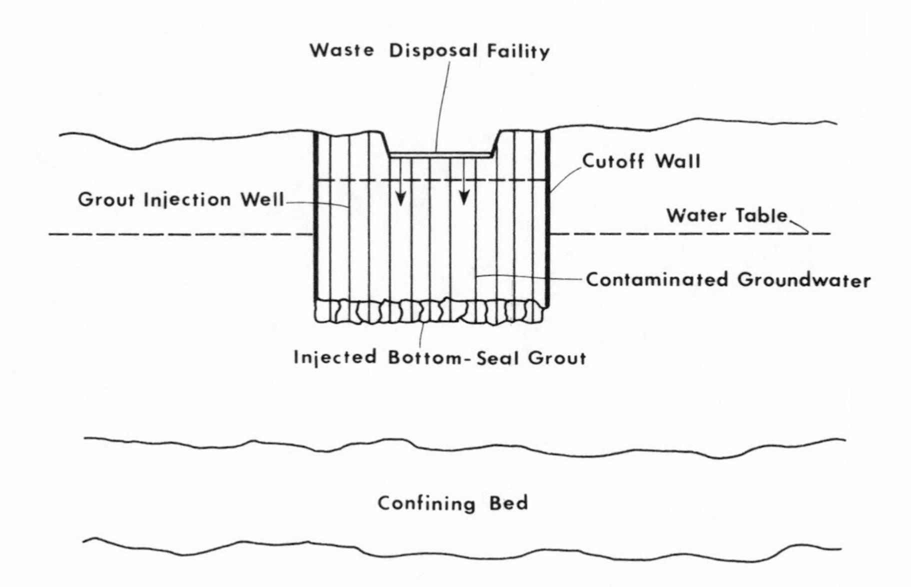

Figure 9–3. Drainage by Gravity of Contaminated Groundwater Through a Deep Injection Well

Geraghty & Miller, Inc., *Seminar Proceedings of the Fundamentals of Groundwater Quality Protection* (1981), p. 17. Reprinted by permission of James J. Geraghty.

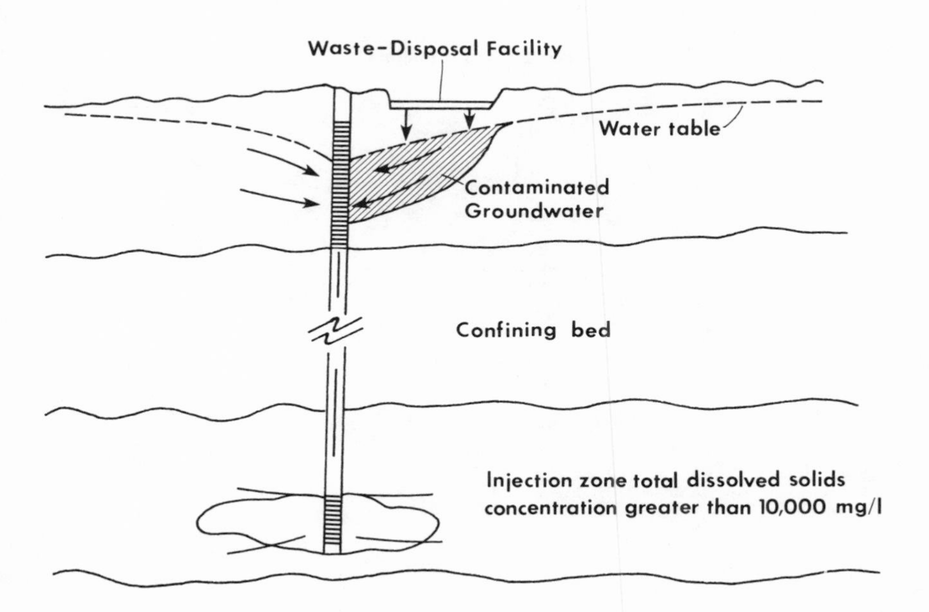

Figure 9–4. Control of Plume Movement by Pumping from a Single Well

Geraghty & Miller, Inc., *Seminar Proceedings of the Fundamentals of Groundwater Quality Protection* (1981), p. 15. Reprinted by permission of James J. Geraghty.

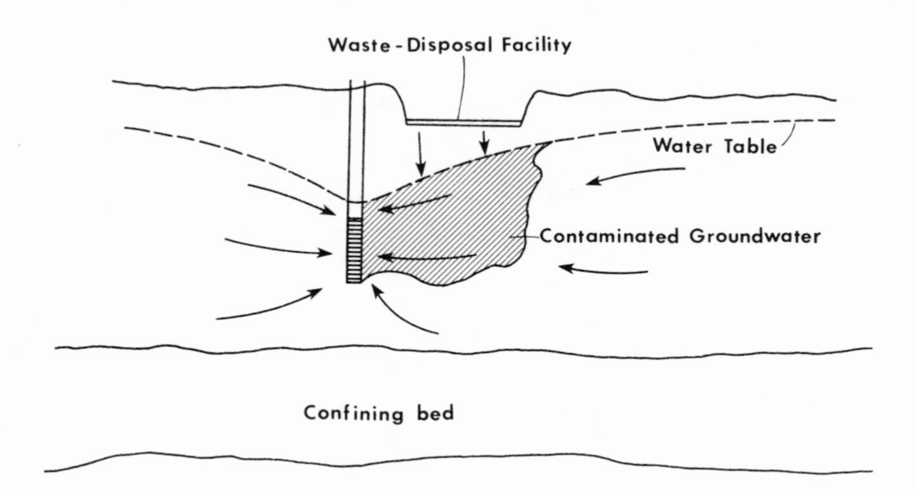

Figure 9–5. Control of Plume Movement Using Buried Perimeter Tile Drains

Geraghty & Miller, Inc., *Seminar Proceedings of the Fundamentals of Groundwater Quality Protection* (1981), p. 14. Reprinted by permission of James J. Geraghty.

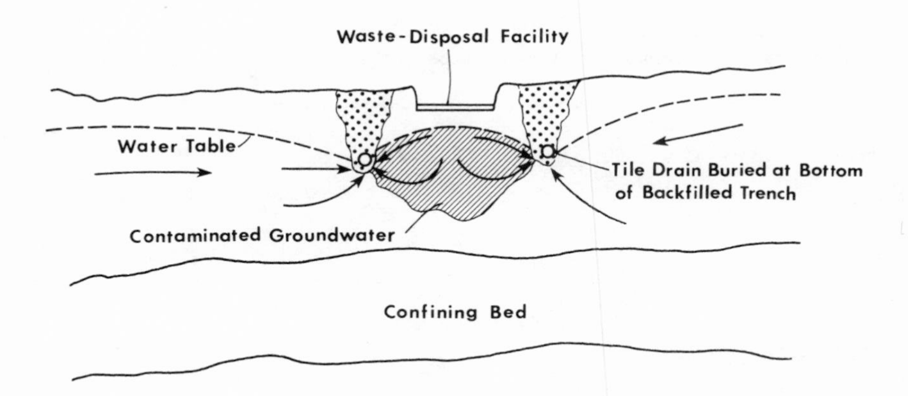

Figure 9–6. Blockage of Plume Movement by Discharge into Drainage Ditch, Brook, or Stream

Geraghty & Miller, Inc., *Seminar Proceedings of the Fundamentals of Groundwater Quality Protection* (1981), p. 13. Reprinted by permission of James J. Geraghty.

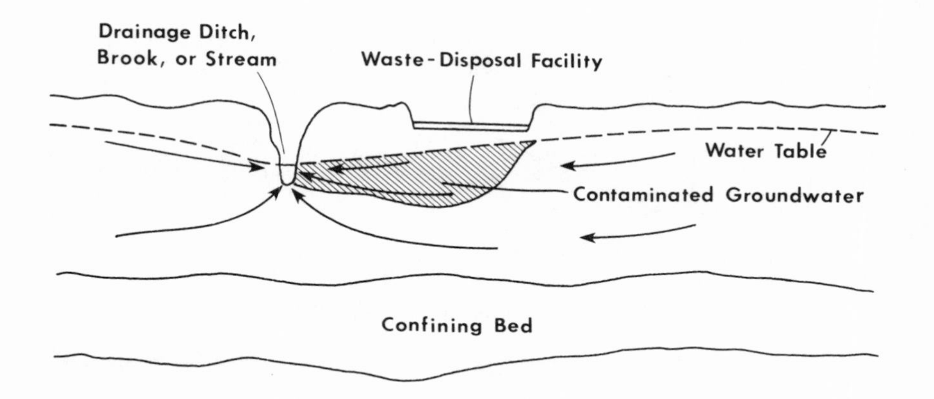

Ten

Proposed Strategies for the Protection of Groundwater

- Because of the difficulty and uncertainity of remedial action, protection of useful, potable aquifers from contamination is a better strategy than curative efforts.
- The EPA 1980 Proposed National Groundwater Strategy is summarized.
- The reactions of the Chemical Manufacturers Association and the Environmental Defense Fund to the 1980 EPA proposed strategy are discussed.
- The procedures that have been followed for the development of an EPA Groundwater Policy since 1980 are outlined, although such a policy has not been released as of April 1983.

EPA Proposed Groundwater Protection Strategy, 1980

The planning process for the proposed Environmental Protection Agency (EPA) groundwater protection strategy began in the winter of 1979 in response to a growing concern for the plight of the nation's groundwaters and in recognition of the need for a preventive program to protect groundwater. Under the direction of then Administrator Douglas M. Costle, the Office of Water and Waste Management was assigned the responsibility for the development of a groundwater strategy with the following emphases:

- Major consideration for future generations
- Exploration of alternative approaches to groundwater protection not included in existing policy or law
- Concentration on broad policy issues
- Participation of representative state officials and other concerned groups
- Cooperation and interaction with other affected institutions
- Recognition of the relation between ground- and surface-waters, including wetlands

A three-phase approach was evolved to fulfill the above requirements. Phase I comprised data gathering by four task groups in the winter and spring of 1980. Information was gathered from as many interests as possible, including public-interest groups, academia, business, industry, state and local governments, the National Drinking Water Advisory Council, and EPA's Science Advisory Board. Background information was collected on groundwater use and contamination, state and federal laws, and current research and development. All results were complied and published for use in the next phase. Phase II consisted of two workshops conducted in June 1980 with eighty participants, representing a cross section of interests, opinion, and knowledge of groundwater protection. The workshops developed the basis for the proposed strategy, and a document was released to the public in November 1980. In January 1981 under Phase III, the proposed strategy was published in the Federal Register, and public hearings were held in five locations throughout the country.

This summary is based on the document released to the public in November 1980. It is written in two parts. The first part describes the development process for the strategy, a synopsis of the Phase II workshops, and a review of groundwater use and contamination. The second part outlines the strategy itself, with the rationale behind it, the assumptions underlying its development, and its goals and objectives.

Strategy Background

The need to establish a comprehensive framework for dealing with the increasingly unmanageable problems of groundwater contamination provided the rationale for the protection strategy. At present, there is no single agency responsible for the protection of groundwater, making the effective management of contamination problems difficult. The EPA Protection Strategy was an attempt to establish a framework which (U.S. EPA, 1980d):

- "facilitates the development of institutional capabilities at the federal/state levels

- "enables consistent groundwater policies and priorities to be set
- "expedites the gathering of data, technological information, and expertise, focuses attention and action on high priority problems
- "promotes longer range planning and identification of more comprehensive future actions."

The Strategy

Ten major assumptions were made for the development of this strategy:

- Threats to groundwater will not be controlled quickly and, therefore, the development of a comprehensive protection program will be a long-term project.
- Because of the complexity of the problem, it is essential that all levels of government work together.
- The strategy will not be able to identify all long-term priorities and policies, therefore, the ultimate groundwater strategy can never be completely defined.
- Programs protecting groundwater quality must go hand-in-hand with those managing quantity; however, the strategy will not directly address quantity issues.
- Until classification standards are developed, all groundwater of drinking quality will be presumed a drinking-water source, ensuring that its use as such will not be impaired.
- Priority needs to be assigned to the gathering of needed scientific and engineering knowledge on groundwater contamination, assessment, enhancement, and protection.
- Due to limited resources, priorities must be established for the allocation of resources to groundwater needs, and strategies must be phased-in over time.
- Innovative approaches to groundwater protection should be encouraged.
- States should develop consistent approaches to groundwater protection.
- With the passage of Superfund (CERCLA), no new federal legislation is anticipated at this time.

The goal of the strategy was preventive rather than curative, recognizing that not all groundwater is of the same value. "It shall be the national goal to assess, protect, and enhance the quality of groundwaters to the levels necessary for current and projected future uses and for the protection of public health and significant ecological systems" (U.S. EPA, 1980d).

The strategy had four short-term objectives to be accomplished by 1985:

1. To initiate groundwater-protection strategies in all states and to develop the necessary personnel, resources, and legal authorities at the state and local levels to put the strategies to work

2. To implement fully the current federal regulations which affect groundwater
3. To begin evaluating groundwater quality, treating and improving conditions at the most hazardous sites, and developing management and technical methods for cleaning up newly discovered contamination plumes
4. To provide a process for state and local governments and the public to set priorities among competing activities which may use or contaminate groundwater

By 1990 it was hoped that the strategy would ensure that appropriate levels of protection were being provided for the groundwater resources in each state and that each state had a program fully implemented to manage all its groundwater.

Suggested Management Approach

The strategy proposed an approach to managing groundwater with four key policies:

- State groundwater protection strategies should be developed by the states. This process may be partially funded by State/EPA Agreements (SEAs).
- A groundwater classification system should be developed which would recognize different levels of protection for different aquifers. Until such a system is developed and adopted, EPA will maintain a policy that wherever groundwater is currently of drinking-water quality or better, it will be provided protection to ensure its use as drinking water.
- Minimum national requirements should be set for high-priority problems, such as highly toxic chemicals and pesticides, and product bans or restrictions should be set where appropriate.
- EPA should coordinate and bring consistency to existing federal programs for groundwater protection.

The development of state strategies would establish a framework for planning, implementation, and enforcement activities at the state and local levels and would help to coordinate state and federal activities. It was of primary importance that the individual states retain their authority over groundwater issues.

A three-phase approach was envisioned by EPA to develop the state strategies. Suggested guidelines for strategy content would be developed and issued by EPA, with contributions from state agencies and other interested groups. The states would prepare the strategies with participation from as many interested and affected groups as possible. Finally, the strategies would be reviewed by EPA for approval and incorporated into State/EPA Agreements (SEAs). Funding for strategy development would have come, to some extent, from existing programs such as Section 208 of the Clean Water Act (CWA), the Resource Conservation and Recovery Act (RCRA), and the Underground Injection Control program (UIC) of the Safe Drinking Water Act (SDWA).

Groundwater classification was a second major element of the protection strategy, in the recognition that not all aquifers have natural yields of the highest quality water and that all uses do not require the same levels of quality. The EPA proposed a model aquifer-classification system which is detailed elsewhere in this report (pages 204–40).

Finally, EPA planned to establish national controls where the threat to groundwater resources is national in scope, complexity, or severity. The following types of incidence were considered serious enough to warrant national action:

- where chemical substances, contamination pathways, and treatment processes are extremely widespread
- where special regulatory remedies such as product bans or use restrictions dictate unified actions
- where interstate issues are significant, as in waste disposal
- where uniformity among states is needed to avoid major economic dislocations and the establishment of de facto pollution havens.

Further priorities for EPA were:

- to develop maximum-contaminant levels and no adverse-risk levels for organics and other compounds in drinking water
- to develop national guidelines for the conduct of monitoring
- to develop procedures for dealing with instances of detected contamination
- to identify high-priority sources of contamination, such as underground storage tanks.

Groundwater-protection action would have been implemented with existing federal legislation. There were no plans for introducing new legislation. RCRA and UIC would be of major importance in implementing the groundwater-protection effort. EPA would also have made full use of emergency powers delegated to it by RCRA and SDWA.

EPA would have sought to coordinate its own regulatory programs with other programs related to groundwater protection. The agency would also work with other federal agencies, such as the Nuclear Regulatory Commission, the U.S. Geological Survey (USGS), Water Resources Council, Council on Environmental Quality, and the Departments of Agriculture, Interior, Transportation, and Housing and Urban Development toward achieving the goals of this strategy.

EPA, under the 1980 proposed strategy, would have tried to keep its in-house activities consistent with the groundwater-protection strategy by doing research in areas such as contaminant transport and fate, groundwater modeling, monitoring techniques, effects on public health, the effects of water reuse, aquifer rehabilitation, contamination by individual sources such as septic tanks, landfills, or lagoons, information transfer and data management, and institutional arrangements and legal issues affecting the strategy.

The proposed strategy would protect groundwater quality according to its value and end-use. Therefore, technical requirements vary in degree and approach as appropriate to the aquifer. There are four major technical approaches:

- siting and design practices
- best management practices specifying best operating practices
- technology based on effluent standards
- performance standards not geared to specific technologies can be used to encourage innovative and alternative technologies.

To a lesser extent, numerical standards of groundwater quality and economic incentives may be used. Economic incentives are desirable but not well defined. They offer local flexibility and lower societal costs than remedial action. The strategy should be seen as an evolving program which will maintain its flexibility for exploration, evaluation, and change. EPA recognized that not all questions could be answered in the initial stages of the protection program.

Summary of the Chemical Manufacturers Association's Position on EPA's Proposed Groundwater Protection Strategy

In response to EPA's 1980 proposed national groundwater strategy, the Chemical Manufacturers Association (CMA, 1980) proposed a groundwater policy in October 1980. The CMA recognizes the potential adverse effects on health and the environmental damage due to chemical or biological contamination of groundwater, and their position paper emphasizes the need for proper management of this valuable resource. For the CMA, a scientifically well-balanced groundwater policy would result in proper management if it achieves responsible protection of human health and the environment consistent with the social and economic needs and well-being of the nation. Using EPA's conceptual framework, the CMA's proposed strategy includes a restated fundamental goal and suggests management strategies, technical options, and the proper federal and state roles. These are summarized below.

Goal

The goal of any national groundwater policy should be to protect human health and the environment and to maintain the multiple uses of the resource responsibly. In elaborating the stated goal, the CMA disapproves of the implementation of any simplistic policies, such as a blanket nondegradation policy, which will not achieve the multiple-use objective. Instead, the paper advocates the development of innovative and flexible techniques to accommodate the diverse nature of occurrences, uses, and existing qualities of the nation's groundwater. According to the CMA, multiple use may not be applicable to aquifers which are a sole source of drinking water and degradation of any aquifer should not prevent the use for which that aquifer is classified. According to the CMA, the formulation of a groundwater policy must take into account the current quantity and quality of groundwater resulting from both natural characteristics and past usage. The states should deal with this existing contamination on a site-specific basis.

Management Approach

The recommended management approach to achieve the stated goal is to identify use-classes and to develop a comprehensive data base on groundwater contaminants and sources of groundwater pollution. The data base would be used to designate classes of groundwater.

The CMA's management approach requires the classification of groundwater according to present and potential uses. The states would assign use classifications on the basis of accumulated scientific data after considering societal needs, intended uses, and the present quantity and quality of the groundwater. The data base should include environmental chemistry, toxicity, physical properties, transport fate, potential impact, and mitigating measures for various types of potential contaminants. The CMA proposes that the use classifications should determine the priorities for management action, with those classes of use relating directly to human health or resource conservation being given the highest priority.

Technical Approach

A flexible technical approach is needed to achieve the stated groundwater-policy goal. Technical requirements should be assigned for each of the use-classes. Alternative requirements should be allowed when it can be demonstrated that the classification will not be impaired.

The CMA emphasizes that no one technical control mechanism, such as water-quality standards, best management practices, or best available technology, is appropriate for every classification of use. Again, the position paper stresses the need for flexibility in groundwater policy.

Federal, State, and Other Roles

The individual states should have the primary responsibility for implementing groundwater policy. The federal role in groundwater policy should be to identify broad national goals, to develop use-classes, and to provide supplemental technical and financial assistance to the states sufficient to implement their management programs.

The CMA believes that the states have the sole right of water allocation and therefore the sole right to assign the use-classes and to determine appropriate management techniques. The states should, however, be aware of the need for regional cooperation. The federal government's role, according to the position paper, is one of advisor, funder, and supplier of technical assistance and scientific information.

Questions Regarding Groundwater Policy

In responding to a hypothetical question concerning the possibility of classifying all groundwater as drinking water in order to safeguard the water for any potential use, the CMA states its opposition to any arbitrary designations of groundwater until their present or projected use is identified. The position paper allows for strict land-use control as a management technique only where there is an overriding need to protect certain resources and where it is not technically or administratively feasible to allow variances in that control. According to the CMA, construction of industrial sites should be allowed above a sole-source aquifer so long as they meet stringent technical requirements which protect the aquifer from contamination. In monitoring the impairment of groundwater, or its being rendered unusable for its classified purpose, the paper recommends a monitoring program consisting of a series of wells starting at the potential source of contamination and extending to the property line.

The transfer of this program should accompany the transfer of the ownership of the property. The CMA believes that any state retains the right of refusal to participate in a national groundwater program, but that existing laws and economic pressures will prevent the development of any pollution havens.

Critique of the CMA Position Paper

The Chemical Manufacturers Association's Position Paper on EPA's Proposed Groundwater Strategy presents a set of assumptions which serve as the basis for the goals and approaches of an alternate groundwater strategy. These assumptions include the need for the protection of human health, for the multiple use of resources, and for flexibility in accommodating the diversity in the quality, quantity, and location of groundwater. Although the protection of human health is recognized as the goal of highest priority, the position paper presents the concept of multiple uses—historic, present, and future—as the primary cornerstone on which its proposed strategy is built. The right of the states to allocate groundwater is the other key component of the CMA's groundwater strategy. Therefore, this critique must examine the validity and suitability of these two concepts as applied by the CMA in a national groundwater strategy.

In stating its goal, management approaches, and technical approach, the CMA position paper defines the concept of multiple use and the need for flexibility. The positions taken by the CMA fail, however, to mention any goal of preserving ecosystems or protecting the environment. The paper stresses the importance of maintaining multiple uses of groundwater in order to meet a variety of societal needs, but fails to explain whether the term groundwater means all of the nation's groundwater, each groundwater aquifer, or one site's groundwater. The paper also fails to consider effectively a time scale in its goals, management, and technical approaches. The CMA feels a blanket nondegradation policy would conflict with the need for innovation and flexibility in the strategy. Conceivably, as a greater understanding of the properties of groundwater develops, a nondegradation policy applied now could result in a more efficient and even a more flexible application of multiple uses at a later time. The CMA supports the policy of evaluating the resource as it currently exists and of classifying aquifers by present and projected use. With these classifications, degradation would not be allowed below a level suitable for use. There are two inherent weaknesses in this classification system: the inaccuracies inherent in trying to predict future uses and the difficulty in determining and implementing water-quality levels for each use. There is also the question of how, or if, the aquifer may be used until the future uses are identified.

The position paper attempts to shift the emphasis on contamination away from industrial sites to the less sensational non-point sources. In doing so, however, the CMA does not mention the significance of the degree and type of contamination when it stresses the need for flexibility in management and technical approaches. The paper proposes the implementation of land-use controls only if no other techniques are available to protect a resource, but it does not consider the potential effectiveness of land-use controls in achieving multiple use. The importance of siting as a control technique is not included in a list of methods used to prevent the contamination of groundwater. Finally the CMA fails to justify its goal of multiple use or of its management and technical approaches on the grounds of economic efficiency.

In defining the federal and state role in a groundwater protection strategy, the CMA believes that a practical approach is the development of individual state management programs. It is important to question how much individual freedom these programs would be allowed and the practicality of the approach. The position paper supports federal guidance and funding, but maintains that the states should create their own programs. The CMA states that any fears of potential pollution havens as a result of political and economic forces on the states are unfounded, but it does not provide any data or cite any studies supporting that statement. Individual state programs may not necessarily ensure more flexibility in the management of groundwater. Although both the quality and type of groundwater sources in many states vary greatly, the states may find that without federal oversight it is more efficient to implement a blanket program which either omits technical controls or includes a nondegradation policy.

The Environmental Defense Fund's Position on EPA's Proposed Groundwater Strategy

The Environmental Defense Fund's (EDF, 1981) paper not only suggests changes in the EPA's proposed strategy itself, but also in the approach the EPA has taken in designing and eventually implementing the strategy. Noting past inefficiencies by the EPA in the implementation of existing legislation and the need to develop policy in an orderly manner, the EDF believes that an incremental approach would be valuable to the groundwater-strategy development. The EDF believes that there are two advantages to this approach: state groundwater strategies would evolve faster and more completely if they were initially based on policies derived from existing programs pursuant to federal law, and the conditions for acceptable degradation of groundwater must be defined before the strategy progresses. Especially important to the EDF is the potential contamination of drinking-water sources by the siting of new facilities before water-quality standards and mitigating technology can be developed. The EDF proposed alternative plan consists of two phases:

Phase I: Federal Efforts

- vigorously enforce existing rules and regulations, with the allocation of adequate resources to enforce compliance and to monitor state programs
- build groundwater-protection components into existing federal programs and fully implement existing laws, i.e., develop an internal federal groundwater policy
- increase research and development in areas outlined on p. VII-12, 13 and 14 of the proposed strategy
- cleanup existing significant sources of groundwater contamination
- provide assistance to the states for aquifer characterizations and other state activities
- develop the necessary drinking-water and groundwater-quality standards to implement a classification scheme. Until standards are

developed, the siting of significant new sources of contamination which require a federal permit should be banned

- develop policies to discourage the use of aquifer contaminants

Phase I: State Efforts

- vigorously enforce existing rules and regulations
- utilize sole-source aquifer designations available under the SDWA
- characterize groundwater resources, with particular emphasis on identifying aquifers subject to Level I and Level III control. States should begin preserving Level I aquifers by addressing point and non-point sources of contamination and permit siting of new localized sources of pollution only over aquifers subject to Level III control
- assess the need for enabling legislation to carry out groundwater strategy, identify lead agency and demarcating agency responsibilities

Phase II: Federal and State Roles

- assess the full extent of groundwater contamination, the sources of contamination, and the need for new legislation
- implement a system of groundwater-quality standards before any siting of new sources of contamination over Level II areas
- apply groundwater-protection standards as required to fully implement classification scheme

Although the EDF believes that the differences between states and localities must be accommodated in both the strategy and its goals, the Fund sees a need for federal oversight to ensure consistency. A strong federal component is necessary, according to the EDF, because of the lack of well-structured, fully implemented state programs and the shortcomings even of those groundwater protection programs that do exist, for example, that of New York. A strong federal role would also ensure the development of a consistent, strong classification scheme. Like EPA, the EDF suggests a three-class aquifer system of classification with the following comments:

> Class I aquifers are those in which some groundwater segments contain high-quality water which should not be degraded at all. This is especially true where the groundwater segments contribute to a national or regional water supply or have ecological significance. Controls, including land-use controls, on significant non-point sources of pollution should be imposed.
>
> Class II aquifers should be protected as sources of drinking water until the development of maximum-contaminant levels and of national interim primary drinking-water standards. This woud replace the EPA's proposal to rely solely on technical requirements in the siting of sources in the interim.

> Class III aquifers must be identified on the basis of their presently poor water quality or inaccessability for economic or technological reasons. An activity that could cause significant pollution may be sited in these places, where it can do the least harm.

The EDF paper elaborates the issue of the federal and state role by stating that the necessary central role in the implementation of a national groundwater-protection program is with the states, but the EDF questions whether all states would be willing to assume that role. The EDF realizes that financial and political obstacles, especially the necessary increase in personnel and the ambiguous division of responsibilities among state and local agencies, prevent or impede the adoption of a groundwater program.

If the EPA initially incorporates groundwater-protection requirements into regulations promulgated under existing laws and their programs, the EDF maintains that the states can begin the task of characterizing groundwater resources and classifying aquifers.

The EDF does not consider a classification scheme to be the best method of ensuring groundwater protection and believes that the ultimate solution lies in the reduction of the use of aquifer contaminants. The EDF therefore suggests the incorporation of incentives into the groundwater-protection strategy in order to discourage the use of these contaminants. This approach would involve a national strategy of economic incentives and market mechanisms to facilitate industrial investments in the reduction of sources of hazardous waste. The objectives of this strategy would include reduction and elimination of the use of toxic substances, recycling, recovery, and reuse of toxics, and their safe disposal when disposal is required. Incentives should stress the financial cost of using toxics and should include: the removal of liability restrictions for generators of hazardous wastes; expensive, stringent regulations under TSCA, RCRA, and SDWA; tax credits, and a deposit-refund system of tax on the transport and discharge of toxics.

The EDF's comments on EPA's proposed groundwater strategy have emphasized the need for a cautious approach to the siting of any facilities that may pose potential threats to groundwater until a definite protective strategy can be installed. As part of this concept, the EDF has suggested an incremental, two-phased approach to the development of the protection strategy. In its comments on the strategy itself, the EDF favors a strong federal role which accommodates the central authority of the state as well as the diversity of groundwater resources and problems. The EDF also believes that the development of maximum contaminant levels and drinking-water standards are essential for the protection of the nation's groundwater resources. Finally, the EDF proposes the adoption of incentives to reduce the use and necessary disposal of toxic substances.

Critique of EDF's Comments

The Environmental Defense Fund position paper on EPA's proposed groundwater-protection strategy takes a conservative approach toward protecting groundwater from contamination. The EDF does not work toward a goal of multiple use or even of protection of ecosystems, but only a goal of the protection of human health. Even though the EDF states the need for flexibility in the national program, this position is not borne out in many of its later recommendations. The EDF also supports a strong federal component in the strategy in order to offset the possibility of haphazard administration and enforcement at the state level. Whether the federal agencies have been shown to be more efficient and cost-effective than the states in previous environmental programs is a subject of considerable political debate. The EDF pushes for the protection of all groundwater until classifications can be made. In this classification scheme, Class I aquifers would be identified first, have a non-degradation requirement, and have the siting of any toxic-waste facility prohibited even if control methods were to be used. The EDF Class II aquifer would contain drinking water for future use and have the siting of toxic-waste facilities prohibited pending further scientific information. Finally the Class III aquifers would also be identified as soon as possible. The key problem with this classification scheme is its questionable viability. The confined or naturally contaminated Cass III aquifers may not have a recharge area and therefore no area for siting of waste facilities. With this scheme, areas with no Class III recharge area would have no place to site hazardous- or toxic-waste facilities. The scheme also depends heavily on the development of water-quality standards by the EPA. National standards and their implementation for surface water has been the source of much criticism against the EPA. The method for determining standards may need changing, but the EDF proposes no solution.

As stated previously, the EDF supports a strong federal role in the protection strategy. The EDF mentions the strong political and economic obstacles to the states' independent adoption of a groundwater strategy but makes no mention of those forces in the states pushing for a strategy nor any analysis of the balance between them. The question of federal authority over groundwater is addressed by suggesting that the programs be developed as far as possible within existing federal laws. Whether these laws provide the federal government with authority over groundwater is still a question for the courts. Throughout all of its comments the EDF fails to consider the economic aspects of its proposals. Whether the classification scheme is efficient and especially whether water-quality standards may be more efficient than effluent charges, for example, are subjects for economic analysis. In its proposal for incentives to reduce and eliminate the generation of hazardous wastes, the EDF does not consider the trade-offs of cost and benefits nor even suggest that the EPA consider these costs if they adopt the suggestion.

EPA Groundwater Policy Since 1980

In 1981 the EPA Administrator was questioned by the Chairman of the House Government Operations Subcommittee on Environment, Energy and Natural Resources concerning the agency's lack of action on the proposed national groundwater strategy, surface-impoundment assessment and maximum containment levels for the prevalent groundwater contaminants. In November 1981 the Administrator of EPA created two separate groundwater task forces. Their aim was to develop a groundwater-options paper that would provide a consistent agency-wide strategy. The two groups considered the extent of the drinking-water problem; the current technical capacity to deal with the problem, and the options available for developing a consistent regulatory approach that could be incorporated into such EPA programs as the Resource Conservation and Recovery Act, Superfund, and the Safe Drinking Water Act. One task force was responsible for gathering data on the extent and nature of the problem and for assessing the scientific and technical resources to meet it. The other group was responsible for making policy decisions. Both groups were to take into account the outside comments received during the preparation of the 1980 proposed strategy and to seek new contributions from individual experts and environmental groups. In addition, the groups were to review the EPA laws and regulations applicable to groundwater. The product of the efforts of both groups was to be an options paper which would outline a consistent EPA groundwater strategy.

Early in its deliberations, the policy group decided to take a more focused look at groundwater problems. In February 1982 the groups were reportedly (*Inside EPA,* 5 February 1982) considering three options:

- no change to current groundwater policy
- moderate change, probably including a new groundwater strategy
- substantial change requiring a new groundwater program

The range of statutory, regulatory, and management possibilities was to be outlined for the three options.

In March 1982 a draft of the paper outlined three approaches. The first required a minimum investment of resources and time, sought no amendments to the current laws and no formal management structure that would be exclusively responsible for groundwater, and anticipated that groundwater research would remain at current projected levels. The second approach aimed to provide an effective framework for state and existing federal protection with a minimum of additional investment. The third approach required a significant commitment of resources and time to develop a high-profile groundwater-protection program. The draft also recommended that the groundwater-policy group meet on a continuing basis, that a lead office within the agency be designated, with resources allocated to it, that consultations between the agency and the states continue, that a review and revision of all relevant agency regulations be undertaken, that EPA should provide guidance to the regions on implementing the groundwater strategy and offer assistance to the states in preparing their individual strategies and, finally, that the EPA research and development program for groundwater should be reviewed (*Inside EPA,* 12 March 1982).

In April 1982 it was reported (*Inside EPA,* 9 April 1982) that the EPA policy group recommended a shift in the responsibility for groundwater protection from EPA to the states, resulting in the states' being the main agencies both for protection and fundamental regulatory decisions. A stumbling block to this course of action was identified as the distribution of authority among different state institutions. EPA's role would be to facilitate state efforts and to improve the consistency and coordination of its own and of other federal programs. Also in April 1982 the Chairman of the House Government Operations Subcommittee on Environment, Energy and Natural Resources, disturbed by the lack of a national groundwater policy after nearly two years of agency review, informed the EPA Administrator that he "may be forced to call upon my colleagues in Congress to enact legislation directing that EPA immediately develop such a policy" (*Environment Reporter,* 23 April 1982, p. 1714).

In May 1982 Rep. James Florio (D. NJ), Chairman of the Subcommittee on Commerce, Transportation and Tourism of the Energy and Commerce Committee, proposed amendments to the Resource Conservation and Recovery Act, including the establishment of a groundwater-quality commission, similar to the study groups previousy mandated for air and water. The commission would assess the nationwide groundwater-contamination problems caused by hazardous wastes and would make recommendations to Congress (*Inside EPA,* 7 May 1982).

In June 1982 it was announced that a groundwater policy that recognizes the primary role of the states in groundwater protection was under preparation and would be released by EPA by September 30 (*Air/Water Pollution Report,* 21 June 1982). In addition EPA would conduct a year-long "public outreach process" to develop a final groundwater policy by September 1983. This would occur after the Administrator approves the draft policy statement and the work plan has been published in the Federal Register for comment (*Inside EPA,* 6 August 1982). As of April 1983 the groundwater policy statement due to be published by 30 September 1982 has not been released by EPA.

Eleven

Aquifer Classification

- Aquifer classification is used by several states as a groundwater management and protection strategy. Classification systems are being considered by several other states.
- Selective protection of different aquifers to different quality levels would require a classification system. Preservation and restoration of all aquifers to drinking water use or the prohibition of degradation of present water quality would not require such a system.
- The benefits and the disadvantages of classification systems are discussed.
- State Aquifer Classification Systems at present in existence are detailed and compared. They fall into those distinct groups ranging from simple non-degradation systems to sophisticated differentiated systems incorporating land-use criteria and numerical water-quality standards.

As groundwater becomes an increasingly valuable resource in the United States, strategies for its protection and management are becoming the focus of detailed study in several states. Aquifer classification is one management tool being used by some states and considered by several others. An analysis of the implications of adopting an aquifer-classification system has recently been completed by Magnuson (1981). A summary of her report and summaries of the Environmental Protection Agency's (EPA) model and actual state aquifer-classification systems follow. Aquifer classification is further discussed in Chapter 13 under state and local groundwater-quality protection measures.

The purpose of aquifer classification is to establish water-quality goals for each aquifer and to identify standards or controls necessary to assure that water quality meets that goal. It is one approach for implementing the state's water policy by formally designating use and water-quality goals for groundwater resources. A state's choice of policy largely determines the appropriateness of classification as part of its overall groundwater-management program. There are three major policy options: to preserve and restore all aquifers for drinking-water use, to prohibit degradation of existing water quality, and to protect selectively different aquifers at different levels of quality. The first two policies are blanket policies, while the last would require the classification of aquifers.

As a groundwater-protection strategy, aquifer classification has both benefits and drawbacks. The benefits provided by aquifer classification include:

legal protection for valuable aquifers and a basis for siting potential contamination sources in low-risk areas

a reduction in unnecessary economic burdens on waste-facility operators by requiring that stringent water-quality standards be met throughout the state

a common basis for critical regulatory decisions affecting future use of groundwater resources

an opportunity for public involvement in critical policy decisions

guidance for planning and for programs to protect water quality at all levels of government

The classification of aquifers has the following drawbacks:

the difficulty in putting the system into place and making it effective

the difficulty of delineating the boundaries of aquifers

the possibility of serious legal and public-policy limitations on the feasibility of classification. Without the acknowledgement of some form of degradation zones, a classification system could offer very little flexibility in levels of protection given to groundwater areas.

the difficulty in gaining public acceptance for formally designated waste-receiving zones.

The Process of Classification

There is no aquifer-classification system in place today which could serve as a model to other states which would want to develop classification systems. Geologic and hydrologic conditions are too variable. Also, programs and policies governing the use of groundwater vary greatly from state to state.

In 1980 EPA drew up a model protection strategy which is detailed on page 189. The central concept of the proposed strategy is that different levels of protection should be provided for different areas of groundwater on the basis of present and projected uses. This strategy is similar to the one given to surface water. With groundwater, however, it may be necessary to acknowledge certain industrial and other activities as having higher priority than the protection of groundwater. Activities which may conflict with groundwater protection are: fuel extraction and processing, agricultural practices related to irrigation return-flow and fertilizer use, waste disposal, and highway deicing.

EPA has been empowered by the Safe Drinking Water Act to designate aquifers as sole or principal sources of drinking water if they are the only aquifers in an area providing all the drinking water. No federal funds can be committed to projects in these areas that would pollute the groundwater or create public-health hazards. For a discussion of the Sole Source Aquifer program, see pages 250–52.

The Definition of Aquifer Boundaries

Groundwater classes can be developed only after some sort of aquifer boundaries are defined. There are several ways to define boundaries:

In some areas of the country, distinct aquifer units can be identified that are hydraulically isolated from any other aquifer systems, as, for example, the Cohansey Aquifer in the New Jersey Central Pine Barrens, the glacial aquifer of Cape Cod, the valley-fill deposits located in glaciated regions of New England and intermountain systems of the western United States, and the St. Peter Sandstone Aquifer of Texas. In most areas of the country, however, identification of isolated hydraulic systems is virtually impossible.

The identification of flow systems such as recharge areas, discharge areas, regional flow, and multi-aquifer systems is another aid in defining the boundaries of aquifers. Water quality may serve to delineate aquifer zones. Natural quality is controlled by precipitation, evaporation, geology, and the amount of time the water remains in the groundwater system. As a general rule, the total content of dissolved solids increases with the depth and length of time that the water has traveled through an aquifer from the point of discharge. High evaporation and low precipitation may result in poor-quality groundwater. On the other hand, shallow aquifers in areas of high precipitation often contain water of very good quality with a total dissolved solids content (TDS) of less than 500 mg/l.

From a review of the hydrogeologic and water-quality data as described above, a state should be able to decide whether or not it can delineate distinct aquifer zones. There may be no method for distinguishing aquifer regions, and in that event they can only be described rather than mapped. Narrative criteria should, however, be used with caution. They are most effectively applied if used to identify regional aquifer characteristics.

Groundwater Classification

Having determined the boundaries of its aquifers, a state can begin to devise a structure for classifying groundwater. Existing systems recognize from two to eight classes. Wyoming has the greatest number of classes—agricultural, livestock, industrial (2 classes), mining, domestic uses, aquaculture, and "non-usable." The fundamental question to ask is whether or not an aquifer should be designated as being of drinking-water quality. Further breakdowns can be made to reflect land use, existing physical factors, and sensitive environmental systems. Connecticut is an example of a state where the drinking-water category is divided into three sub-categories based on existing uses and conditions.

Classification categories are structured according to combinations of the following factors:

- existing use
- water quality, primarily based on its total content of dissolved solids
- the determination to use either criteria or standards of quality (standards are more specific than criteria)
- land use
- other aquifer characteristics, i.e., soils and geology
- yield and availability of water regardless of quality (less than 350 gallons per minute (gpm) is considered uneconomical for community water-supply development)
- ability of an aquifer to attenuate and assimilate wastes
- multi-aquifer flow systems (a plan for the management of groundwater resources based on flow systems has been developed for Nassau and Suffolk Counties on Long Island)
- an aquifer associated with mineral deposits and geothermal sources may be classified for production purposes
- contribution to surface waters
- socio-economic factors

Magnuson (1981) believes that classified aquifers may be controlled by numerical standards for water quality, effluent-discharge limitations, or non-numerical rules for land use and waste disposal.

EPA Model for Aquifer Classification

In 1980 EPA proposed a model for aquifer classification as part of a comprehensive groundwater-protection strategy. The model suggests that the most important factor to be considered in classifying aquifers is the identification of current or projected uses of the aquifer, recognizing that not all aquifers have high-quality yields nor do all uses require the same level of quality (U.S. EPA, 1980d). There could be as many as seven categories of use:

1. highly valuable drinking water (sole source or pristine)
2. drinking water after minimal treatment
3. drinking water after extensive treatment
4. agricultural use (irrigation, livestock)
5. industrial use (cooling, process water)
6. mining and energy development
7. limited waste disposal

Additional important considerations are aquifer yield, the natural quality of the groundwater, and alternative sources of water in the area. Until an aquifer classification system is adopted, it would be presumed that all groundwater presently suitable for drinking would have a projected future use as a source of drinking water. Decisions to allocate groundwater of drinking quality to less protected uses would be based on assessments of future drinking-water needs, the quantity and quality of presently available drinking-water supplies, the availability of adequate protection for significant ecological systems, and the protection of public health.

The model then proposed three levels of control. Level I would warrant the most stringent regulations for the protection of water that is highly valuable for human use or ecological function. Level II would allow limited sitings of facilities dealing with hazardous and toxic wastes, while ensuring groundwater quality suitable for drinking. The majority of fresh groundwater would be found in this class. Level III would be more lenient, having technical requirements for facilities involved with hazardous and toxic wastes, but would require strict monitoring to ensure the protection of public health.

Critiques of the Proposed EPA Aquifer-Classification System from the Environmental Defense Fund and the American Water Works Association

The Environmental Defense Fund (EDF) thinks that too little is known about either groundwater or contamination to maintain the quality of drinking water and still allow some degradation (Environmental Defense Fund, 1981). "Priority should . . . be given to ascertaining appropriate aquifers for Level I and Level III controls, the former to prevent further contamination, the latter to provide siting locations for potentially polluting activities." The Defense Fund thinks that EPA is a long way from setting adequate groundwater-quality standards for protecting drinking water and that its history in working to establish such standards is not encouraging.

The American Water Works Association (AWWA) is primarily concerned with the logistics of implementing a classification system (Atkinson, 1981). "While it is possible to classify aquifers, to do it effectively may require a costly, time-consuming process and, to be a valuable tool, should also address classification of each total hydrologic flow system. An adequate information base is essential since many recharge areas for groundwater systems are currently unknown." The AWWA stresses the point that groundwater classification should be a flexible tool. A more detailed description of all the points of the Environmental Protection Agency's groundwater strategy proposed in 1980, together with critiques of the proposed scheme, are given on pp. 189–203.

State Aquifer-Classification Systems

The U.S. Water Resources Council identified fifteen states with aquifer-classification systems in use (Connecticut, Florida, Iowa, Maine, Maryland, Minnesota, Nebraska, New Jersey, New Mexico, New York, North Carolina, South Carolina, Utah, Virginia, and Wyoming) and three states in the process of developing systems (Kentucky, New Hampshire, and Missouri) (U.S. Water Resources Council, 1981). This list formed the basis for the summary of aquifer-classification systems contained in this report. Thirteen of the above states as well as Massachusetts and Arizona were asked to supply information. The appropriate authorities in Minnesota, Utah, Virginia, Maryland, and Kentucky, however, either could not be reached or did not send information. Only ten states were found actually to have classification systems (Connecticut, Florida, Maine, Nebraska, New Hampshire, New Jersey, New Mexico, New York, North Carolina, and Wyoming). Arizona, Iowa, and Massachusetts are working on groundwater-protection strategies that may include aquifer-classification systems. Massachusetts's approach to aquifer classification will be summarized at the end of this chapter. Missouri (D. Miller, Missouri Department of Natural Resources, personal communication) and South Carolina (D. Dunkin, South Carolina Department of Heath and Environmental Control, personal communication) do not have classification systems and depend on EPA Drinking Water Standards for chemical constituency parameters to protect their aquifers. To help protect their groundwater, several states, including Arizona, Iowa, and Missouri, presently have licensing procedures for all well drilling.

This summary does not intend to be comprehensive. Rather, it intends to recognize a variety of protection policies being used or being considered by some states, reflecting their needs and philosophies on regulation. The ten aquifer-classification systems identified in this report vary considerably. In two states, New Hampshire and Maine, aquifer classification is of a general nature. All groundwater is designated as potential drinking water, and it is the goal of those two states simply to prevent degradation. Magnuson (1981) does not consider this to be true classification because there is no selective process for protecting one aquifer more than another. This report will, however, consider the aquifer-protection plans of New Hampshire and Maine as the first step towards a classification system in those states since they themselves refer to their plans as classification systems. Florida, Nebraska, and New Mexico both have two-class systems based on the total content of dissolved solids in the groundwater. Connecticut, New Jersey, New York, North Carolina, and Wyoming have considerably more complex systems that recognize that an abundance of groundwater is in demand by several interests which have varying requirements for quality.

Connecticut

Connecticut is considered to be something of a model among the states having applied aquifer-classification systems. In September 1980 the state adopted a 4-class system as follows (Connecticut Department of Environmental Protection, 1980, Table 11–1):

1. Class GAA groundwater is to be used for public and private drinking supplies without treatment. The only allowable discharges into groundwater of this class are wastewaters of human or animal origin and other minor cooling and clean-water discharges.
2. Class GA is assigned to groundwater to be used for private drinking-water supplies without treatment. Discharges are restricted to those which pose no permanent threat to untreated drinking-water supplies.
3. Class GB groundwater may have to be treated to be potable because of existing or past land uses. Allowable discharges include certain treated industrial wastewaters that can be filtered by the soils but do not cause degradation threatening future potability without treatment.
4. Class GC groundwater may be suitable for some waste-disposal practices if land-use practices or hydrogeologic conditions render it more suitable for that purpose than for development as a potable-water supply. Down-gradient surface water must, however, be of medium-to-poor quality,

Table 11–1. Connecticut Groundwater Classifications

CLASS GAA	
Existing or proposed public drinking-water use without treatment.	
1. Dissolved oxygen	As naturally occurs.
2. Oils and grease	None other than of natural origin.
3. Color and turbidity	None other than of natural origin.
4. Coliform bacteria per 100 ml	Not to exceed a monthly arithmetic mean of 1 or more than 4 in any individual sample collected.
5. Taste and odor	None other than of natural origin.
6. pH	As naturally occurs or as may result from normal agricultural, horticultural silviculture, lawn maintenance or construction activity provided all reasonable controls are used.
7. Chemical constituents	The waters shall be free from chemical constituents in concentrations or combinations which would be harmful to human, animal or aquatic life for the most sensitive and governing water use class. Criteria for chemical constituents contained in guidelines published by the U.S. Environmental Protection Agency shall be considered. In areas where fisheries are the governing consideration and numerical limits have not been established, bioassays may be necessary to establish limits on toxic substances. The recommendations for bioassay procedures contained in "Standard Methods for the Examination of Water and Wastewater" and the application factors contained in EPA water quality guidelines shall be considered. For groundwaters classified for use as public or private drinking water (Classes GAA and GA), the raw water sources must be maintained or restored at a quality as defined by criteria developed by the U.S. EPA or the State, whichever is more stringent, so that criteria for finished water can be met without treatment.
CLASS GA	
May be suitable for public or private drinking water use without treatment.	
1. Dissolved oxygen	As naturally occurs.
2. Oils and grease	None other than of natural origin.

Table 11–1. (continued)

3. Color and turbidity	None other than of natural origin.
4. Coliform bacteria per 100 ml	Not to exceed a monthly arithmetic mean of 1 or more than 4 in any individual sample collected.
5. Taste and odor	None other than of natural origin.
6. pH	As naturally occurs or as may result from normal agricultural, horticultural silvicultural, lawn maintenance or construction activity provided all reasonable controls are used.
7. Chemical constituents	The waters shall be free from chemical constituents in concentrations or combinations which would be harmful to human, animal or aquatic life for the most sensitive and governing water use class. Criteria for chemical constituents contained in guidelines published by the U.S. Environmental Protection Agency shall be considered. In areas where fisheries are the governing consideration and numerical limits have not been established, bioassays may be necessary to establish limits on toxic substances. The recommendations for bioassay procedures contained in "Standard Methods for the Examination of Water and Wastewater" and the application factors contained in EPA water quality guidelines shall be considered. For groundwaters classified for use as public or private drinking water (Classes GAA and GA), the raw water sources must be maintained or restored at a quality as defined by criteria developed by the U.S. EPA or the State, whichever is more stringent, so that criteria for finished water can be met without treatment.

Class GB

May not be suitable for public or private use as drinking water without treatment. No quantitative or qualitative limits apply since the groundwaters specified as GB are known or presumed to be degraded.

Class GC

May be suitable for certain waste disposal practices because past land use or hydrogeologic conditions render these groundwaters more suitable for receiving permitted discharges than development for public or private water supply.

No qualitative or quantitative limits apply.

Source: Connecticut Department of Environmental Protection, 1980.

and wastewater discharges must not result in the degradation of surface waters below the classification goals established by the state.

"It is the policy of the State to restore or maintain the quality of the ground water to a quality consistent with its use for drinking without treatment" (GAA or GA), except where it has been classified GB and is not needed as a potable water supply, or GC where restoration is not feasible (Connecticut Department of Environmental Protection, 1980). The criteria for chemical constituents are determined by EPA standards or the state standards, whichever are more stringent, and apply always to waters classified for use as public or private drinking supplies (GAA or GA).

North Carolina

In June of 1979 North Carolina adopted a classification system in recognition of the fact that land uses were changing from agriculture and silviculture to housing, commerce, and industry, all of which would increase the potential and incidence of groundwater contamination (North Carolina Environmental Management Commission, 1979). North Carolina has a five-class system whose major parameters are the suitability of water for drinking, culinary use, and food processing; chloride concentration, and the depth at which the water occurs below the land surfaces (Table 11–2).

"The regulations . . . are intended to maintain and preserve the quality of groundwater, prevent and abate pollution and contamination, protect public health and permit management of groundwater for best usage by the citizens of North Carolina " (North Carolina Environmental Management Commission, 1979).

1. Class GA waters are best used for human drinking, culinary use, and food processing. They have chloride concentrations $\leq$250 mg/l, and do not need treatment except to reduce naturally occurring concentrations to meet the National Interim Primary Drinking Water Regulations. They occur at depths greater than 20 feet below the land surface and in the saturated zone at depths less than 20 feet below the land surface where those waters are the principal source of potable water supply.
2. Class GSA waters are different from class GA waters in that they are also sources of potable mineral water and are suitable for conversion to fresh water. They occur at depths similar to class GA waters.
3. Class GB waters are suitable for recharging aquifers of class GA quality. They occur in the saturated zone above a depth of 20 feet. This class was created in recognition of the fact that water in the upper 20 feet of the earth's surface is particularly

Table 11–2. North Carolina Groundwater Classifications

1. Class GA waters:
   - (a) Arsenic: not greater than 50 μ/l
   - (b) Cadmium: not greater than 10 μ/l
   - (c) Chloride: allowable increase not to exceed 50 percent of the naturally occurring chloride concentration or result in a concentration of more than 250 mg/l.
   - (d) Chromium: not greater than 50 μ/l
   - (e) Coliform group total: not greater than 1.0/100 ml
   - (f) Color: less than 5.0 units
   - (g) Lead: not greater than 50 μ/l
   - (h) Mercury: not greater than 2.0 μ/l
   - (i) Nitrate (as N): not greater than 10 mg/l
   - (j) Nitrite (as N): not greater than 1.0 mg/l
   - (k) Oil and grease: free from taste or odor
   - (l) Pesticides: shall not exceed maximum limits recommended or established by the National Interim Primary Drinking Water Regulations.
   - (m) Phenol: not greater than 1.0 μ/l
   - (n) Phthalate esters: none in measurable quantities.
   - (o) Polychlorinated biphenyls: none in measurable quantities
   - (p) Radioactive substances: shall not exceed maximum limits recommended or established by the National Interim Primary Drinking Water Regulations.
   - (q) Selenium: not greater than 10 μ/l
   - (r) Silver: not greater than 50 μ/l
   - (s) Total dissolved solids: allowable increase not to exceed 50 percent of the naturally occurring total dissolved solids concentration or result in a concentration of more than 1000 mg/1.

2. Class GSA waters:
   - (a) Arsenic: not greater than 50 μ/l
   - (b) Cadmium: not greater than 10 μ/l
   - (c) Chloride: allowable increase not to exceed 100 percent of the naturally occurring chloride concentration.
   - (d) Chromium: not greater than 50 μ/l
   - (e) Coliform group, total: not greater than 1.0 per 100 ml.
   - (f) Color: less than 5.0 units
   - (g) Lead: not greater than 50 μ/l
   - (h) Mercury: not greater than 2.0 μ/l
   - (i) Nitrate (as N): not greater than 10 mg/l
   - (j) Nitrite (as N): not greater than 1.0 mg/l

Table 11–2. (continued)

(k) Pesticides: shall not exceed maximum limits recommended or established by the National Interim Primary Drinking Water Regulations.

(l) Phenol: not greater than 1.0 μ/l

(m) Phthalate esters: none in measurable quantities

(n) Polychlorinated biphenyls: none in measurable quantities

(o) Radioactive substances: shall not exceed maximum limits recommended or established by the National Interim Primary Drinking Water Regulations.

(p) Selenium: not greater than 10 μ/l

(q) Silver: not greater than 50 μ/l

3. Class GB Waters.

   All chemical, radioactive, biological, taste producing, odor producing, thermal, and other deleterious substances will be allowed only in such amounts, whether alone or in combination with other substances, as will not result in the contravention of established water quality standards

4. Class GSB Waters.

   All chemical, radioactive, biological, taste producing, odor producing, thermal and other deleterious substances will be allowed only in such amounts, whether alone or in combination with other substances, as will not result in the contravention of established water quality standards

5. Class GC Waters.

   All chemical, radioactive, biological, taste producing, odor producing, thermal, and other deleterious substances shall not exceed the concentration existing at the time of classification

Source: North Carolina Environmental Management Commission, 1979.

vulnerable to contamination and should be considered to be in a cycling zone. In North Carolina, most of the water in this zone is of drinking-water quality.

4. Class GSB waters are suitable for recharging aquifers of GSA quality and, otherwise, are similar to waters of class GB.
5. Class GC waters are best used for activities other than drinking, culinary use, or food processing. They do not meet the quality standards of the higher classifications, and it is not possible to upgrade them for technical and economic reasons.

New York

New York State adopted a 3-class system in September 1978, which was similar to North Carolina's but lacked the classifications for recharge waters and specifications for depth of occurrence of groundwater. "The purpose of these classes, quality standards, and effluent standards and/or limitations is to *prevent* pollution of groundwaters and to protect the groundwaters for use as a potable water" (New York Department of Environmental Conservation, 1978).

1. Class GA waters are fresh and potable and are protected by the most stringent quality standards determined by the state and EPA. The waters are found in the saturated zone of unconsolidated deposits and consolidated rock and bedrock (Tables 11–3 and 11–4).
2. Class GSA waters are saline waters containing between 250 mg Cl/l and 1000 mg Cl/l that can be used for potable mineral water, converted to freshwater, or as a raw material in the manufacture of sodium chloride or its derivatives or similar products (Table 11–5).
3. Class GSB waters have chloride concentrations in excess of 1000 mg/l. They are found in the saturated zone and best used for the disposal of wastes. This class is only assigned if adjacent and tributary groundwaters will not be impaired (Table 11–5).

Wyoming

Wyoming adopted groundwater classification in April 1980 "in order to apply standards to protect water quality. Groundwaters of the State are classified by use, and by ambient water quality" (Wyoming Department of Environmental Quality, 1980). The Wyoming system is more intricate than the four described above and appears to accomodate all the major competitors for groundwater use in the state: people, crops, livestock, fish and aquatic life, industry, excavation of hydrocarbons and minerals, geothermal energy. The four classes are:

1. Class I—suitable for domestic use
2. Class II—suitable for agricultural use where all other conditions (i.e., soil) are adequate
3. Class III—suitable for livestock
4. Class Special (A)—suitable for fish and aquatic life

Each of the above classes has a set of parameters limiting its chemical constituents (Table 11–6). In addition, those waters may not contain biological, hazardous, toxic, or potentially toxic materials or substances in concentrations greater than those determined by the EPA under the *National Interim Primary Drinking Water Regulations* (see page 76). Discharges into water of these four classes are only permitted if the water can be returned to its original quality.

5. Class IV—suitable for industry; quality standards vary with type

Table 11–3. New York Groundwater Classifications: Quality Standards for Class GA

The following quality standards shall be applicable to Class GA waters.

Items	*Specifications*
1. Sewage, industrial waste or other wastes, taste or odor producing substances, toxic pollutants, thermal discharges, radioactive substances or other deleterious matter.	1. None which may impair the quality of the ground waters to render them unsafe or unsuitable for a potable water supply or which may cause or contribute to a condition in contravention of standards for other classified waters of the State.
2. The concentration of the following substances or chemicals:	2. Shall not be greater than the limit specified, except where exceeded due to natural conditions:
(1) Arsenic (As)	(1) 0.025 mg/l
(2) Barium (Ba)	(2) 1.0 mg/l
(3) Cadmium (Cd)	(3) 0.01 mg/l
(4) Chloride (Cl)	(4) 250 mg/l
(5) Chromium (Cr) (Hexavalent)	(5) 0.05 mg/l
(6) Copper (Cu)	(6) 1.0 mg/l
(7) Cyanide (CN)	(7) 0.2 mg/l
(8) Fluoride (F)	(8) 1.5 mg/l
(9) Foaming Agents[1]	(9) 0.5 mg/l
(10) Iron (Fe)[2]	(10) 0.3 mg/l
(11) Lead (Pb)	(11) 0.025 mg/l
(12) Manganese (Mn)[2]	(12) 0.3 mg/l
(13) Mercury (Hg)	(13) 0.002 mg/l
(14) Nitrate (as N)	(14) 10.0 mg/l
(15) Phenols	(15) 0.001 mg/l
(16) Selenium (Se)	(16) 0.02 mg/l
(17) Silver (Ag)	(17) 0.05 mg/l
(18) Sulfate (SO_4)	(18) 250 mg/l
(19) Zinc (Zn)	(19) 5 mg/l
(20) pH Range	(20) 6.5–8.5
(21) Aldrin, or 1,2,3,4,10,10-hexachloro-1,4,4a,5,8,8a-hexahydro-*endo*-1, *4*-exc-5,8-dimethanonaphthalene.	(21) not detectable[3]

Table 11–3. (continued)

(22) Chlordane, or 1,2,4,5,6,7,8,8-octachloro-2,3,3a,4,7,7a-hexahydro-4,7-methanoindene.	(22) 0.1 μ/l
(23) DDT, or 2,2-bis-(p-chlorophenyl)-1,1,1-trichloroethane and metabolites.	(23) not detectable[3]
(24) Dieldrin, or 6,7-epoxy aldrin.	(24) not detectable[3]
(25) Endrin, or 1,2,3,4,10,10-hexachloro-6,7-epoxy-1,4,4a,5,6,7,8,8a-octahydro-endo-1,4-*endo*-5,8-dimethanonaphthalene.	(25) not detectable[3]
(26) Heptachlor, or 1,4,5,6,7,8,8-heptachloro-3a,4,7,7a-tetrahydro-4,7-methanoindene and metabolites.	(26) not detectable[3]
(27) Lindane and other Hexachlorocyclohexanes or mixed isomers of 1,2,3,4,5,6-hexachlorocyclohexane.	(27) not detectable[3]
(28) Methoxychlor, or 2,2-*bis*-(*p*-methoxyphenyl)-1,1,1-trichloroethane.	(28) 35.0 μ/l
(29) Toxaphene (a mixture of at least 175 chlorinated camphene derivatives).	(29) not detectable[3]
(30) 2,4-Dichlorophenoxyacetic acid (2,4-D)	(30) 4.4 μ/l
(31) 2,4,5-Trichlorophenoxypropionic acid (2,4,5-TP) (Silvex)	(31) 0.26 μ/l
(32) Vinyl chloride (chloroethene)	(32) 5.0 μ/l
(33) Benzene	(33) not detectable[3]
(34) Benzo(a) pyrene	(34) not detectable[3]
(35) Kepone or decachlorooctahydro-1,3,4-metheno-2H-cyclobuta (cd) pentalen-2-one (chlordeone).	(35) not detectable[3]
(36) Polychlorinated biphenyls (PCB) (Aroclor)	(36) 0.1 μ/l
(37) Ethylene thiourea (ETU)	(37) not detectable[3]
(38) Chloroform	(38) 100 μ/l
(39) Carbon tetrachloride (tetrachloromethane)	(39) 5 μ/l
(40) Pentachloronitrobenzene (PCNB)	(40) not detectable[3]

Table 11–3. (continued)

(41) Trichloroethylene	(41) 10 μ/l
(42) Diphenylhydrazine	(42) not detectable[3]
(43) bis (2-chloroethyl) ether	(43) 1.0 μ/l
(44) 2,4,5-Trichlorophenoxyacetic acid (2,4,5-T)	(44) 35 μ/l
(45) 2,3,7,8-Tetrachlorodibenzo-p-dioxin (TCDD)	(45) 3.5×10^{-5} μ/l
(46) 2-Methyl-4-chlorophenoxy-acetic acid (MCPA)	(46) 0.44 μ/l
(47) Amiben, or 3-amino-2,5-dichlorobenzoic acid (chloramben)	(47) 87.5 μ/l
(48) Dicamba, or 2-methoxy-3,6-dichlorobenzoic acid	(48) 0.44 μ/l
(49) Alachlor, or 2-chloro-2′,6′-diethyl-*N*-(meth oxymethyl)-acetanilide (Lasso)	(49) 35.0 μ/l
(50) Butachlor, or 2-chloro-2′,6′-diethyl-N-(butoxymethyl)-acetanilide (Machete)	(50) 3.5 μ/l
(51) Propachlor, or 2-chlor-N-isopropyl-N-acetanilide (Ramrod)	(51) 35.0 μ/l
(52) Propanil, or 3′,4′-dichloropropionanilide	(52) 7.0 μ/l
(53) Aldicarb, [2-methyl-2-(methylthio) propionaldehyde *0*-(methyl carbamoyl) oxime] and methomyl [1-methylthioace-taldhyde *0*-(methyl-carbamoyl) oxime]	(53) 0.35 μ/l
(54) Bromacil, or 5-broma-3-sec-butyl-6-methluracil	(54) 4.4 μ/l
(55) Paraquat, or 1,1′ βdimethyl-4,4′-dipyridylium	(55) 2.98 μ/l
(56) Trifluralin, or α,α,α-trifluoro-2,6-dinitro-N-dipropyl-p-toluidine (Treflan)	(56) 35.0 μ/l
(57) Nitralin, or 4-(methylsulfonyl)-2,6-dinitro-N,N-dipropylaniline (Planavin)	(57) 35.0 μ/l
(58) Benefin, or N-butyl-N-ethyl-α,α,α-trifluoro-2,6-dinitro-p-toluidine (Balan)	(58) 35.0 μ/l

Table 11–3. (continued)

(59) Azinphosmethyl, or *0,0*-dimethyl-*S*-4-oxo-1,2,3-benzotriazin-3(4H)-ylmethylphosphorodithioate (Guthion)	(59) 4.4 μ/l
(60) Diazinon, or *0,0*-diethyl *0*-(2-isopropyl-4-methyl-6-pyrimidinyl)-phosphorothioate.	(60) 0.7 μ/l
(61) Phorate (also for Disulfoton), or *0,0*-diethyl-*S*-[(ethylthio)methyl]-phosphorodithioate (Thimet R), and disulfoton, or *0,0*-diethyl-*S*-[(2-ethylthio)ethyl] phosphorodithioate (Di-System R)	(61) not detectable[3]
(62) Carbaryl, or 1-naphthyl-N-methylcarbamate	(62) 28.7 μ/l
(63) Ziram, or zinc salts of dimethyl-dithiocarbamic acid.	(63) 4.18 μ/l
(64) Ferbam, or iron salts of dimethyl-dithiocarbamic acid.	(64) 4.18 μ/l
(65) Captan, or *N*-trichloromethylthio-4-cyclohexene-1,*2*-dicarboximide.	(65) 17.5 μ/l
(66) Folpet, or *N*-trichloromethylthiophthalimide.	(66) 56.0 μ/l
(67) Hexachlorobenzene (HCB)	(67) 0.35 μ/l
(68) Paradichlorobenzene (PDB) (also orthodichlorobenzene)	(68) 4.7 μ/l
(69) Parathion (and Methyl parathion), or (*0,0*-diethyl-*O*-*p*-nitrophenylphosphorthioate, and methyl parathion, or *0,0*-dimethyl-*O*-*p*-nitrophenylphosphorothioate.	(69) 1.5 μ/l
(70) Malathion, or *S*-1,2-*bis* (ethoxycarbonyl) ethyl-*0,0*-dimethylphosphorodithioate.	(70) 7.0 μ/l
(71) Maneb, or manganese salt of ethylene-bis-dithiocarbamic acid.	(71) 1.75 μ/l
(72) Zineb, or zinc salt of ethylene-bis-dithiocarbamic acid.	(72) 1.75 μ/l
(73) Dithane, or zincate of manganese ethylene-bis-dithiocarbemate.	(73) 1.75 μ/l

Table 11–3. (continued)

(74) Thiram, or tetramethylthiuramdisulfide	(74) 1.75 μ/l
(75) Atrazine, or 2-chloro-4-ethylamino-6-isopropylamino-S-triazine.	(75) 7.5 μ/l
(76) Propazine, or 2-chloro-4,6-diisopropyl-amino-S-triazine.	(76) 16.0 μ/l
(77) Simazine, or 2-chloro-4,6-diethylamino-S-triazine.	(77) 75.25 μ/l
(78) Di-n-butylphthalate	(78) 770 μ/l
(79) Di (2-ethylhexyl) phthalate (DEHP)	(79) 4.2 mg/l
(80) Hexachlorophene, or 2,2′-methylene-bis (3,4,6-trichlorophenol)	(80) 7 μ/l
(81) Methyl methacrylate	(81) 0.7 mg/l
(82) Pentachlorophenol (PCP)	(82) 21 μ/l
(83) Styrene	(83) 931 μ/l

1. Foaming agents determined as methylene blue active substances (MBAS) or other tests as specified by the Commissioner.
2. Combined concentration of iron and manganese shall not exceed 0.5 mg/l.
3. "Not detectable" means by tests or analytical determinations referenced in Section 703.4.

Source: New York Department of Environmental Conservation, 1978.

of industry

a) Class IV (A)—TDS ≤10,000 mg/l.

b) Class IV (B)—TDS >10,000 mg/l.

Discharges into industrial-use aquifers are allowed as long as the water remains fit for its intended use. Oil and grease concentrations cannot be greater than 10 mg/l. Radiation concentrations may not exceed the limits of the first four classes. EPA standards for maximum chemical constituents may not be exceeded.

6. Class V—groundwater closely associated with hydrocarbon deposits or other minerals, or groundwater considered a geothermal resource. Discharges into these waters is for the purpose of recovering the resources.
7. Class VI—groundwater that is unsuitable for any use.

New Jersey

New Jersey has adopted a four-class system that has the total content of dissolved solids as its prime criteria for defining protection (New Jersey Department of Environmental Protection, 1981b). "It is the policy

(Text continued on p. 225.)

Table 11–4. New York Groundwater Classifications: Effluent Standards or Limitations on Class GA

Applicability. The following effluent standards or limitations shall apply to all Class GA waters in New York State.

Biological organisms. Coliform and/or pathogenic organisms shall not be discharged in amounts sufficient to render fresh ground waters detrimental to public health, safety or welfare.

Chemical Characteristics

Substance	Maximum Allowable Concentration in mg/l (unless otherwise noted)
(1) Aluminum	(1) 2.0
(2) Arsenic	(2) 0.05
(3) Barium	(3) 2.0
(4) Cadmium	(4) 0.02
(5) Chloride	(5) 500
(6) Chromium (Cr) (Hexavalent)	(6) 0.10
(7) Copper	(7) 1.0
(8) Cyanide	(8) 0.40
(9) Fluoride	(9) 3.0
(10) Foaming Agents[1]	(10) 1.0
(11) Iron[2]	(11) 0.6
(12) Lead	(12) 0.05
(13) Manganese[2]	(13) 0.6
(14) Mercury	(14) 0.004
(15) Nickel	(15) 2.0
(16) Nitrate (as N)	(16) 20
(17) Oil and Grease	(17) 15
(18) Phenols	(18) 0.002
(19) Selenium	(19) 0.04
(20) Silver	(20) 0.1
(21) Sulfate	(21) 500
(22) Sulfide	(22) 1.0
(23) Zinc	(23) 5.0
(24) pH Range[3]	(24) 6.5–8.5
(25) Aldrin, or 1,2,3,4,10,10-hexachloro-1,4,4a,5,8,8a-hexahydro-*endo*-1,*4*-exc-5,8-dimethanonaphthalene	(25) not detectable[4]
(26) Chlordane, or 1,2,4,5,6,7,8,8-octachloro-2,3,3a,4,7,7a-hexahydro-4,7-methanoindene	(26) 0.1 μ/l
(27) DDT, or 2,2-bis-(p-chlorophenyl)-1,1,1-trichloroethane and metabolites	(27) not detectable[4]
(28) Dieldrin, or 6,7-epoxy aldrin	(28) not detectable[4]

Table 11–4. (continued)

(29) Endrin, or 1,2,3,4,10,10-hexachloro-6,7-epoxy-1,4,4a,5,6,7,8,8a-octahydro-endo-1,4-*endo*-5,8-dimethanonaphthalene	(29) not detectable[4]
(30) Heptachlor, or 1,4,5,6,7,8,8-heptachloro-3a,4,7,7a-tetrahydro-4,7-methanoindene and metabolites	(30) not detectable[4]
(31) Lindane and other Hexachlorocyclohexanes or mixed isomers of 1,2,3,3,5,6-hexachlorocyclohexane	(31) not detectable[4]
(32) Methoxychlor, or 2,2-*bis*-(*p*-methoxphenyl)-1,1,1-trichloroethane	(32) 35 μ/l
(33) Toxaphene (a mixture of at least 175 chlorinated camphene derivatives)	(33) not detectable[4]
(34) 2,4-Dichlorophenoxyacetic acid (2,4-D)	(34) 4.4 μ/l
(35) 2,4,5-Trichlorophenoxypropionic acid (2,4,5-TP) (Silvex)	(35) 0.26 μ/l
(36) Vinyl chloride (chloroethene)	(36) 5.0 μ/l
(37) Benzene	(37) not detectable[4]
(38) Benzo(a) pyrene	(38) not detectable[4]
(39) Kepone or decachlorooctahydro-1,3,4-metheno-2H-cyclobuta (cd) pentalen-2-one (chlordeone)	(39) not detectable[4]
(40) Polychlorinated biphenyls (PCB) (Aroclor)	(40) 0.1 μ/l
(41) Ethylene thiourea (ETU)	(41) not detectable[4]
(42) Chloroform	(42) 100 μ/l
(43) Carbon tetrachloride (tetrachloromethane)	(43) 5 μ/l
(44) Pentachloronitrobenzene (PCNB)	(44) not detectable[4]
(45) Trichloroethylene	(45) 10 μ/l
(46) Diphenylhydrazine	(46) not detectable[4]
(47) bis (2-chloroethyl) ether	(47) 1.0 μ/l
(48) 2,4,5-Trichlorophenoxyacetic acid (2,4,5-T)	(48) 35 μ/l
(49) 2,3,7,8-Tetrachlorodibenzo-p-dioxin (TCDD)	(49) 3.5×10^{-5} μ/l
(50) 2-Methyl-4-chlorophenoxyacetic acid (MCPA)	(50) 0.44 μ/l
(51) Amiben, or 3-amino-2,5-dichlorobenzoic acid (chloramben)	(51) 87.5 μ/l
(52) Dicamba, or 2-methoxy-3,6-dichlorobenzoic acid	(52) 0.44 μ/l
(53) Alachlor, or 2-chloro-2′,6′-diethyl-*N*-(methoxymethyl)-acetanilide (Lasso)	(53) 35.0 μ/l
(54) Butachlor, or 2-chlor-2′,6′-diethyl-N-(butoxymethyl)-acetanilide (Machete)	(54) 3.5 μ/l
(55) Propachlor, or 2-chlor-N-isopropyl-N-acetanilide (Ramrod)	(55) 35.0 μ/l
(56) Propanil, or 3′,4′-dichloropropionanilide	(56) 7.0 μ/l
(57) Aldicarb, [2-methyl-2-(methylthio) propionaldehyde	(57) 0.35 μ/l

Table 11–4. (continued)

O-(methyl carbamoyl) oxime] and methomyl [1-methylthioacetaldhyde *O*-(methyl-carbamoyl) oxime]	
(58) Bromacil, or 5-broma-3-sec-butyl-6-methluracil	(58) 4.4 μ/l
(59) Paraquat, or 1,1′-dimethyl-4,4′-dipyridylium	(59) 2.98 μ/l
(60) Trifluralin, or α,α,α-trifluoro-2,6-dinitro-N-dipropyl-p-toluidine (Treflan)	(60) 35.0 μ/l
(61) Nitralin, or 4-(methylsulfonyl)-2,6-dinitro-N-N-dipropylaniline (Planavin)	(61) 35.0 μ/l
(62) Benefin, or N-butyl-N-ethyl-α,α,α-trifluoro-2,6-dinitro-p-toluidine (Balan)	(62) 35.0 μ/l
(63) Azinphosmethyl, or *O,O*-dimethyl-*S*-4-oxo-1,2,3-benzotriazin-3(4H)-ylmethylphosphorodithioate (Guthion)	(63) 4.4 μ/l
(64) Diazinon, or *O,O*-diethyl *O*-(2-isopropyl-4-methyl-6-pyrimidinyl)-phosphorothioate	(64) 0.7 μ/l
(65) Phorate (also for Disulfoton), or *O,O*-diethyl-*S*-[(ethylthio)methyl]-phosphorodithioate (Thimet R), and disulfoton, or *O,O*-diethyl-*S*-[(2-ethylthio)ethyl] phosphorodithioate (Di-System R)	(65) not detectable[4]
(66) Carbaryl, or 1-naphthyl-N-methylcarbamate	(66) 28.7 μ/l
(67) Ziram, or zinc salts of dimethyldithiocarbamic acid	(67) 4.18 μ/l
(68) Ferbam, or iron salts of dimethyldithiocarbamic acid	(68) 4.18 μ/l
(69) Captan, or *N*-trichloromethylthio-4-cyclohexene-1,*2*-dicarboximide	(69) 17.5 μ/l
(70) Folpet, or *N*-trichloromethylthiophthalimide	(70) 56.0 μ/l
(71) Hexachlorobenzene (HCB)	(71) 0.35 μ/l
(72) Paradichlorobenzene (PDB) (also orthodichlorobenzene)	(72) 4.7 μ/l
(73) Parathion (and Methyl parathion), or (*O*, -*O*-diethyl-*O*-*p*-nitrophenylphosphorthioate, and methyl parathion, or *O,O*-dimethyl-*O*-*p*-nitrophenylphosphorothioate	(73) 1.5 μ/l
(74) Malathion, or *S*-1,2-*bis* (ethoxycarbonyl) ethyl-*O,O*-dimethylphosphorodithioate	(74) 7.0 μ/l
(75) Maneb, or manganese salt of ethylene-bis-dithiocarbamic acid	(75) 1.75 μ/l
(76) Zineb, or zinc salt of ethylene-bis-dithiocarbamic acid	(76) 1.75 μ/l
(77) Dithane, or zincate of manganese ethylene-bis-dithiocarbemate	(77) 1.75 μ/l

Table 11–4. (continued)

(78) Thiram, or tetramethylthiuramdisulfide	(78) 1.75 μ/l
(79) Atrazine, or 2-chlor-4-ethylamino-6-isopropylamino-S-triazine	(79) 7.5 μ/l
(80) Propazine, or 2-chloro-4,6-diisopropylamino-S-triazine	(80) 16.0 μ/l
(81) Simazine, or 2-chloro-4,6-diethylamino-S-triazine	(81) 75.25 μ/l
(82) di-n-butylphthalate	(82) 770 μ/l
(83) Di (2-ethylhexyl) phthalate (DEHP)	(83) 4.2 mg/l
(84) Hexachlorophene, or 2,2′-methylene-bis (3,4,6-trichlorophenol)	(84) 7 μ/l
(85) Methyl methacrylate	(85) 0.7 mg/l
(86) Pentachlorophenol (PCP)	(86) 21 μ/l
(87) Styrene	(87) 931 μ/l

In addition to the effluent standards and/or limitations the following also apply in the counties of Nassau and Suffolk

Chemical Characteristics

Substance	Maximum Allowable Concentration in mg/l
Dissolved Solids, Total	1000
Nitrogen, Total (as N)	10

1. Foaming agents determined as methylene blue active substances (MBAS) or other tests as specified by the Commissioner.
2. Combined concentration of iron and manganese shall not exceed 1.0 mg/l.
3. When natural ground waters have a pH outside the range indicated above, that natural pH may be one extreme of the allowable range.
4. Not detectable means by tests or analytical determinations referenced in Section 703.4.

Source: New York Department of Environmental Conservation, 1978.

of this State to restore, enhance, and maintain the chemical, physical and biological integrity of its waters, to protect public health, to safeguard fish and aquatic life and scenic and ecological values and to enhance the domestic, municipal, recreational, industrial, and other uses of water" (New Jersey Department of Environmental Protection, 1981b).

"Existing and potential uses of groundwater shall be maintained and protected." The State will upgrade the quality of any water which does not meet the standards for its intended use.

1. Class GW1 was established specifically to protect the groundwaters of the unique and fragile ecosystem of the Central Pine Barrens. The groundwater reservoir is of extremely

Table 11–5. New York Groundwater: Quality Standards for Class GSB

The following quality standards shall be applicable to Class GSB waters.

Items	Specifications
1. Sewage, industrial wastes or other wastes, color, taste or odor producing substances, toxic pollutants, thermal discharges, radioactive substances or other deleterious matter.	1. None which may be deleterious, harmful, detrimental or injurious to the public health, safety or welfare or which may cause or contribute to a condition in contravention of standards for other classified waters of the State.

(3) Class GSB shall not be assigned to any groundwaters of the State unless the Commissioner finds that adjacent and tributary ground waters and the best usage thereof will not be impaired by such classification.

(2) The following quality standards shall be applicable to Class GSA waters.

Items	Specifications
1. Sewage, industrial wastes or other wastes, color, taste or odor producing substances, toxic pollutants, thermal discharges, radioactive substances or other deleterious matter.	1. None which may impair the waters for use as sources of saline waters for the best usage outlined above or as to cause or contribute to a condition in contravention of standards for other classified waters of the State.

Source: New York Department of Environmental Conservation, 1978.

high quality but also very vulnerable to contamination. No activity which would cause degradation is allowed in this area. Class GW1 groundwater "shall be suitable for potable water supply, agricultural water supply, continual replenishment of surface waters to maintain the existing quantity and high quality of the surface waters in the Central Pine Barrens, and other reasonable uses" (New Jersey Department of Environmental Protection, 1981b). Table 11–7 lists the quality criteria applicable to groundwater of this class.

2. Class GW2 groundwater has a natural concentration of total dissolved solids of 500 mg/l or less and shall be suitable for potable, industrial, or agricultural uses; or for the replenishment of quantity and quality of surface waters.

(Text continued on p. 230.)

Table 11–6. Wyoming Groundwater Classification

UNDERGROUND WATER CLASS Use Suitability Constituent or Parameter	I Domestic Concentration*	II Agriculture Concent.*	III Livestock Concent.*
Aluminum (Al)	—	5.0	5.0
Ammonia (NH)	0.5	—	—
Arsenic (As)	0.05	0.1	0.2
Barium (Ba)	1.0	—	—
Beryllium (Be)	—	0.1	—
Boron (B)	0.75	0.75	5.0
Cadmium (Cd)	0.01	0.01	0.05
Chloride (Cl)	250.0	100.0	2000.0
Chromium (Cr)	0.05	0.1	0.05
Cobalt (Co)	—	0.5	1.0
Copper (Cu)	1.0	0.2	0.5
Cyanide (CN)	0.2	—	—
Fluoride (F)	1.4–2.4	—	—
Hydrogen Sulfide (H_2S)	0.05	—	—
Iron (Fe)	0.3	5.0	—
Lead (Pb)	0.05	5.0	0.1
Lithium (Li)	—	2.5	—
Manganese (Mn)	0.05	0.2	—
Mercury (Hg)	0.002	—	0.00005
Nickel (Ni)	—	0.2	—
Nitrate ($NO_3 - N$)	10.0	—	—
Nitrite ($NO_2 - N$)	1.0	—	10.0
$(NO_3 + NO_2) - N$	—	—	100.0
Oil & Grease	Virtually Free	10.0	10.0
Phenol	0.001	—	—
Selenium (Se)	0.01	0.02	0.05
Silver (Ag)	0.05	—	—
Sulfate (SO_4)	250.0	200.0	3000.0
Total Dissolved Solids (TDS)	500.0	2000.0	5000.0
Uranium (U)	5.0	5.0	5.0
Vanadium (V)	—	0.1	0.1
Zinc (Zn)	5.0	2.0	25.0
pH	6.5–9.0s.u.	4.5–9.0s.u.	6.5–8.5s.u.

Table 11–6. (continued)

SAR	—	8	—
RSC	—	1.25 meq/l	—
Combined Total Radium 226 and Radium 228	5pCi/l	5pCi/l	5pCi/l
Total Strontium 90	8pCi/l	8pCi/l	8pCi/l
Gross alpha particle radioactivity (including Radium 226 but excluding Radon and Uranium)	15pCi/l	15pCi/l	15pCi/l

*mg/l, unless otherwise indicated

UNDERGROUND WATER CLASS Use Suitability Constituent or Parameter	Special (A) Fish/Aquatic Life Concentration*
Aluminum (Al)	0.1
Ammonia (NH_3)	0.02
Arsenic (As)	0.05
Barium (Ba)	5.0
Beryllium (Be)	0.011–1.1
Boron (B)	—
Cadmium (Cd)	0.0004–0.015
Chloride (Cl)	—
Chromium (Cr)	0.05
Cobalt (Co)	—
Copper (Cu)	0.01–0.04
Cyanide (CN)	0.005
Fluoride (F)	—
Hydrogen Sulfide (H_2S)	0.002
Iron (Fe)	0.5
Lead (Pb)	0.004–0.15
Lithium (Li)	—
Manganese (Mn)	1.0
Mercury (Hg)	0.00005
Nickel (Ni)	0.05–0.4
Nitrate (NO_3-N)	—
Nitrite (NO_2-N)	—
$(NO_3+NO_2)-N$	—
Oil & Grease	Virtually free
Phenol	0.001
Selenium (Se)	0.05
Silver (Ag)	0.0001–0.00025
Sulfate (So_4)	—
Total Dissolved Solids (TDS)	500.0 –1000.0 –2000.0
Uranium (U)	0.03–1.4
Vanadium (V)	—
Zinc (Zn)	0.05–0.6
pH	6.5s.u.–9.0s.u.

Table 11–6. (continued)

Combined Total Radium 226 and Radium 228	5pCi/l
Total Strontium 90	8pCi/l
Gross alpha particle radioactivity (including Radium 226 but excluding Radon and Uranium)	15pCi/l

Source: Wyoming Department of Environmental Quality, Water Quality Division, 1980.

Table 11–7. New Jersey Groundwater Classification: Quality Criteria for the Central Pine Barrens: Class GW1

Ground-Water Quality Criteria for the Central Pine Barrens: Class GW1

Pollutant, Substance or Chemical	Ground-Water Quality Criteria
1. Aldrin/Dieldrin	1. 0.003 μ/l
2. Arsenic and Compounds	2. 0.05 mg/l
3. Barium	3. 1.0 mg/l
4. Benzidine	4. 0.0001 mg/l
5. Cadmium	5. Natural Background
6. Chromium (Hexavalent) and Compounds	6. Natural Background
7. Cyanide	7. 0.2 mg/l
8. DDT and Metabolites	8. 0.001 μ/l
9. Endrin	9. 0.004 μ/l
10. Lead and Compounds	10. 0.05 mg/l
11. Mercury and Compounds	11. 0.002 mg/l
12. Nitrate-Nitrogen	12. 2.0 mg/l
13. Phenol	13. 0.3 mg/l
14. Polychlorinated Biphenyls	14. 0.001 μ/l
15. Radionuclides	15. Prevailing regulations adopted by the U.S.-EPA. pursuant to sections 1412, 1415 and 1450 of the Public Health Services Act as amended by the Safe Drinking Water Act (PL 93-523)
16. Selenium and Compounds	16. Natural Background
17. Silver and Compounds	17. 0.05 mg/l

Table 11–7. (continued)

18. Toxaphene	18. 0.005 μ/l
19. Ammonia	19. 0.5 mg/l
20. BOD (5-day)	20. 3 mg/l
21. Chloride	21. 10 mg/l
22. Coliform Bacteria	22. a) by membrane filtration, not to exceed four per 100 ml in more than one sample when less than 20 are examined per month, or b) by fermentation tube, with a standard 10 ml portion, not to be present in three or more portions in more than one sample when less than 20 are examined per month, or c) prevailing criteria adopted pursuant to the Federal Safe Drinking Water Act (PL 93-523)
23. Color	23. None Noticeable
24. Copper	24. 1.0 mg/l
25. Fluoride	25. 2.0 mg/l
26. Foaming Agents	26. 0.5 mg/l
27. Iron	27. 0.3 mg/l
28. Manganese	28. 0.05 mg/l
29. Odor and Taste	29. None Noticeable
30. Oil and Grease and Petroleum Hydrocarbons	30. None Noticeable
31. pH (Standard Units)	31. 4.2–5.8
32. Phosphate, Total	32. 0.7 mg/l
33. Sodium	33. 10 mg/l
34. Sulfate	34. 15 mg/l
35. Total Dissolved Solids	35. 100 mg/l
36. Zinc and Compounds	36. 5 mg/l

Source: New Jersey Department of Environmental Protection, 1981b.

Conventional water treatment may be necessary. Table 11–8 lists quality criteria for this class.

3. Class GW3 has a natural concentration of total dissolved solids of between 500 mg/l and 10,000 mg/l. It is suitable for conversion to fresh potable waters. Quality criteria are listed in Table 11–9.
4. Class GW4 has a natural concentration of total dissolved solids in excess of 10,000 mg/l. It is suitable for any reasonable

(Text continued on p. 232.)

Table 11–8. New Jersey Groundwater Classification: Quality Criteria for Class GW2

Ground-Water Quality Criteria Statewide where the Total Dissolved Solids (TDS, Natural Background) Concentration is less than or equal to 500 mg/l: Class GW2

Pollutant, Substance Or Chemical	Ground Water Quality Criteria
Primary Standards/Toxic Pollutants	
1. Aldrin/Dieldrin	1. 0.003 μ/l
2. Arsenic and Compounds	2. 0.05 mg/l
3. Barium	3. 1.0 mg/l
4. Benzidine	4. 0.0001 mg/l
5. Cadmium and Compounds	5. 0.01 mg/l
6. Chromium (Hexavalent) and Compounds	6. 0.05 mg/l
7. Cyanide	7. 0.2 mg/l
8. DDT and Metabolites	8. 0.001 μ/l
9. Endrin	9. 0.004 μ/l
10. Lead and Compounds	10. 0.05 mg/l
11. Mercury and Compounds	11. 0.002 mg/l
12. Nitrate-Nitrogen	12. 10 mg/l
13. Phenol	13. 3.5 mg/l
14. Polychlorinated Biphenyls	14. 0.001 μg/l
15. Radionuclides	15. Prevailing regulations adopted by the U. S. EPA pursuant to sections 1412, 1415, and 1450 of the Public Health Services Act as amended by the Safe Drinking Water Act (PL 93-523)
16. Selenium and Compounds	16. 0.01 mg/l
17. Silver and Compounds	17. 0.05 mg/l
18. Toxaphene	18. 0.005 μ/l
Secondary Standards	
19. Ammonia	19. 0.5 mg/l
20. Chloride	20. 250 mg/l
21. Coliform Bacteria	21. a) by membrane filtration, not to exceed four per 100 ml in more than one sample when less than 20 are examined per month, or b) by fermentation tube, with a standard 10 ml portion, not to be present in three or more portions in more than one sample when less than

Table 11–8. (continued)

	20 are examined per month, or c) Prevailing criteria adopted pursuant to the Federal Safe Drinking Water Act (PL 93-523)
22. Color	22. None Noticeable
23. Copper	23. 1.0 mg/l
24. Fluoride	24. 2.0 mg/l
25. Foaming Agents	25. 0.5 mg/l
26. Iron	26. 0.3 mg/l
27. Manganese	27. 0.05 mg/l
28. Odor and Taste	28. None Noticeable
29. Oil and Grease and Petroleum Hydrocarbons	29. None Noticeable
30. pH (Standard Units)	30. 5–9
31. Phenol	31. 0.3 mg/l
32. Sodium	32. 50 mg/l
33. Sulfate	33. 250 mg/l
34. Total Dissolved Solids	34. 500 mg/l
35. Zinc and Compounds	35. 5 mg/l

Source: New Jersey Department of Environmental Protection, 1981b.

beneficial use. Quality criteria are determined on a case-by-case basis.

Florida

Florida, at present has a two-class system that designates all groundwater with a total content of dissolved solids of no more than 10,000 mg/l. as potable and all groundwater with a total content of dissolved solids greater than 10,000 mg/l. as non-potable (R. Dehan, Florida Department of Environmental Regulation, personal communication). The state has drafted a three-class system as follows (Florida Department of Environmental Regulation 1981c and d):

1. Class G–I—all groundwaters in single-source aquifers having a TDS content of less than 10,000 mg/l.
2. Class G–II—all groundwaters obtained from other than single-source aquifers with a TDS content of less than 10,000 mg/l.
3. Class G–III—all groundwater with a TDS content ≥10,000 mg/l. Discharges into these waters will be considered on a case-by-case

Table 11–9. New Jersey Groundwater Classification: Quality Criteria for Class GW3

Pollutant, Substance or Chemical	Ground-Water Quality Criteria
Ground Water Quality Criteria Statewide where the Total Dissolved Solids (TDS, Natural Background) Concentration is between 500 mg/l and 10,000 mg/l: Class GW3	
Primary Statewide/Toxic Pollutants	
1. Aldrin/Dieldrin	1. 0.003 μ/l
2. Arsenic and Compounds	2. 0.05 mg/l
3. Barium	3. 1.0 mg/l
4. Benzidine	4. 0.0001 mg/l
5. Cadmium and Compounds	5. 0.01 mg/l
6. Chromium (Hexavalent) and Compounds	6. 0.05 mg/l
7. Cyanide	7. 0.2 mg/l
8. DDT and Metabolites	8. 0.001 μ/l
9. Endrin	9. 0.004 μ/l
10. Lead and Compounds	10. 0.05 mg/l
11. Mercury and Compounds	11. 0.002 mg/l
12. Nitrate-Nitrogen	12. 10 mg/l
13. Phenol	13. 3.5 mg/l
14. Polychlorinated Biphenyls	14. 0.001 μ/l
15. Radionuclides	15. Prevailing regulations adopted by the U. S. EPA pursuant to sections 1412, 1415 and 1450 of the Public Health Services Act as amended by the Safe Drinking Water Act (PL 93-523)
16. Selenium and Compounds	16. 0.01 mg/l
17. Silver and Compounds	17. 0.05 mg/l
18. Toxaphene	18. 0.005 μ/l
Secondary Standards	
19. Ammonia	19. 0.5 mg/l
20. Chloride	20. Natural Background
21. Coliform Bacteria	21. a) by membrane filtration, not to exceed four per 100 ml in more than one sample when less than 20 are examined per month, or b) by fermentation tube, with a standard 10 ml portion, not to be present in three or more portions in more

Table 11–9. (continued)

	than one sample when less than 20 are examined per month, or c) Prevailing criteria adopted pursuant to the Federal Safe Drinking Water Act (PL 93-523)
22. Color	22. None Noticeable
23. Copper	23. 1.0 mg/l
24. Fluoride	24. 2.0 mg/l
25. Foaming Agents	25. 0.5 mg/l
26. Iron	26. 0.3 mg/l
27. Manganese	27. 0.05 mg/l
28. Odor and Taste	28. None Noticeable
29. Oil and Grease and Petroleum Hydrocarbons	29. None Noticeable
30. pH (Standard Units)	30. 5–9
31. Phenol	31. 0.3 mg/l
32. Sodium	32. Natural Background
33. Sulfate	33. Natural Background
34. Total Dissolved Solids	34. Natural Background
35. Zinc and Compounds	35. 5 mg/l

Source: New Jersey Department of Environmental Protection, 1981b.

basis to insure against danger to the public health, safety, and welfare.

There is a set of criteria for any discharge into classes G-I and G-II aquifers (see Table 11–10) that may not be exceeded unless the background value for a particular criteria is greater than the stated maximum. These same criteria may not necessarily apply to G-III groundwaters, as long as there is no danger to health, safety, or welfare of the public.

Nebraska

Like Florida and New Mexico, Nebraska protects its groundwater on a fairly subjective basis, using the total content of dissolved solids as a guideline to quailty. Standards (Table 11–11) were adopted in 1978 to be applied to groundwater with a total content of dissolved solids of less than 10,000 mg/l. (Nebraska Department of Environmental Control, 1978).

It is the "public policy of Nebraska to protect and improve the quality of groundwater for human consumption, agriculture, industry and other productive beneficial uses; to achieve the standards set out in Rule

Table 11–10. Florida Groundwater Classification

Class G-I Ground Waters. All ground waters in single source aquifers and having a total dissolved solids content of less than 10,000 mg/l are classified as Class G–I ground waters.

(a) The criteria and requirements contained in Section 17-3.051 and the criteria specified below apply to discharges to waters of this classification and also Class G–II waters.

1. Antimony—shall not exceed 0.146 milligrams per liter (mg/l).
2. Arsenic—shall not exceed 0.000 mg/l.
3. Bacteriological Quality—Total coliform shall not exceed 4 per 100 milliliters.
4. Barium—shall not exceed 1.0 mg/l
5. Cadmium—shall not exceed 0.01 mg/l
6. Chloride—shall not exceed 250 mg/l
7. Chlorinated hydrocarbons:

Endrin	shall not exceed .0002 mg/l
Lindane	shall not exceed .000 mg/l
Methoxychlor	shall not exceed .1 mg/l
Toxaphene	shall not exceed .00 mg/l

8. Chlorophenoxys:

2,4,—D	shall not exceed .10 mg/l
2,4,5,—TP Silvex	shall not exceed .01 mg/l

9. Chromium (hexavalent)—shall not exceed 0.05 mg/l
10. Color—shall not exceed 15 color units as measured by the Platinum-Cobalt Method.
11. Copper—shall not exceed 1.0 mg/l
12. Cyanide—shall not exceed 0.01 mg/l
13. Dissolved Solids—shall not exceed 500 mg/l
14. Fluoride—shall not exceed 1.5 mg/l
15. Iron—shall not exceed 0.3 mg/l
16. Lead—shall not exceed 0.05 mg/l
17. Manganese—shall not exceed .05 mg/l
18. Mercury—shall not exceed 0.00014 mg/l
19. Nitrate—shall not exceed 10.0 mg/l as N
20. Nickel—shall not exceed 0.013 mg/l
21. Odor—shall not exceed a threshold number of 3
22. pH—shall not be greater than 8.5 nor less than 6.5
23. Phenolic compounds—shall not exceed 0.001 mg/l
24. Radioactive Substances—combined radium 226 and 228—shall not exceed five picocuries per liter. Gross alpha particle activity (including radium 226 but excluding radon and uranium) shall not exceed 15 pCi/l.

Table 11–10. (continued)

25. Selenium—shall not exceed 0.01 mg/l
26. Silver—shall not exceed 0.05 mg/l.
27. Sulfates—shall not exceed 250 mg/l
28. Trihalomethane (Total)—shall not exceed 0.00 mg/l
29. Zinc—shall not exceed 5 mg/l

(b) If the concentration for any constituent listed in (a) in background quality of the ground water is greater than the stated maximum, the background value shall be the prevailing standard for discharges to G–I ground waters. If the pH in the background quality of the ground water is less than the stated minimum, or greater than the stated maximum, the pH of the background water shall be the prevailing standard.

(c) A substance which is either not specified in (a) or is not present in the background water and which is a known or suspected carcinogen, mutagen, or teratogen shall not be detectable in discharges to Class G-1 groundwaters.

Source: Florida Department of Environmental Regulation, 1980.

4 (Table 11–11) wherever possible'' (Nebraska Department of Environmental Control, 1978). Environmental, technological, social, and economic factors should be taken into consideration when determining whether standards are attainable for any specific aquifer. In selected cases, degradation may be allowed as a result of necessary and widespread economic or social development. Degradation, however, must not interfere with existing water uses.

New Mexico

New Mexico has a two-class system similar to Florida's. Groundwater with a TDS content greater than 10,000 mg/l. is considered non-potable, and water with a TDS content of less than 10,000 mg/l. is protected for potable use (M. Goad, Environmental Improvement Division of New Mexico, personal communication).

Maine

Maine has classified all its groundwater under one classification for which the highest standards apply (A. Tolman, Geologist, State of Maine, personal communication). Water must be free of radioactive matter or any matter imparting color, turbidity, taste, or odor, impairing the use of the water, other than that occurring from natural phenomena (Maine Department of Environmental Protection, 1979).

New Hampshire

New Hampshire has just adopted a program to protect all groundwater as a potential drinking-water supply (P. Piattoni, New Hampshire Water

Table 11–11. Nebraska Groundwater Classification

RULE 4. **DESCRIPTION AND APPLICATION OF STANDARDS**

(1) **General Criteria**

Wastes or toxic substances introduced directly or indirectly by man in concentrations which are hazardous to or which produce undesirable physiological effects in humans, animals or plants or which cause taste, odor or color problems shall not be allowed to enter groundwater by leaching or by direct contact.

(2) **Maximum Contaminant Levels**

The following standards are the maximum contaminant levels in groundwater for the specified contaminants. The standards apply to all groundwater which has an existing TDS concentration less than 10,000 mg/l. When a maximum contaminant level is exceeded by the existing contaminant level, as determined by the Department, the latter shall be used in place of the former, except where the existing concentration is the result of an identified point source of pollution.

(a) **Primary (Health)**

Contaminant	**Maximum Contaminant Level (mg/l)**
Arsenic (As)	0.05
Barium (Ba)	1.
Cadmium (Cd)	0.01
Chromium (Cr)	0.05
Fluoride (F)	2.4
Lead (Pb)	0.05
Mercury (Hg)	0.002
Nitrate-nitrogen (NO_3-N)	10.
Selenium (Se)	0.01
Silver (Ag)	0.05
Chlorinated hydrocarbons	
Endrin	0.0002
Lindane	0.004
Methoxychlor	0.1
Toxaphene	0.005
Chlorophenoxys	
2,4-D	0.1
2,4,5-TP Silvex	0.01

Contaminant	**Level (pCi/l)**
Radionuclides	
Combined radium-226 and radium-228	5
Gross alpha particle activity	15

Table 11–11. (continued)

(including radium-226 but excluding radon and uranium)	
Gross beta particle activity	50

(b) **Secondary (Aesthetic)**

Contaminant	**Maximum Contaminant Level (mg/l except as indicated)**	
Color	15	Color Units
Copper	1	
Foaming Agents (detergents)	0.5	
Hydrogen Sulfide	0.05	
Iron	1.0	
Manganese	0.2	
Odor	3	Threshold Odor Number
pH	6.5–8.5	Standard Units
Zinc	5	
Oil and Grease	1	

Source: Nebraska Department of Environmental Control, 1978.

Supply and Pollution Control Commission, personal communication). Through a permit system for aquifer use, the State will attempt to regulate all discharge into and contamination of its aquifers. Regulation on the local level is strongly encouraged, and a few communities have taken the initiative to regulate their groundwaters (New Hampshire Office of State Planning, 1981). One community has amended its zoning ordinance to include an Aquifer Protection District. Only certain activities are allowed in the district, lot sizes are limited to 6 acres, and covering more than 10% of a lot with material impervious to water is prohibited.

Massachusetts

Massachusetts is representative of a state trying to develop an aquifer-classification system. The State is beginning a five-year program (as of fiscal year 1982) to develop a groundwater strategy (Massachusetts Department of Environmental Quality and Engineering, Groundwater Strategy, n.d.). Groundwater classification is a major priority of the program. Following a year-long study of other classification systems a three-class system has been drafted based on the philosophy that classification should be a tool for guidance in future decision-making on waste-disposal sites rather than a course for definitive action. Groundwater classification should be subjective, and without exact site controls or numerical standards for the following reasons:

- There are not enough data on the effects of contaminants on health.
- Many dangerous contaminants are not limited by existing standards.
- Treatment or containment technology is presently unreliable.
- There is a lack of personnel, data base, and lab resources to acquire data and to administer such a program.

The Massachusetts Water Resources Commission voted on 9 February 1981 to adopt an approach similar to Connecticut's classification system, with the following major assumptions:

- All groundwater deserves some level of protection.
- Massachusetts does not subscribe to a policy of non-degradation.
- The focus of classification will be on the prevention of contamination rather than the restoration of water to better conditions.
- The classification system is a guide for decisions rather than a regulator of activities.
- Classification will not be dependent on numerical standards.

Sub-basins will be placed in one of three classes ranging from high quality (G–1) to known contamination areas (G–3). Judgment for classification will be based on both factual knowledge on the status of groundwater quality and on a knowledge of surface land-uses and their presumed impact on groundwater. These judgments are aimed at assessing the potential "risk of contamination" from existing land use.

Summary of State Aquifer-Classification Systems

The aquifer classification systems summarized in this survey may be divided into three distinct groups, ranging from simple systems that classify all aquifers as non-degradable to sophisticated differentiating systems that incorporate both land-use criteria and numerical standards into the classification of aquifers.

Non-Degradation Policy

The states with relatively low population densities, limited industrial development, high average annual precipitation rates, and low dependence on groundwater maintain blanket policies of non-degradation for their aquifers. New Hampshire and Maine have populations of about one million each (U.S. Department of Commerce, Bureau of the Census, 1980); groundwater usage as a percentage of total water usage is 6% and 4%, respectively, (Lehr, 1981); each state receives thirty to sixty inches of rain annually (U.S. EPA, 1977). It seems reasonable to assume that, because there are no apparent major threats to groundwater in either Maine or New Hampshire and people are not heavily dependent on the resource, there is little urgency to develope a comprehensive protection plan.

Classification Based on Numerical Standards

Florida, Nebraska, and New Mexico classify their aquifers into potable and non-potable water supplies based on the total content of dissolved solids in the water. Those classified as potable are carefully protected to maintain potability. Limited discharging may be allowed into non-potable aquifers. A non-degradation policy in these states would be very unrealistic. Groundwater is a heavily used resource, particularly in Nebraska, where it accounts for 68% of the total water use, and New Mexico, where 50% of the total water used is groundwater (Lehr, 1981). Groundwater in these states is threatened by several potentially contaminating activities as well as by depletion due to meager precipitation, as in Nebraska and New Mexico. In these states groundwater is a precious resource, and it is necessary to protect what can be protected. Classification by numerical standards separates aquifers that need special protection, because they are supplies for drinking water, from those that cannot be used for drinking water.

Classification Based on Land Use and Numerical Standards

The least groundwater dependent, most densely populated, and highly industrialized or agriculturally intensive states studied here have the most sophisticated classification systems, which are based on the understanding that different land uses require different levels of water quality. The states are Connecticut, New Jersey, New York, North Carolina, and Wyoming. Although Wyoming is not densely populated, it relies little on groundwater for its water supply, since only 6% of its total annual water supply comes from groundwater (Lehr, 1981). These states have set up standards of water quality for varying uses such as housing, agriculture and industry. Each state has a classification that may permit waste discharge into a low-quality aquifer. The classification systems based on land use require a good deal of time and labor to design and probably are most sensible for highly developed states where parameters of population growth and industrialization are not likely to change drastically for several years.

Twelve

Federal Statutes Relevant to the Protection of Groundwater

- There is no federal program whose aim is specifically that of groundwater protection. A group of statutes designed primarily for other environmental problems do focus indirectly on groundwater and offer some measure of protection.
- At the federal level the predominant concern has focused upon industrial hazardous wastes through the Resource Conservation and Recovery Act (RCRA) of 1976.
- Other federal statutes affecting groundwater protection are the Safe Drinking Water Act (SDWA), the Clean Water Act (CWA), the Comprehensive Environmental Response, Compensation and Liability Act (CERCLA or "Superfund"), the Toxic Substances Control Act (TOSCA), the National Environmental Policy Act (NEPA), the Surface Mining Control and Reclamation Act (SMCRA), and the Federal Insecticide, Fungicide and Rodenticide Act (FIFRA).

The legal framework established to protect groundwater reflects the efforts of society to deal with the numerous diverse problems of groundwater contamination described in earlier chapters. In approaching this legal framework, it is important to consider the federal regulations in combination with state and local regulations, since the respective bodies of law cover, in some instances, quite different areas of concern. It should also be noted that some activities which may give rise to groundwater contamination do not lend themselves easily to control through traditional regulatory mechanisms and have received less attention from the lawmakers. Accordingly, it can be quite informative to consider the differing extent and nature of regulatory controls that have been established for each of the common types of groundwater contamination.

Another feature of most groundwater-protection statutes is that they are not focused exclusively, or in many instances even primarily, on groundwater protection as such. Instead, they are directed at particular acts or practices likely to cause environmental damage in various ways, with groundwater being one of several natural resources warranting protection. This statutory focus on activities to be controlled rather than on the medium to be protected makes a survey of pertinent laws somewhat more complicated. It also makes it important to consider whether the various statutes, in combination, provide a comprehensive framework for protecting the quality of groundwater or whether there are gaps or weaknesses that need to be addressed. The Environmental Protection Agency (EPA) is currently developing an overall groundwater strategy, although progress toward completing that strategy has been impeded by the large number of difficult technical issues that are involved.

At the federal level, the predominant concern has centered upon industrial hazardous wastes. The principal federal statute relevant to the protection of groundwater is the Resource Conservation and Recovery Act of 1976 (RCRA), which established a comprehensive framework for the management of municipal solid wastes and hazardous wastes. One of the primary motivating factors leading to the enactment of RCRA was the recognition of the need to regulate waste-disposal practices in such a way as to minimize the threat of soil and groundwater contamination.

Other important federal statutes affecting groundwater-protection efforts are the Safe Drinking Water Act of 1974 (SDWA), which was enacted to provide for a sanitary drinking-water supply and to regulate the use of underground injection wells; the Clean Water Act of 1977 (CWA), which established a program to control the discharge of pollutants into navigable waters, and the Comprehensive Environmental Response, Compensation and Liability Act of 1980 (CERCLA), which authorizes the federal government to take direct remedial action to respond to releases or threatened releases of hazardous substances into the environment which may present an imminent and substantial danger to public health. Other statutes bearing less directly on the problem, though relevant to the overall effort to protect groundwater, are the Toxic Substances Control Act, the National Environmental Policy Act, the Surface Mining Control and Reclamation Act, and the Federal Insecticide, Fungicide and Rodenticide Act.

While the above-mentioned statutes were not specifically designed to address all groundwater-policy concerns, taken as a whole, they do offer a legal framework for the support of federal efforts to protect groundwater. As will be described in greater detail below, many of the statutes mentioned above contain broad imminent-hazard provisions which enable EPA to take immediate action to restrain activities posing a threat to any feature of the environment, including groundwater. EPA has invoked the imminent-hazard provisions of RCRA, CWA, CERCLA, and other environmental statutes, the provisions for recovering the cost of cleanup of CERCLA, as well as the federal common law of nuisance, in more than 70 cases filed against owners of waste-disposal sites allegedly causing environmental problems. This enforcement campaign has focused principally on ground- and surface-water pollution attributable to the migration of toxic wastes.

The role of states in environmental-protection efforts has been significantly augmented by several federal environmental statutes which enable the states to obtain EPA authorization to administer and enforce federal environmental programs. When it enacted RCRA, the SDWA and the CWA, Congress envisioned that the states would play a major role in administering these programs, which affect groundwater, once the regulatory framework was in place. Typically, in order to obtain authorization to administer one of these environmental programs, a state would have to propose a program for EPA approval that was substantially equivalent to federal guidelines and would have to obtain the legal authority from its legislature to carry out the program. This process has taken place under the SDWA and CWA and several other programs, and states now play a significant role in carrying out these programs. States have begun to obtain EPA interim authorization of the RCRA program, but until a permitting strategy has been fully developed and implemented, states will ony be able to play a limited role in hazardous-waste management.

The Resource Conservation and Recovery Act of 1976, 42USC §6901 *et seq.,* Pub. L. No. 94–580

The Resource Conservation and Recovery Act of 1976 (RCRA) is foremost among federal statutes aimed at minimizing groundwater contamination. After extremely limited federal involvement in the area of hazardous-waste management, RCRA was enacted in 1976, completely overhauling the Solid Waste Disposal Act as originally adopted in 1965.

Prior to the enactment of RCRA, pollution-control programs such as the Clean Air Act and Clean Water Act significantly increased waste-management activities in and on the land. These unregulated land-disposal practices created many situations where leachate might migrate into groundwater, causing potentially serious contamination. One of the original purposes of RCRA was to fill the gap that existed after the implementation of other pollution-control programs. As stated by Congress in Section 1002 of RCRA:

> As a result of the Clean Air Act, the Water Pollution Control Act and other Federal and State laws respecting public health and the environment, greater amounts of solid waste (in the form of sludge and other pollution treatment residues) have been created. Similarly sound practices for disposal of solid waste have created greater amounts of air and water pollution and other problems for the environment and health.

Thus, Congress enacted RCRA to provide for careful planning and management practices in the treatment, storage, and disposal of hazardous waste.

The most relevant features of the RCRA program are the Subtitle C program, which governs hazardous-waste management, and the Subtitle D program, which covers municipal solid-waste disposal. The most significant feature of the Subtitle C RCRA program is the tracking of hazardous wastes from "cradle to grave." EPA has promulgated regulations imposing manifesting, recordkeeping, and reporting requirements on generators and transporters of hazardous waste. Owners and operators of hazardous-waste treatment, storage, and disposal facilities must obtain interim-status approval by submitting RCRA permit applications and must comply with EPA regulations applicable to interim-status facilities in order to continue operations until EPA begins to issue draft permits. Construction of new hazardous-waste facilities (i.e., those not in existence before 19 May 1980) may not begin until permits are issued. Interim-status facilities, and in the future, new hazardous-waste facilities are required to comply with strict design and operating standards, in addition to the normal requirements for recordkeeping, reporting, and financial responsibility.

Subtitle D of RCRA calls for federal supervision of municipal solid-waste disposal. RCRA also gives EPA broad emergency powers to abate imminent hazards caused by improper waste-disposal practices that pose a threat to the environment.

Under Section 1004(27) of RCRA, solid waste is defined as any garbage, refuse, sludge, or any other discarded material. Specifically excluded from regulation under RCRA are solids or dissolved materials in domestic sewage, irrigation return-flows, industrial point-source discharges subject to Federal Water Pollution Control Act, nuclear wastes, exploration and production waste, and certain wastes associated with mining activities. Section 1004(5) defines hazardous waste as any solid waste that may present specified risks or harm to human health and the environment. That RCRA was intended to regulate disposal activities affecting groundwater is clearly shown by Section 1004(3), which defines disposal as "the discharge, deposit, injection, dumping, spilling, leaking, or placing of any solid waste or hazardous waste into or on any land or water so that such solid waste or hazardous waste or any constituent thereof may enter the environment or be emitted into the air or discharged into any waters, including groundwaters."

Solid-Waste Disposal Program

Subtitle D of RCRA provides for limited federal supervision of state and municipal practices of solid-waste disposal. EPA is required to provide technical and financial assistance to the states in the development of methods of solid-waste disposal that are environmentally sound and to encourage resource conservation. Under Section 4006 of RCRA, states are required to develop plans for the management of solid wastes and the conservation of resources in conformance with EPA guidelines. The plans must be approved by EPA and are subject to their continuous review and revision.

The key to the Subtitle D solid-waste program is Section 4004 of RCRA, which requires EPA to establish guidelines for classifying facilities for the disposal of solid waste as either "open dumps" or "sanitary landfills." The Act provides that at a minimum, a facility may be classified as a sanitary landfill and not as an open dump "only if there is no reasonable probability of adverse effects on health or the environment from the disposal of solid waste at such facility." States with approved subtitle D plans then use the EPA criteria to classify their facilities for solid-waste disposal and take appropriate action to upgrade or close any that are classified as open dumps.

EPA has established eight criteria to be used by the states in classifying solid waste facilities (40 Codes of Federal Regulations. §257.3 1981). One deals specifically with effects on groundwater, while the others address other types of environmental concerns (40 C.F.R. §257.3–4, 1981).

The Subtitle D groundwater criteria state that a facility for solid-waste disposal is an open dump if it contaminates groundwater that either is being used as a source of drinking water or contains less than 10,000 mg/l total dissolved solids. Contamination is deemed to occur whenever the concentration of a contaminant in the groundwater at the "solid-waste boundary" is increased so as to exceed any of the National Interim Primary Drinking Water Standards, which cover nine inorganic chemicals and six pesticides. If the groundwater at the "solid-waste boundary" already exceeds any of these standards, then any further increase in the concentration of that contaminant is also deemed to be contamination. While the Subtitle D groundwater criteria represent a clear effort to prevent contaminants from migrating into the groundwater, it should be noted that National Interim Primary Drinking Water Standards have been set for only a fraction of the contaminants now found in groundwater.

Although the EPA groundwater criteria measure contamination at the "solid-waste boundary," i.e., at the outermost perimeter of the solid-waste facility, the states are allowed to establish alternative boundaries for particular facilities based upon a number of site-specific factors. These include the nature of the wastes involved, the present quality and quantity of the groundwater, and the availability of alternate supplies of drinking water.

Once a state with an approved Subtitle D plan classifies a facility as an open dump, section 4005 of RCRA requires that it must then provide for either the upgrading or the closure of that facility. The state may issue a compliance schedule to a facility that plans to upgrade, thereby insulating the facility from possible citizen suits to enjoin the prohibited act of "open dumping" under Section 4005(a).

Hazardous-Waste Disposal Program

As mentioned earlier under Subtitle C of RCRA, EPA is authorized to regulate hazardous wastes from "cradle to grave." This enables EPA to impose manifesting, recordkeeping, and reporting requirements on generators and transporters of hazardous waste. The key to the Subtitle C program, however, is Section 3004 of the Act which directs EPA to establish standards for all hazardous waste management facilities as may be necessary to protect human health and the environment. These standards are to be incorporated into RCRA permits for individual facilities. Under Section 3005 of the Act, effective 19 November 1980, it is unlawful to treat, store, or dispose of any hazardous waste without a RCRA permit.

Because the more than 10,000 hazardous-waste facilities in existence on the effective date of the program could not be permitted overnight, RCRA provides that they are accorded interim status. This means that these existing facilities can be treated as though they have received individual RCRA permits and may therefore continue to operate pending final action on their permit applications if they comply with the procedures required to obtain interim status. Under the regulations, if an owner or operator of an existing facility notified EPA as required by Section 3010, and filed a timely application for a RCRA permit, then the facility is considered to be operating under a permit until such time as EPA takes final action on the permit application. Thus, interim status is essential for all existing facilities that treat, store, or dispose of hazardous waste.

Several different sets of EPA regulations apply to various categories of RCRA facilities. First, the interim-status standards set out in 40 Codes of Federal Regulations Part 265 apply to existing facilities that are operating under interim status pending final action on their permit application. Second, the permitting standards in 40 C.F.R. Part 264 apply to both new and existing facilities, and only facilities meeting these standards will receive RCRA permits. Interim-status facilities that cannot meet the permitting standards will be required to cease handling hazardous waste following a denial of their permit applications. The interim-status standards and the permitting standards are discussed separately below.

Similar to the Subtitle D program, Congress designed the Subtitle C program so that it also could be administered by the states. The state-authorization process takes place in two phases. First, in order to obtain interim authorization, the state must submit a description of the program it proposes to administer, including a description of the agency that will administer it, the staff, the estimated cost, and the type of forms and papers that will be used. After EPA review and opportunity for public notice, hearing, and comment, EPA will grant interim authorization to the state if the program is substantially equivalent to the federal program. A state with interim authorization must receive final authorization by 26 January 1985. If no final authorization has been obtained by that date, the authority of the state agency to issue RCRA permits will terminate, and EPA will have to reinstitute a federal program in that state. In order to obtain final authorization, a state program must: be equivalent to the federal program, be consistent with the federal program and other state programs, and provide for adequate enforcement. Once final authorization has been received, hazardous-waste generators and transporters and owners and operators of hazardous-waste facilities are governed by the state program in lieu of EPA regulations.

Interim-Status Standards

EPA has developed two basic types of interim-status standards: non-technical standards that apply to all hazardous-waste facilities and technical standards applicable to specific types of facilities, such as landfills or surface impoundments. The non-technical standards apply uniformly to all hazardous-waste facilities regardless of the type of waste-management activity, whether it be treatment, storage, or disposal, and regardless of the type of facility, such as incinerator, landfill, land-treatment unit, or container. The non-technical standards include waste analysis and inspection requirements and other housekeeping measures, including standards designed to assure financial responsibility for proper closure and post-closure care of RCRA facilities. The non-technical standards also include groundwater-monitoring requirements intended to provide both a current profile of background-groundwater quality and a timely indication of any significant contamination from the facility.

The technical standards cover specific types of RCRA facilities and vary for each type. The technical standards impose specific design, operating, and maintenance requirements on specific types of hazardous-waste facilities in order to insure that each type of facility is managed in an environmentally safe manner. The technical standards dictate what kind of specific measures an owner or operator of a specific type of facility must observe in order to continue operation. Thus, facilities that use containers to store hazardous wastes must insure that the containers are in good condition and are not leaking. They must conduct weekly inspections. Tanks used to manage hazardous wastes must allow two feet of freeboard unless they are equipped with containment structures designed to handle leaks of overflows from the tanks.

Surface impoundments must also allow adequate freeboard to prevent any overtopping of dikes. The dikes must have a protective cover to minimize erosion. Waste piles must be covered or otherwise managed to prevent wind dispersal. Land-treatment facilities must be managed so as to render the wastes non-hazardous or less hazardous, and monitoring in the unsaturated zone is required in order to detect any migration of waste constituents. Landfills are subject to special restrictions on the disposal of liquid wastes.

Permitting Standards

On 26 July 1982 EPA promulgated permitting standards as required by Section 3004 of RCRA for new and existing hazardous-waste land-treatment, storage, and disposal facilities (47 Federal Register 32,274, 26 July 1982). These permitting standards will be found at 40 Codes of Federal Regulations Part 264 and are the basis for issuing permits to new facilities. Ongoing operations of other existing facilities will become subject to these permitting standards only as EPA and authorized state agencies process their permit applications and bring them under these additional controls through the issuance of permits. These regulations are applicable to surface impoundments, waste piles, land-treatment units, and landfills. Two basic elements embodied in EPA's permitting standards are a "liquids-management strategy" and a "groundwater-monitoring and response program." The liquids-management strategy is intended to minimize the generation of leachate and to remove it from the waste-management unit before it enters the groundwater. This strategy reflects EPA's awareness that when hazardous waste is in liquid form or in a mixture with other liquids, it presents the greatest threat to groundwater because of the potential for migration below the surface. The most significant feature of the liquids-management strategy is the use of liners and leachate-collection systems on new surface impoundments, waste piles, and landfills.

The groundwater-monitoring and response program is intended to detect the migration of contaminants that have escaped from a facility and, where they exceed specified limits, to require removal of such leachate from the groundwater. All facilities are required to have a groundwater-monitoring and response program in effect, subject to a few exceptions. The brief description below of the design and operating standards applicable to specific RCRA facilities will demonstrate that groundwater protection was a primary objective of the RCRA program.

The specific design and operating standards for surface impoundments, waste piles, and landfills require these facilities to have a liner and a leachate-collection and removal system that is designed to prevent migration of waste to adjacent subsurface soil, groundwater, or surface water. An exemption is allowed for "existing portions" of such facilities because of the difficulties associated with retrofitting. These existing facilities do, however, remain subject to groundwater monitoring requirements, which can lead to the imposition of treatment or removal requirements when groundwater is contaminated.

In addition to these general design and operating requirements, surface impoundments and waste piles must be constructed and maintained so as to prevent overtopping from run-on, rainfall, and other causes. In general, ignitable or reactive wastes must not be placed in surface impoundments or waste piles unless special steps are taken to prevent ignition or reaction. Landfills are subject to the same controls as waste piles. The permitting standards provide a special prohibition against placing bulk or non-containerized liquid wastes or wastes containing free liquid in landfills unless special requirements are met. A similar prohibition also applies to the landfilling of containers holding free liquids, subject to specified exceptions.

Land-treatment facilities are not subject to the liner and leachate-collection and removal requirements applicable to other land-disposal facilities; instead there are specific requirements for land-treatment units. No hazardous wastes may be placed in a land-treatment unit unless the facility owner or operator demonstrates that the hazardous constituents have been completely degraded, transformed, or immobilized within the "treatment zone" of the facility. The treatment zone is a soil area within the land-treatment unit where wastes will be applied under conditions that will allow for effective degradation, transformation, or immobilization of the hazardous constituents. The treatment zone must have a maximum depth of no more than five feet and must be more than three feet above the seasonal high-water table. Land-treatment units must also have specified run-on and run-off management systems to protect against flooding and are subject to specific inspection and monitoring requirements.

Land treatment, storage, and disposal facilities are also subject to locational standards aimed at limiting off-site migration of hazardous wastes through either seismic activity or flooding. Tanks and containers must meet specified design and operating standards to allow for efficient drainage and to protect against collapse or rupture. The permitting standards also include financial responsibility requirements to insure closure and post-closure care of the RCRA facility to allow for safe containment, removal, or decontamination of waste residues at the end of the active life of a facility.

Imminent-Hazard Authority

Section 7003 of the RCRA empowers the Administrator, upon receipt of evidence that the handling of any solid waste or hazardous waste is presenting or may present an "imminent and substantial endangerment to health or the environment," to bring suit in district court to restrain such handling of solid waste or hazardous waste. Alternatively, the Agency may issue such administrative orders "as may be necessary to protect public health and the environment." Willful violation of an administrative order subjects the violator to additional civil penalties, which may be collected in a separate action in federal district court.

250

Safe Drinking Water Act of 1974, 42 USC §§ 300f to 300j–9, Pub. L. No. 93–523.

The Safe Drinking Water Act (SDWA) was enacted by Congress to provide for sanitary drinking-water supplies and to establish a program to control underground injection in order to prevent endangerment of subsurface waters. The underground-injection-control (UIC) program under the Safe Drinking Water Act was the first federal effort that was directly aimed at the prevention of groundwater contamination. Under the UIC program, EPA asserts direct authority over underground waste-disposal wells. Although there would be sufficient statutory authority under RCRA to regulate underground waste-disposal wells, the UIC program continues to be managed under the Safe Drinking Water Act, and EPA has largely deferred exercising this authority under RCRA because of the UIC program.

Under the UIC program established under Section 1421 of the SDWA, underground injection is prohibited without an authorized state permit. In order to obtain a state permit, the applicant must satisfy the state that the underground injection will not endanger drinking-water sources. Inspection, monitoring, recordkeeping, and reporting requirements are imposed under the UIC program. There was legislation pending in the 97th Congress that would have significantly affected the UIC program if it had been enacted. The bill would have absolutely prohibited the disposal of hazardous wastes by injection into or above underground sources of drinking water. This would also have abolished the current variance under Section 1421(b) which allows direct injection into an underground source of drinking water upon a showing of no endangerment to drinking-water supplies.

An important feature of the SDWA program is the establishment of primary and secondary drinking-water standards which have been promulgated by EPA on interim final form under Section 1412. These standards apply to every public water system in each state. The Natural Interim Primary Drinking Water Standards list contaminants which have been determined by EPA to have an adverse effect on human health. The primary drinking-water standards also specify a maximum contaminant level for each such contaminant and contain criteria and procedures to assure that supplies of drinking water are in compliance with the prescribed maximum contaminant levels. The secondary drinking-water standards specify maximum contaminant levels for contaminants that may adversely effect the odor or appearance of drinking water in such a way as to cause a substantial number of persons to discontinue its use. The secondary drinking-water standards also prescribe maximum contaminant levels for any contaminant that may in any other way adversely affect public welfare. As mentioned earlier, it should be noted that primary and secondary drinking-water standards have not been set for many of the contaminants now found in surface waters and groundwater. Under Section 1414(a) EPA may commence civil action against a state not in compliance with primary drinking-water standards.

Another aspect of the SDWA program specifically aimed at groundwater protection is the "sole-source aquifer" program under Section 1424 which enables EPA to take special measures to protect those areas which have only one aquifer as their principal source of drinking water. No new underground injection wells can be drilled in these areas without a permit. In order to obtain a permit the applicant must prove that the injection will not cause contamination to the aquifer. Section 1424(e) gives EPA broad authority to protect a sole-source aquifer. Under this provision, if EPA determines that a sole-source aquifer, if contaminated, "would create a significant hazard to public health," no commitment of federal financial assistance through grants, contracts, or loan guarantees may be given to any program which EPA determines may contaminate such an aquifer so as to create a significant hazard to human health.

When Congress enacted the SDWA, it envisioned that the states would have primary responsibility for assuring compliance with SDWA regulations. Under Section 1413, EPA is authorized to give the states primary enforcement responsibility for assuring compliance with the primary and secondary drinking-water standards. In order to obtain such authorization, the state must adopt drinking-water standards in conformance with the federal standards and adopt implementing procedures for the enforcement of the state standards. Similarly, the SDWA enables states to have primary enforcement responsibility for programs to control underground injection. Under Section 1422, EPA is required to list all states that should have such programs, and all states that are listed by EPA must adopt such a program which meets the requirements specified by EPA. EPA is authorized to take over these programs if a state fails to insure their enforcement.

As with RCRA, the SDWA contains an imminent-hazard provision which is relevant to the implementation of groundwater-protection measures. In order to protect drinking-water supplies, Section 1431 of the SDWA allows EPA to institute a civil action or take any other measures when it receives information that a contaminant is present or likely to enter a public water system and present an imminent and substantial endangerment to the health of persons. This authority may only be exercised if the state or local authorities have failed to act.

252

The Clean Water Act of 1977, 33 USC §1251 *et seq.*, Pub. L. No. 95–217

The Clean Water Act (CWA) is the most comprehensive federal water-pollution-control program in existence. The primary objective of the CWA is the reduction and control of the discharge of pollutants into the nation's navigable waters. While the CWA does not specify control of groundwater pollution as one of its explicit objectives, it nevertheless offers limited statutory authority to implement groundwater-protection measures, and in many instances the reduction of pollution in surface waters will protect the quality of groundwater. As part of the overall program to prevent and eliminate sources of water pollution, Section 104 of the CWA requires EPA to "establish, equip and maintain a water quality surveillance system for the purpose of monitoring navigable waters and ground waters." This section has been implemented most completely with regard to surface waters, with only limited surveillance of groundwater.

Section 208 of the CWA, which deals with the development and implementation of area-wide plans for the management of waste treatment, is potentially the most effective means of controlling groundwater pollution as part of the entire program. Section 208 was enacted to eliminate the problems in the control of water quality occurring in urban and industrial areas. It has led to the reduction in use of such things as septic tanks, which have been known to contribute to groundwater contamination in urban areas. Under Section 208, in coordination with state authorities, EPA is required to publish guidelines for "the identification of those areas which as a result of urban-industrial concentrations or other factors have substantial water quality problems." The state must develop plans that identify the type of treatment facility necessary to meet municipal and industrial waste-treatment needs. The plan should also identify agriculturally and silviculturally related non-point sources of pollution, including irrigation return-flows and their cumulative effects, and set procedures to control these non-point sources of pollution. The plan is also required to identify methods of controlling salt-water intrusion into rivers and lakes as a result of the reduction of fresh-water flow due to the migration, obstruction, or extraction of groundwater. The waste-treatment plan should contain similar remedial measures to control pollution from mining and construction activities.

The programs implemented under Section 208 have received lower priority and achieved much more limited results than have other parts of the Clean Water Act, but these programs nevertheless possess the potential for having a significant bearing upon the protection of groundwater.

Two other highlights of the Clean Water Act are the effluent limitations that apply to all point sources of discharge of pollutants and the water-quality standards. These features of the Clean Water Act apply exclusively to surface water and are relevant to the extent that there are situations where surface water may be leaching into groundwater. Section 304 of CWA directs the Administrator to provide guidelines for effluent limitations in the form of regulations which identify the degree of effluent reduction attainable through the application of varying levels of pollution-control technology applicable to any point source. Section 304 also requires EPA to establish water-quality standards consistent with the purposes of the Act.

The information and guideline requirements of Section 304(e) of the Clean Water Act are more relevant to groundwater issues, but the purpose of that particular Section is education, not regulation. Section 304 requires EPA to publish information including guidelines for identifying and evaluating the nature and extent of non-point sources of pollutants, and processes, procedures, and methods to control pollution resulting from agriculture and silviculture, mining and construction, excavation, salt-water intrusion, and changes in surface or groundwater flow.

One of the most important features of the Clean Water Act is the National Pollution Discharge Elimination System (NPDES) under Section 402, which allows EPA or authorized states to issue permits for the discharge of any pollutant or combination of pollutants if certain specified conditions are met. These permits require compliance with specific standards in order to release certain types of industrial and municipal wastes into the nation's waters and are the principle mechanism for enforcing measures to reduce and control the discharge of pollutants into surface waters.

One significant feature of Section 402 is subsection (b)(1)(D) which states that as a condition to authorizing a state NPDES program, the state must have adequate authority to control the disposal of pollutants into wells. Thus, it seems clear that a state with EPA authorization to administer a NPDES program would have the authority to protect groundwater by way of its authority to regulate the disposal of pollutants into wells. It should be noted, however, that under Section 502(6), the term pollutant would not include materials associated with oil and gas production. Therefore, well-disposal activities associated with oil and gas production cannot be regulated by the states under Section 402.

Another provision of the CWA that offers some limited authority to regulate activities that may cause groundwater contamination is Section

404, which regulates the discharge of dredged or fill material into navigable and non-navigable waters and wetlands. Dredged materials are defined as materials that are excavated or dredged from navigable waters. Fill materials are materials used in replacing an aquatic area with dry land or used in elevating the bottom of a body of water (33 Codes of Federal Regulations §323.2, 1981). The Secretary of the Army and authorized states are required to issue permits to control the adverse effects of point-source discharges of dredged or fill material into the nation's waters. Before the enactment of the Clean Water Act Amendments in 1977, it was believed that this authority was limited to waterways susceptible to use for navigation. The 1977 amendments made clear congressional intent to regulate the discharge of dredged or fill material into lakes, tributaries, rivers, streams, swamps, marshes, and other waters outside of those commonly considered as navigable waters. Section 404 was enacted to prevent the destruction or degradation of aquatic resources that results from replacing water with dredged or fill material and to prevent the contamination of water resources by toxic substances contained in these materials.

One significant feature of the CWA which affects groundwater in a more direct way is the imminent-hazard authority granted to EPA to bring suit or to take any other action that may be necessary to restrain persons or activities allegedly causing the discharge of pollutants. Specifically, Section 504 states that where a pollution source or combination of sources presents an imminent and substantial endangerment to human health or where the endangerment is to the livelihood of such persons, EPA may go to court to restrain any persons causing such pollution. Because this provision gives EPA broad authority to protect against environmental as well as economic injury, i.e., injury to livelihood or welfare, it could possibly be very effective in restraining activities threatening to contaminate groundwater supplies.

Comprehensive Environment Response, Compensation and Liability Act of 1980, 26 USC §4611 *et seq.,* Pub. L. No. 96–510

The Comprehensive Environmental Response, Compensation and Liability Act (CERCLA) was enacted in 1980 to allow the federal government to respond immediately to the release or threatened release of hazardous substances into the environment which may present an imminent and substantial danger to public health. Since this type of incident represents the most immediate threat to groundwater quality, CERCLA is an extremely important statute for groundwater protection.

CERCLA gives the federal government the basic operating authority to take direct action to remove and provide remedial measures whenever hazardous substances or pollutants or contaminants are released or there is the threat of a release which poses a serious and imminent risk to public health or the environment. That authority includes conducting investigations, testing, and monitoring of disposal sites. It also includes the authority to implement actual remedial measures to remove contaminants from the groundwater. These activities are to be carried out under the terms of a National Contingency Plan.

The remedial measures carried out by the federal government under CERCLA are financed by a $1.6 billion Hazardous Substance Response Trust Fund, a financing mechanism in the Act commonly referred to as "Superfund." Seven-eighths of the Trust Fund money is provided by industry through taxes, and one-eighth through appropriations from general revenues.

In cases where the responsibility for the wastes causing contamination can be traced to companies with financial resources, CERCLA requires that the financial responsibility for the cleanup is placed on those companies. The statute establishes a new and far-reaching set of federal laws under which liability can be imposed on such companies even though they were never directly involved in the ownership or operation of the facilities where the wastes were disposed of. After the government has identified a site as one that threatens environmental damage, it may call upon those companies which can be held liable in that instance to undertake the cleanup at their own cost. Alternatively, if such companies refuse to assume the responsibility for the cleanup, the government can carry out the remedial program using money from the Fund and then bring suit against the companies for reimbursement.

National Contingency Plan

On 16 July 1982 EPA published revisions to the National Contingency Plan (NCP) to ensure an effective response to both CERCLA and the Clean Water Act. (47 Federal Register 31,180, 1982, to be codified at 40 C.F.R. Part 300). This revised NCP is of particular importance to groundwater protection. The procedure for moving from discovery, to investigation, to a plan of removal has been outlined in seven phases of response. Phase I—Discovery and Notification, Phase II—Preliminary Assessment, Phase III—Immediate Removal, Phase IV—Evaluation and Determination of Appropriate Response, Phase V—Planned Removal, Phase VI—Remedial Action, and Phase VII—Documentation and Cost Recovery.

The NCP also includes criteria for determining priorities for remedial actions among releases, and based upon these criteria EPA has developed a Hazard Ranking System (HRS). This HRS will be the foundation for determining a list of at least 400 top-priority response targets. EPA has not completed this list, which will be included as Appendix B to the NCP in the future.

The HRS takes into account the following considerations: the population at risk, the hazard potential of hazardous substances at such facilities, the potential for contamination of drinking-water supplies, the potential for direct human contact, and the potential for destruction of sensitive ecosystems. With these considerations in mind, EPA looked at five potential "pathways" of exposure to the human population or a sensitive environment and other factors to arrive at an HRS mathematical score for relative ranking of the priority list. The mathematical computations are subject to some uncertainty, and the actual selection of sites for remedial action will depend not only on the relative-risk rankings but also on the availability of cost-sharing and other state assurances.

A critical question confronting EPA in the development of the NCP was the degree to which it would define the appropriate extent of a remedy. The system adopted by EPA does not include any requirement to achieve specific environmental standards. Instead, EPA has developed a flexible methodology which considers environmental effects as one of several criteria to be taken into account in determining the appropriate extent of a remedy. In general, the appropriate extent of a remedy is "the lowest cost alternative that is technologically feasible and reliable and which effectively mitigates and minimizes damage to and provides adequate protection of public health, welfare, or the environment."

The NCP also lists several specific engineering methods for the control of various types of releases, including pollution of groundwater.

Enforcement and Implementation

EPA has made sufficient progress in the implementation of the CERCLA program to indicate the general outlines of the approach it will follow. In October of 1981 the Agency published an interim list of the 115 top-priority sites in the United States. It added an additional 45 sites, making a total of 160 sites, in July of 1982. Those two lists of selected priority sites will clearly provide the target situations at which EPA will be aiming virtually all of its early enforcement efforts.

Similar to the imminent-hazard provisions found in RCRA, SDWA, and the CWA, Congress established an extremely broad imminent-hazard authority under Section 106 of CERCLA, which enables EPA to take any action when there is a risk to the environment. These powers include securing judicial relief and the issuance of administrative orders to protect public health, welfare, and the environment.

EPA has instituted enforcement actions against responsible parties at some of the 160 identified sites and has also initiated response financed by the Trust Fund at several other sites. Usually each site involves a large number of companies whose wastes may have been disposed of at that particular site, and who are therefore potentially liable for the cleanup costs. CERCLA bars the government from undertaking cleanup financed by the Superfund (CERCLA) if it is determined that the owner or operator of the facility, or any other responsible party, will properly conduct the necessary remedial work.

There are stringent liability standards under CERCLA that are worthy of a brief description. Under Section 107 of CERCLA, any owner or operator of any vessel or facility from which there is a release or a threatened release of a hazardous substance is liable. Past owners and operators of facilities from which hazardous substances are or threaten to be released, as well as persons who arranged for disposal or treatment of hazardous substances, or those who accepted hazardous substances for transport to disposal or treatment facilities from which there is a release or a threatened release are also liable. Liability under CERCLA extends to all removal and remedial costs incurred by the United States or a state not inconsistent with the National Contingency Plan, any other necessary response cost incurred by any other person consistent with the National Contingency Plan, and damages for injury to natural resources belonging to, or held in trust by, or otherwise controlled by any governmental entity.

Liability under CERCLA attaches without regard to fault or negligence and is subject only to a few narrowly drawn defenses. Liability can be avoided by a showing that the release of hazardous substances resulted solely from an act of God, an act of war, or an act or omission of a third party, other than an employee or a person with a direct or indirect contractual relationship with the defendant, provided that the defendant exercised due care and took precautions against foreseeable acts and omissions of the third party.

Toxic Substances Control Act, 15 USC § 2601 *et seq.*, Pub. L. No. 94–469

The Toxic Substances Control Act (TSCA) was enacted in 1976 to regulate the manufacture, use, and disposal of chemical substances and mixtures that pose a significant risk of injury to health and the environment. Although groundwater protection is not a specific statutory objective of TSCA, to the extent that TSCA regulates the disposal of toxic chemicals, it is relevant to any discussion of groundwater protection.

TSCA provides a comprehensive framework for the regulation of the manufacture and use of chemical substances and mixtures. It requires extensive testing, notification, labeling, and record keeping. EPA has the authority under TSCA to prohibit or limit the quantity of the manufacture, processing, distribution, and use of chemicals. But most importantly for groundwater concerns, TSCA gives EPA the authority to prohibit or regulate the manner or method of disposal of chemicals or of any article containing a chemical. This authority extends to the manufacturer and processor as well as to any person who uses or disposes of a chemical substance for commercial purposes.

Another feature of TSCA significant for groundwater protection is the imminent-hazard provision under Section 7. Pursuant to this Section, EPA has emergency powers to commence civil action to seize imminently hazardous chemical substances and mixtures. An imminently hazardous chemical substance is one which poses immediate threat of serious or widespread injury to health or the environment.

The Surface Mining Control and Reclamation Act of 1977, 30 USC §1201 *et seq.*, Pub. L. No. 95–87

In 1977 Congress enacted the Surface Mining Control and Reclamation Act (SMCRA) to protect the environment from the adverse effects of surface mining. Generally SMCRA enables the Secretary of the Interior or authorized states to take measures to ensure that surface mining is conducted in an environmentally sound manner, to ensure that steps are promptly taken to reclaim areas where surface mining has taken place, and to prevent surface mining where reclamation is not feasible.

Under Section 1265 of the Act, all permitted surface coal mining and reclamation operations must be in compliance with environmental-protection performance standards, which specify the restoration and reclamation activities that must be conducted contemporaneously with production operations. Included among these measures are the requirements under Section 1265(10) to take special measures to minimize disturbances to the prevailing hydrologic balance of the mine site and surrounding areas and to minimize disturbances to the quality and quantity of surface and groundwater systems. Section 1265 (b)(10)(A) lists special design and operating requirements which must be observed by all permitted surface-mining operations in order to prevent toxic drainage liquids from entering groundwater.

Similarly, under Section 1258, in order to obtain a permit to conduct a surface-mining operation, the permit applicant must submit a reclamation plan which must include, among other things, a detailed description of measures that will be taken during the mining and reclamation process to protect groundwater.

Section 1237 gives the Secretary of the Interior the authority to enter upon land adversely affected by past coal-mining practices and do whatever is necessary to control or abate any adverse affects upon land or water resources.

Federal Insecticide, Fungicide and Rodenticide Act, 7 USC §136 *et seq.*, Pub. L. No. 92–516

The Federal Insecticide, Fungicide and Rodenticide Act (FIFRA) was enacted to provide for the establishment of procedures for the registration, classification, sale, use, research, monitoring, and disposal of pesticides. Because pesticides have been known to be the source of some groundwater contamination, it is appropriate to consider briefly some of the key provisions of FIFRA.

FIFRA gives EPA broad powers to regulate all pesticides. Under Section 3(a) no pesticide may be bought, sold, distributed, or otherwise handled if it is not registered. Pursuant to Section 3(c)(2)(A), EPA is required to make the stringency of standards which must be met in order to register a pesticide commensurate with the anticipated pattern of use and the degree of potential exposure of man and the environment to the pesticide.

One of the most significant features of FIFRA for groundwater protection is Section 3(d), which enables EPA, as part of the registration process, to classify pesticides for either general or restricted use. A pesticide classified for general use has been determined by EPA generally not to cause unreasonable adverse effects on the environment. For pesticides classified for restricted use, it has been determined that their use may cause unreasonable adverse effects on the environment without additional regulatory restrictions. Under Section 3(d) restricted-use pesticides may only be used or applied by a certified applicator, a person authorized by EPA to use or supervise the use of any pesticicde.

EPA has broad power under Section 6(b) to change the classification or to cancel the registration of a pesticide if it appears generally to cause unreasonable adverse effects on the environment. A hearing must be held before such action can be taken. Thus, in order to take immediate steps in the case of an emergency, Section 6(c) authorizes EPA to suspend the registration of a pesticide if necessary to prevent an imminent hazard during the time required for cancellation or change in classification.

National Environmental Policy Act of 1969, 42 USC § 4321 *et seq.*, Pub. L. No. 91–190

In any review of federal statutes affecting groundwater, it is appropriate to consider the National Environmental Policy Act of 1969 (NEPA), which could be used very effectively to prevent groundwater contamination. The basic goal of NEPA is to require the federal government to consider the environmental effects on any governmental legislation, regulation, or program. Section 102 of NEPA requires that as part of any recommendation or report on a proposal for legislation or any other major federal action significantly affecting the quality of the environment, the federal agency must prepare an environmental-impact statement assessing the environmental effect of the proposed action, the unavoidable environmental effects if the proposal were implemented, alternatives to the proposed action, the short-term uses of man's environment in comparison with the maintenance and enhancement of long-term productivity, and any irreversible and irretrievable commitments of resources which would be involved if the proposal were implemented. Thus NEPA enables major projects sponsored by or permitted by the various federal agencies to be evaluated and studied for their potential adverse effects on the environment, including groundwater.

Conclusion

It is clear from the brief summary of the federal environmental statutes given above that Congress has responded to various environmental concerns by enacting legislation to limit specific practices which threaten health and the environment. The desire to prevent contamination of groundwater appears to be only one of many enunciated environmental objectives in these statutes. Although there is no one single statute specifically aimed at protecting groundwater, there are more than a half dozen federal statutes which, in combination with each other, are directed at accomplishing that objective. Most significant among these are RCRA, SDWA, CWA, and CERCLA. A review of these and other environmental statutes discussed in this chapter indicates that there is a legal framework which can significantly aid in the implementation of a groundwater-protection strategy.

Thirteen

State and Local Measures for the Protection of Groundwater Quality

- At the state and local level there is a broad mixture of regulations that can protect groundwater from contamination.
- The diversity of regulations reflects the differences among the various regions in the types of contamination problems that have been experienced.
- There are three main types of controls in effect. These include specific source controls, for example those dealing with septic tanks; controls implementing quality standards for groundwater; controls which regulate land use.
- As pollution and depletion, quality and quantity may be intimately related in certain instances, a discussion is given of groundwater allocation law in various states.
- Summaries of State Groundwater Programs that are already in effect are given for selected states.

The unique characteristics of groundwater pollution have given rise to a body of state regulation which is quite different from that which governs surface water. Although in some instances the direct discharge of waste into ground—for example, through septic tanks or injection wells—can be monitored and quantitatively controlled in much the same way as surface-water pollution, much of the groundwater contamination is attributable to sources unrelated to waste disposal—spills and leaks, mine drainage, saltwater intrusion, water wells, oil and gas wells, surface-water infiltration, agricultural activities, highway deicing salts, and many others. Discharges from both of these categories of activity occur underground and out of sight and are so diffuse that they cannot ordinarily be reached by direct regulation, but only indirectly through restrictions on the activities that generate them. Moreover, because of the slowness with which water moves underground and its low rate of dispersion, the self-cleansing process characteristic of surface waters is not so evident in the case of groundwater. Protective regulation, therefore, aims primarily at prevention rather than cleanup.

State and local regulations to protect groundwater are varied. This diversity in part reflects the differences among regions in the problems of groundwater contamination that have been experienced. In part it may also reflect simply the historical differences in the adoption of controls by different legislative bodies. Finally, further differences have also developed in the manner in which different states have responded to federal programs calling for specific types of state actions. This review will not attempt to describe state and local requirements in any comprehensive way but will indicate the types of controls at the state and local level that are typical.

The states vary widely in the quantity and quality of their groundwater, their degree of dependence on it, and the nature of the sources and activities which pollute it. The tremendous variation in the characteristics of groundwater and the sources of its pollution may account for the diversity in state regulatory mechanisms and organizational structures. Despite the diversity, however, state regulations generally fall into three broad categories: those dealing with particular sources of pollution, such as septic systems and waste-disposal sites; those establishing and implementing water-quality standards for groundwater aquifers, the latter sometimes classified according to current or projected uses, and those which regulate the use of land in areas overlying critical aquifer-recharge zones. These three categories of regulations are discussed in the sections which follow.

Finally, in view of the close relation between pollution and depletion, the qualitative and quantitative side of groundwater conservation, a brief description of the applicable state-law rules governing the allocation of the right to withdraw groundwater is also included in this survey.

Specific Source Controls

As already noted, the characteristics of groundwater pollution generally necessitate regulatory efforts that focus on prevention of groundwater contamination through restrictions on the activities that generate it. Regulations applicable to specific sources of contamination typically require a discharger to obtain a permit from the state's environmental protection agency. Before receiving a permit, the applicant may be required to meet various design, construction, monitoring, and reporting specifications.

The controls that effectively protect groundwater often are not designed solely for that purpose. Even when a regulation is adopted with groundwater protection in mind, protection of surface water or prevention of other forms of environmental damage may be of equal or greater importance. Regulations governing solid-waste disposal, for example, typically have provisions specifically concerned with groundwater, but their broader purpose is the overall prevention of health hazards. For still other contamination sources, such as the land spreading of pollutants, few regulations have been adopted. State regulatory programs for the control of particular sources of groundwater contamination will be discussed in this section.

Sources of Groundwater Contamination Related to Waste Disposal

Waste-Management Sites. Although the federal government now regulates waste-disposal sites under the Resource Conservation and Recovery Act (RCRA), regulation at the state level will normally provide the controlling requirements. Many states are adopting programs that will meet federal criteria and thereby replace the federal regulation. In addition, many states have also established controls at their own initiative. As called for by the federal requirements under RCRA, a typical state's regulations prohibit the disposal of wastes without a permit and require the permit applicant to submit detailed design specifications and information on the geological characteristics of the site and to agree to meet operation, reporting, and monitoring requirements. Regulations may also restrict the types of waste that may be disposed of at specified classes of sites and may prohibit the disposal, without agency approval, of wastes defined as hazardous.

Regulations affecting solid-waste disposal, animal feedlots, and deep-well disposal often contain provisions for storage, as distinct from disposal. Many states, however, do not have special regulations governing the storage of wastes, relying merely on general statutory provisions relating to water pollution. A state environmental protection agency may, therefore, find itself unable to prohibit or control the operation of surface impoundments unless an effect on water quality from storage activities can be demonstrated. Several states have expanded their authority in order to regulate storage areas more effectively. Florida, for example, requires a permit for the construction of all waste-management facilities, including surface impoundments (U.S. EPA, 1977). The Pennsylvania water-quality statute allows regulation of impoundment and storage where necessary to avoid contamination. States have used their authority to establish regulations for location, construction, operation, and maintenance of storage facilities. With the stimulus of federal funding and federal controls under RCRA, the development of such regulations is now under active consideration in nearly all states where comprehensive control over waste-management sites is not already in effect.

Well Disposal of Wastes. The subsurface disposal of industrial and municipal wastes by means of deep injection wells is regulated by about half the states (Lehr et al., 1976). Some states specifically prohibit the practice, and certain others allow it only if no other waste-disposal method is available. The latter typically require permits for construction and operation, including specifications for pre-testing, monitoring, reporting, and financial responsibility.

In contrast to the strict regulatory treatment of deep wells is the relative inattention that has been given to the widespread use of shallow wells to discharge a variety of non-toxic liquid wastes, such as stormwater sewage and industrial effluent, into freshwater aquifiers. This practice has been regulated minimally, if at all, and indeed is even encouraged by some state agencies.

Septic-Tank Systems. Septic tanks are the most frequently reported source of groundwater contamination and are regulated by all states. The chief purpose of this regulation is to protect the health of the septic tank user and of his neighbors. Landowners are typically required to obtain a permit before installing a system and, as a precondition, they must furnish soil reports, detailed plans of the system design, and equipment specifications. In addition, some states restrict the density of septic systems in a given area so that attenuation and dilution processes can operate effectively. The administration of septic-tank regulations is handled primarily through local health departments.

Land Spreading of Pollutants. Although the spraying of treated sewage wastes on agricultural land for irrigation is a widespread practice that poses potential risks of groundwater pollution, it is specifically regulated by only a few states. Pennsylvania's Spray Irrigation Manual contains comprehensive regulations, fixes guidelines for locating and evaluating sites, and sets standards for treatment, storage, screening controls, piping, sprinklers, spacing, and application rate (Pennsylvania Department of Environmental Resources, 1972). Maryland issues permits for spray irrigation as part of its program to enforce water-quality standards (Lehr et al., 1976), and New York requires that the design specifications for the spraying system be submitted for approval (Lehr et al., 1976).

The land spreading of municipal and industrial sludge is regulated in approximately 20 states. Some states, such as Minnesota and Oregon, have separate regulations for the problem of municipal sludge, while others deal with it as part of the general regulation of municipal waste-treatment plants. Colorado's criteria for the review of wastewater facilities, for example, require that submitted plans include a description of the process for stabilizing sludge (Colorado Department of Health, 1973). Illinois's waste-treatment regulations require that a permit be obtained from the Division of Land Pollution to dispose of non-liquid sludges or from the Division of

Water Pollution Control to dispose of liquid sludges (Illinois Environmental Protection Agency, 1971).

To regulate industrial sludges, most states rely on the general provisions of statutes governing water pollution. Under such statutes, effective enforcement is hampered by the fact that the state has the burden of showing that sludge disposal has actually resulted in pollution. A few states, including New York, have avoided the burden-of-proof problem by invoking instead their laws governing solid-waste or hazardous-waste disposal as a basis for the regulation of the land spreading of pollutants (U.S. EPA, 1977).

Animal Feedlots. Since animal feedlots are considered point sources under section 502(14) of the Water Pollution Control Act, they are subject to the requirements of the NPDES permit program. These requirements are directed chiefly at surface-water protection, but may also provide protection against groundwater contamination. In addition, some states have adopted regulations for feedlots in which the ratio of animals to land area is deemed high enough to threaten groundwater quality. The regulations generally demand that water be diverted above the lot and that a settling pond and lagoon be provided below it. To obtain a state permit, operators may be required to submit information concerning building and lot areas, lagoons, and direction of surface drainage. Some of the more detailed rules contain specifications for the operation of facilities and for the storage and disposal of wastes.

Sources of Groundwater Contamination Not Related to Waste Disposal

Aside from waste-disposal practices, a wide variety of other activities may contribute to the deterioration of groundwater quality. For the most part, the impact of these activities had not been systematically studied nor extensively regulated. The most significant efforts at control, such as they are, are the following:

The Construction and Operation of Wells. Recognizing that water wells, if poorly designed or constructed, can be wasteful of groundwater and, worse, a conduit for polluting groundwaters, many states have undertaken to regulate the installation and abandonment of such wells. These regulations, varying in detail from state to state, contain requirements for location, design, construction, drilling equipment, pumps, water testing, and record keeping. With more than 500,000 new water wells drilled each year, enforcement of construction standards is no easy task, but the licensing of drilling contractors appears to have been somewhat effective in improving well-construction practices.

Many states also impose controls on the drilling of oil and gas wells. Although primarily designed to promote the orderly development of the oil resource and to prevent its waste, many of the provisions for well construction and abandonment also serve to prevent groundwater pollution. Almost all states require the installation of surface casing to protect aquifers and the filing of a performance bond to insure compliance. The regulations may also contain specifications for drilling, cementing, waste disposal, reporting, fluid injection, abandonment, and plugging.

Mine Drainage. Mining operations, prevalent in the Northeast, Northwest, and Southwest, often create groundwater contamination through drainage of mineralized and acidic solutions. Several states regulate these activities, some for the express purpose, among others, of protecting groundwater quality. Both Illinois and Pennsylvania require permits for all mining operations (U.S. EPA, 1977). Applicants must describe the proposed method of mining and the disposal of refuse and must meet the requirements for plugging holes, monitoring, and reporting.

Saltwater Intrusion. Intrusion of salt water into fresh-water aquifers is a serious contamination problem both in coastal and inland areas. Large-scale pollution has occurred in the coastal northeastern states, California, and Florida. Several northeastern states have reduced coastal salt-water intrusion by imposing strict controls on pumpage, so as to prevent excessive depletion. California, moreover, has been successful in reversing the flow of salt water by means of "barriers," wells paralleling the shoreline which inject fresh water into previously depleted aquifers.

A problem that has received less attention than coastal saltwater intrusion is the contamination of fresh-groundwater aquifers in inland areas by salt-water from hydrologically connected saline aquifers. This condition has been studied but little and regulated scarcely at all.

Spills and Leaks. Although contaminants from accidental spills of liquid wastes, toxic fluids, and gasoline often travel through the soil into groundwater aquifers, many state programs designed to handle spills do not take their impact on groundwater into account. In some cases, for example, liquids spilled on highways have simply been transferred to nearby soils, causing contamination through seepage into shallow aquifers.

In addition to the applicable federal programs, some states have adopted spill regulations that attempt, among other things, to protect groundwater quality. In Pennsylvania, for example, anyone responsible for a spill must immediately notify the Department of Environmental Resources (U.S. EPA, 1977). A geologist from the Groundwater Section will survey the scene of the spill and suggest procedures for its removal that will be the least detrimental to groundwater quality.

Highway Deicing-Salts. Soluble salts used for road maintenance may, through highway runoff or seepage from salt storage piles, raise the chloride and sodium concentrations of groundwater aquifers. Although no adequate substitute for deicing salts has been found, some states, aware of this danger, have begun to reduce the quantities of salt spread or to enclose salt storage piles to avoid dispersal through precipitation.

Standards and Classification Systems for Groundwater

While every state has adopted at least some regulations for the control of the sources of groundwater contamination, only 25–30% of the states have, thus far, adopted groundwater-quality standards (see Chapter 11). The trend in many states, however, is toward the adoption of such standards (United States Water Resources Council, 1981).

Groundwater-quality standards generally specify a maximum numerical level of concentration for each of several pollutants. New York has established such levels for no fewer than 83 contaminants. In contrast, some states have numerical standards for only a few contaminants, while still others rely on purely descriptive standards. Many states borrow their standards, in whole or in part, from the interim maximum-contaminant levels established by the Environmental Protection Agency (EPA) for various drinking-water pollutants under the Safe Drinking Water Act. Such standards are available, however, for only a few of the contaminants now found in groundwater. In addition to adopting groundwater-quality standards, many states divide aquifers into categories based upon their current or projected uses, as does Connecticut, for example; (see Chapter 11). At least two states, Maine and New Hampshire, however, aim to make all aquifers suitable for drinking water.

Many states which have developed groundwater standards use permit systems to implement them. Some issue permits for groundwater discharge as part of their general National Pollution Discharge Elimination System (NPDES) program, while other maintain a separate permit program for groundwater. These permit requirements, however, generally apply only to the deep-well injection of wastes and other selected discrete sources of pollution. They do not apply to the full range of activities that may cause groundwater contamination. Thus, there is no comprehensive mechanism for applying the groundwater-quality standards.

In those cases where permits are required, they often contain effluent limitations which translate the general requirements of water-quality standards into specific limits for each discharger by describing the amount of pollutants that can be released legally by a particular source. Effluent limitations may be based on the availability of technology to control pollution, as in Connecticut, or they may be based on a level of water quality that is to be achieved consistent with an aquifer's use, as in New York. At least one state, New York, has established uniform effluent limitations for all aquifers. The typical approach, however, is to establish effluent limitations on a case-by-case basis depending on the geohydrologic characteristics of the receiving aquifer.

Some states do not establish effluent limitations for all dischargers, but instead require each polluter to submit a plan specifying how its discharge will be consistent with the state's groundwater-quality standards. In New

Mexico, for example, a discharge plan must describe "the methods or techniques the discharger proposes to use or processes expected to naturally occur which will ensure compliance with these regulations" (New Mexico Health and Environment Department, 1982). A plan might contain design and construction specifications or it might establish effluent limitations designed to meet the water-quality standards.

Rather than allow aquifers of above-standard quality to deteriorate to the level of the standards, some states, for example, Connecticut, New Jersey, and New York, have adopted a non-degradation policy similar to that established for surface waters, which requires, in theory at least, that high-quality aquifers be maintained in that condition. In view of the difficulty of reversing groundwater contamination, the unique problems of monitoring, the lack of knowlege concerning the safety thresholds of various contaminants, and the extraordinary importance of groundwater to human life and health, the nondegradation principle has even greater theoretical appeal here than in the case of surface waters. In practice, however, few states, including those that pay statutory lip service to nondegradation, seem actually to have enforced such a policy; most appear to allow deterioration to the level of the standards (Hines, 1977).

Land-Use Regulations

In recognition of the fact that intensive land development is often a serious threat to groundwater quality, state and local governments have adopted a variety of measures in certain localities to prevent land uses that might contaminate critical recharge zones. The most common method, typically employed at the local level, is zoning—the division of land into districts in which specified uses are permitted, subject to certain conditions. Initially enacted largely for the purpose of preserving property values, zoning regulations today clearly have broader aims, including environmental protection (Grad, 1981), and have been widely upheld by the courts as a means of preserving ecological values and drinking-water quality. Zoning techniques for the protection of groundwater include the regulation of minimum lot size to prevent intensive residential or commercial development over recharge areas, bans on the location of facilities for the disposal of solid waste and on waste lagoons in areas where groundwater pollution is likely, and restrictions on the density of septic systems in a given area. Even conventional urban zoning, though not primarily designed to protect groundwater, may have that effect by limiting the density of residential development or by channeling industrial activities into specified areas.

Almost all of the earliest land-use regulations were enacted by local governments. States soon began to realize, however, that environmental problems often cannot be addressed within a narrowly defined jurisdiction and that land-use regulation must extend beyond parochial local concerns. State governments, therefore, have imposed a variety of land-use controls. One such regulation is the designation of areas as environmentally critical. A critical area has been defined as "an area which contains or affects state or regional environmental, historical or archaeological resources; or an area which affects or is affected by a proposed public facility or an area of major development potential" (Florida Statutes Annotated § 380.012 et seq.). A prime example of such a regulation is New Jersey's designation of the Central Pine Barrens as a critical area for sewage purposes and its prescription of stringent groundwater-quality standards to protect aquifers in that area (New Jersey Administrative Code § 7:9–10, 1978). Critical-area regulation has proven politically palatable to local governments because it affects only a small geographic region of a state. While the state's authority is dominant in a critical area, municipalities outside of the area remain free to apply their own zoning and planning mechanisms.

Land-use controls, it has been argued, are an essential mode of groundwater protection (Tripp and Jaffe, 1979). Discharges from non-point sources, for reasons noted earlier, are not susceptible to technological controls. The procedures that have been devised to minimize the escape of wastes have proven inadequate. Preventive measures such as land-use regulations, moreover, are less costly and more effective than efforts at remedial cleanup, particularly since the irreversibility of groundwater pollution makes cleanup virtually impossible. Land-use controls have, however, not yet been applied in any state except in reference to special, localized situations.

Groundwater-Allocation Law

Pollution and depletion, quality and quantity, are intimately related problems where groundwater is concerned. Depletion often brings pollution in train, permitting invasion of the aquifer by salt water or other contaminating substances. Moreover, depletion-control measures may have adverse effects on the quality of groundwater while, conversely, pollution-abatement efforts may sometimes exacerbate the depletion problem. Thus, no survey of state groundwater-management regulation is complete without at least a brief description of the rules governing the quantitative allocation of groundwater supplies.

In the United States, groundwater allocation is governed by two fundamentally distinct bodies by law. In the 31 states that comprise the eastern half of the country—from the Atlantic seaboard to the tier of states extending from Minnesota to Louisiana—the right to withdraw groundwater depends on judicially developed and generally permissive rules of tort liability based originally on the English Common Law. In Alaska and the 17 contiguous western states stretching from the North Dakota to Texas tier to the Pacific Ocean, in most of which chronic water scarcity is the prevailing condition, groundwater use is controlled instead by statutes and aministrative regulations and is based on the principle of prior appropriation. A brief description of these two approaches will suffice for our purposes.

Common Law Approaches

From the middle of the nineteenth century until early in the twentieth, nearly all American states adhered to the English Common Law rule of absolute ownership. A landowner was entitled to withdraw unlimited amounts of groundwater from his land, however much this might deplete his neighbor's supply, provided only, in some states, that he was not acting for the very purpose of hurting his neighbor. This rule assumed an abundance of groundwater and encourged its liberal and unregulated use, perhaps in the view that each landowner was the best judge of his own needs, that any resultant injury to others would be of short duration, and that temporary inefficiencies could be avoided through bargaining. In the course of this century, however, most states have abandoned the all-permissive English rule in favor of what has come to be known as the American rule of reasonable use, under which a landowner is subject to liability for injury inflicted through "unreasonable" withdrawal of groundwater. This restriction, however, is less significant than it sounds, since, under the American rule a withdrawal is deemed reasonable so long as the water is used for the benefit of the land overlying the aquifer and not some other land to which it must be transported.

Some courts, deviating from the American rule, have elaborated the notion of "reasonable use" in what they believe to be a fairer or more socially efficient way. One such variation is the correlative-rights rule, applied by the California courts to percolating groundwater, though not to other kinds, such as definite underground streams or surface-river underflows. Under this rule, a landowner is not entitled to the beneficial use of all the groundwater underlying his property, but only to a fair share reflecting the proportionate size of his holding relative to the total land area overlying the aquifer.

A more substantial departure from the American rule is the open-ended balancing approach embodied in Section 858 of the American Law Institute's Restatement (Second) of Torts and adopted, to date, by one state, Wisconsin. Like the American rule itself, Section 858 would impose liability only for withdrawal of groundwater which "unreasonably causes harm" to a neighboring owner. Reasonableness, however, would be determined more flexibly, by weighing, in all the circumstances of each particular case, the competing interests of the affected private parties and of the public.

The Prior Appropriation System

Under the doctrine of prior appropriation, which governs the use of surface and most groundwaters in the 17 contiguous western states and Alaska, all natural waters belong to the public or to the state, not to the owners of adjacent or overlying land. Private individuals may acquire the right to appropriate public waters for beneficial uses, including distant ones, but this usufructory right has nothing to do with land ownership. Priorities among competing users of the same source of supply are ordered, initially at least, on the basis of seniority of appropriation, according to the principle of "first in time, first in right." This doctrine originated in the customary practices of the California mining camps during the Gold Rush, rapidly spread to the other western states, and by the end of the century had been recognized by statute in nearly all of them. At first, water claims, analogous to mining claims themselves, were established by the simple method of posting notice at the point of diversion and filing that notice in the county record office. By the turn of the century, however, the vast expansion of western agriculture and the consequent need for enormous quantities of water for irrigation made clear the need for a more orderly and efficient system of acquiring and recording water rights. Hence, nearly all the western states established by statute administrative-permit systems for the appropriation of both surface and groundwater. The permit is issued if, and only if, the administrators, upon investigation, are satisfied that the proposed source of supply contains unappropriated water and that the issuance of the permit will neither infringe on existing water rights nor be contrary to the public interest, for example, because the water could be put to some socially superior use. The permit, when issued, specifies the place and purpose of the proposed use, the quantity of water to be withdrawn, the point of diversion, and the facilities to be constructed. Upon completion of the diversion facilities and the commencement of withdrawal, the appropriator receives a second document—sometimes called a licence, more often a certificate—describing in more definitive terms the water rights that have been acquired and detailing the actual circumstances of use and diversion. Neither the permit nor the certificate, however, assures the appropriator that there will in fact be enough water to meet his quota. If the state administrators have overestimated the capacity of the supply source, or in the event of a drought, the available water supply may be insufficient to fill all of the authorized allotments, in which case the junior users must cease to withdraw water until the senior users have fully met their needs.

In most of the western states, the rights of the senior appropriator yield to those of the junior appropriator when the latter has a socially preferred use for the water. The typical statute gives preference to domestic and municipal use, followed by agricultural and then by manufacturing or industrial uses. In light of these statutory preferences, a permit may be denied to a senior applicant in favor of a junior applicant who proposes a higher-ranking use, and even an appropriation already authorized and of long standing may be subordinated to a new appropriation for a higher-ranking use.

Monitoring and Enforcement Programs

Ineffective enforcement appears to be a much more pervasive feature of groundwater regulation than of surface-water regulation. Officials in state agencies regularly complain that monitoring and enforcement programs are understaffed and underfunded (Dawson, 1979).

Part of the problem is that sampling and monitoring of groundwater is a particularly expensive enterprise. Test wells and casings are costly, and because of the absence of mixing in an aquifer, the number of samples needed for an accurate picture of groundwater quality in an area may be quite large. Once samples are obtained, moreover, an assessment of their quality requires repeated measurement by sophisticated and expensive instrumentation (CEQ, 1980). Failing this, state regulators often find themselves without a sufficient data base to prescribe or enforce groundwater standards.

Another obstacle to the effective implementation of groundwater programs is the inadequacy of presently available testing techniques (CEQ, 1980). Several classes of compounds are difficult even to isolate or detect, let alone measure in quantitative terms. Testing techniques are often complex, time-consuming, sensitive to interference from other compounds, and variable in result. Ineffective testing makes it difficult to establish the background quality of aquifers and therefore to assign a responsibility for contamination.

Lack of both staffing and funds may also account for the weakness of enforcement programs. Some regulations are enforced minimally, others not at all (Dawson, 1979). Most violations are handled informally at the agency level, with only light sanctions imposed. Rarely are administrative decisions taken to court.

State Groundwater Protection Programs: Summaries for Selected States

This section will present a detailed description of the groundwater regulatory programs now in effect in selected states. The states chosen have programs which are comprehensive, progressive, or unique in some way. The efforts taken by these states to protect groundwater resources more effectively may serve as a guide for other states that are interested in making improvements in their existing programs.

Arizona

Arizona has recently passed major regulations for groundwater conservation. Its 1980 Groundwater Management Act established four active management areas in which groundwater uses are restricted in order to prevent aquifer overdraft. Within these areas, the law imposes strict controls, requires conservation plans, pumping fees, water-measuring devices, mandatory conservation for farmers, and the adoption of the latest conservation techniques by industries. The law also calls for statewide registration of all water wells and requires the filing of pumpage reports. The Director of a new Department of Water Resources has the power to set limits on per-capita consumption (Wickersham and Canter, 1980).

While this Act is one of the nation's most far-reaching pieces of legislation designed to protect groundwater quantity, the state's efforts to protect groundwater quality have somewhat lagged. Until recently, Arizona exercised little control over important sources of groundwater contamination, such as agricultural and mining activities. The state's water-quality protection efforts are, however, undergoing a period of transition. The Quality Control Council in the State Department of Health Services, which is responsible for planning and policy-making, is in the process of correcting many of the deficiencies in existing programs. Like many other states, Arizona is moving towards the adoption of groundwater-quality standards.

The Bureau has established a Draft Framework for Groundwater Quality Protection, to be implemented beginning in 1983. The draft declares broad water-quality objectives—protection of public health, the preservation of existing and projected water uses, and the promotion of economic welfare—and contains proposed groundwater standards expressed in descriptive rather than numeric terms because of the practical limits of applying specific numbers to varying geohydrologic conditions and the inadequacies of existing data.

Rather than adopt uniform standards statewide, the Bureau, in its draft proposal, has opted to develop discharge limitation on a case-by-case basis. All facilities which discharge waste will be required to submit a discharge plan as a condition of obtaining a permit. The plan must explain how the facility's operation will comply with the goals and standards of the Water Quality Control Council, describe the disposal system, and assess the probable effect of the discharge on the quality of ground- and surface water in the discharge-impact area. In addition, permit recipients must monitor their discharge and submit reports, and official monitoring is also conducted to the extent necessary to verify the accuracy of the submissions (Arizona Division of Health Services, 1982).

It is the general policy of Arizona to prevent all hazardous wastes from entering groundwater aquifers. In order to implement this policy, the Department of Health Services has adopted a special permit program for the disposal of solid and hazardous wastes (U.S. Water Resources Council, 1981b). New solid-waste facilities must meet the requirements of the federal Resource Conservation and Recovery Act. The Bureau of Water Quality Control is also in the process of developing programs to control contamination associated with surface mining and to designate sole-source aquifers under the Safe Drinking Water Act.

California

In California, groundwater varies in quality, quantity, and sources of contamination. In order to manage its diverse resource more effectively, California has divided authority for groundwater-quality control among a State Water Resources Control Board and nine semi-autonomous regional boards. The State Board is responsible for developing statewide policy, including the promulgation of water-quality objectives. It also has the specific authority over groundwater contamination associated with deep-well injection of wastes and from landfill activities. Regional boards are responsible for setting standards and effluent limitations, developing a plan to control water quality, and specifying waste-discharge requirements. The content and level of detail of each regional plan for water-quality control vary. The San Diego Region, with numerous small-volume aquifers, has detailed quality objectives, while the Lahontan region, which stretches from Lake Tahoe to Riverside County, has a much less comprehensive plan (U.S. Water Resources Council, 1981b).

California's policy is that all groundwater suitable for drinking shall be maintained for that use. The Department of Health Services has adopted health-based numerical water-quality standards to protect aquifers used for drinking water. If a drinking-water standard is violated by a waste-disposal practice, the practice must be either modified or discontinued (U.S. EPA, 1980b).

The state has also developed a unique program to regulate treatment, storage, and disposal of solid and hazardous wastes. A three-tiered classification system has been developed for sites, based on the degree of protection from waste disposal they can provide to groundwaters. Wastes are also classified into three groups according to their degree of harmfulness to human health. Group 1 toxic wastes may only be disposed of in the most protective Class I sites, while inert Group 3 wastes may be placed in any site (23 California Administrative Code 2510–2533, 1977).

Groundwater quantity, like groundwater quality, is managed mainly at the regional, rather than the state level. Three counties in Southern California have adopted ordinances regulating the use and export of groundwater. In many overdrawn areas, however, no comprehensive groundwater management has been undertaken. Poor management of groundwater quantity has caused groundwater-quality problems, such as saline intrusion into fresh-water aquifers (U.S. EPA, 1980c).

Connecticut

In Connecticut aquifers are being classified on the basis of a nondegradation policy which, according to the 1980 regulations, means that groundwater classified in Class GA or Class GAA is to be maintained at, or restored to, a quality consistent with its use for drinking without treatment (see Chapter 11). The state's Department of Environmental Protection (DEP) has adopted a four-fold system of classification. The Connecticut Department of Health has promulgated drinking-water standards pursuant to the federal Safe Drinking Water Act.

The state's groundwater-protection policy is implemented through a system of permits. Certain dischargers into groundwaters must submit a discharge plan, which must be approved before a permit may be issued. The permit contains technology-based effluent standards and also specifies a level of quality that the effluent must meet. Certain industrial wastes are not permitted to be discharged into the groundwater. Permits are also required for certain potential sources of groundwater contamination. For example, operators of disposal sites for solid and hazardous waste may be required to obtain three permits before constructing their disposal sites, one from the Solid Waste Unit, which must meet the requirements of the federal Resource Conservation and Recovery Act, another from the Water Compliance Unit, and a third from the Hazardous Waste Unit.

In addition to regulating particular sources of groundwater contamination, Connecticut has utilized land-use controls to protect aquifers. Legislation enacted in 1980 authorizes local governments to use their zoning powers to protect aquifers. A statewide plan for water-quality management has been approved under §208 of the Clean Water Act. The plan contains a model ordinance which local governments may use when establishing zoning regulations to protect critical aquifer-recharge zones.

To obtain a permit, a discharger must agree to conduct self-monitoring and to file monthly reports containing groundwater-quality data. In addition, DEP conducts a limited degree of independent surveillance.

When a violation is detected, DEP may issue a cease and desist order and, in the event of non-compliance, turn the matter over to the Attorney General for criminal prosecution. Heavy fines are imposed for failure to submit monitoring reports. Exemptions and variances are negotiated on a case-by-case basis.

Florida

In Florida, groundwater is a high-quality, inexpensive, and readily available source of water. It is also a critically vital resource, since over 91% of Florida's population depends on groundwater for drinking purposes. For this reason, the Groundwater Section of the Department of Environmental Regulation has adopted a wide range of programs to protect groundwater quality.

DER has developed a groundwater-classification system and groundwater standards similar to those of the states discussed previously. The classification system and standards, however, are in the process of being revised (see Chapter 11). The proposals would establish a three-tiered classification system instead of the two-tiered system now being used, and develop maximum contaminant levels for a broader range of pollutants (Florida Department of Environmental Regulation, 1982a).

All dischargers into the groundwaters of the state must obtain a permit containing effluent limitations designed to meet the groundwater-quality standards. In addition to technology-based effluent limitations, the permits may also specify limitations based on water quality to assure that the water-quality criteria are met. All operators of waste-disposal facilities must obtain construction permits in addition to discharge permits.

As part of its effort to control deep-well disposal of wastes, Florida has assumed the primary enforcement responsibility for an Underground Injection Control Program, administered under the Safe Drinking Water Act, is conducting a statewide drainage-well inventory, and is completing a study which locates, defines, and maps underground sources of drinking water in Florida. The state has also developed a unique program for the control of mining operations, a significant contributor to groundwater pollution. In an attempt to prevent phosphate mining in the Osceola National Forest, a sensitive recharge area, Florida's Environmental Regulation Commission has declared several bodies of water in the forest Outstanding Florida Waters. This effectively limits mining operations and protects groundwater in the area, since no pollutants can be discharged into the designated waters (Florida Department of Environment Regulation, 1982b).

Florida is one of the several states to have adopted special land-use regulations to protect high-quality aquifers. Local governments have been authorized to use their zoning powers to restrict activities over aquifer-recharge zones. The Dade County Commission has enacted a zoning ordinance to protect the Biscayne Aquifer, a largerly undeveloped area containing high-quality groundwater. The area was designated a sole-source aquifer under the Safe Drinking Water Act and rezoned for five-acre lots. The ordinance was upheld over legal challenges claiming that the rezoning bore no relation to legitimate county concerns (Tripp and Jaffe, 1979).

Because of its severe problems of saline intrusion, Florida has taken steps toward the comprehensive management of groundwater withdrawal. In 1972 the state enacted omnibus legislation, the Water Resources Act, which authorizes unified administraton and planning of water resources. Five regional water-management districts issue permits for groundwater withdrawals and are responsible for preparing water-shortage plans (U.S. Water Resources Council, 1981a).

New Jersey

Groundwater quality varies tremendously in New Jersey, with groundwater pollution problems coming from a variety of sources. New Jersey, like New York, has established a groundwater-classification system (see Chapter 11) and groundwater standards through its Department of Environmental Protection (DEP), although the list of contaminants for which maximum levels has been established, 18 toxic substances and 19 other organic and inorganic substances, is much less exhaustive (New Jersey Administrative Code §§7:9–4, 14, 1978).

New Jersey is unique in that it has established special highly protective groundwater standards for one particular region of the state, the Central Pine Barrens, a largely undeveloped region containing large amounts of high-quality water especially susceptible to contamination from development. The groundwaters in the Central Pine Barrens have an important impact on the quality and quantity of surface waters. In 1978 DEP developed two sets of regulations to protect the Central Pine Barrens. The first established water-quality standards for seven parameters that represent existing background conditions. The other set of regulations designates the Central Pine Barrens as a critical area for sewage systems. In addition, the state has established a non-degradation policy for the Central Pine Barrens, meaning that all aquifers must be maintained at their existing quality (New Jersey Administrative Code §7:9–14a(2), 1978).

The stringency of the standards promulgated for the Central Pine Barrens, particularly the nitrates standards, have rendered heavy industrial development and intensive land-use virtually impossible (E. Rashak, Senior Geologist, New Jersey Department of Environmental Protection, personal communication). Several discharges have challenged these standards on federal constitutional grounds, but DEP has prevailed in all litigation to date.

In addition to establishing groundwater classifications and standards, New Jersey has enacted several pieces of legislation to control particular sources of groundwater pollution, the most notable of which is the Solid Waste Management Act (13 New Jersey Statutes Annotated §§1 E–1 to 48, 1978). Enacted in 1978, the Act serves as a statutory framework within which all solid-waste collection can be coordinated. The Act directs DEP to adopt criteria for evaluating the suitability of particular sites for solid-waste facilities that will dispose of hazardous waste.

New Jersey, like New York, enforces its groundwater criteria through a system of permits administered under the New Jersey Pollution Discharge Elimination System (NJPDES). These permits contain non-uniform effluent limitations based on hydrologic factors, such as current flow and size of aquifer, and, in addition, they establish a maximum number of gallons that can be discharged per day.

The NJPDES regulations also establish procedures for monitoring and enforcement. In addition to the self-monitoring reports which must be filed every quarter, DEP sets up monitoring wells for independent surveillance. This program is financed in part by fees assessed upon dischargers. Permit violations are handled informally in the first instance, with unresolved disputes being heard by an Administrative Law Judge. The usual penalty is a fine.

New Mexico

New Mexico's Water Quality Control Commission has adopted quality standards designed to protect groundwater with a total concentration of dissolved solids of 10,000 mg/l or less for domestic and agricultural purposes (see Chapter 11). Groundwater-quality standards, which consist of a pH range and maximum contaminant levels for various organic and inorganic pollutants, are established for three separate categories—human health, domestic water supply, and irrigation (New Mexico Health and Environment Department, 1982).

New Mexico's statute, unlike New York's and Virginia's, does not contain a "non-degradation" provision; contamination is permitted within the limits set by the water-quality standards. Any pollutant concentration that exceeds the standards as a result of human activities must, insofar as is feasible, be reduced; if the excess is due instead to the naturally poor quality of the groundwater, no such reduction is required. In either case, the existing concentration level becomes the operative ceiling, and no further dischargers into the substandard aquifers are permitted.

New Mexico is unique in that it requires all dischargers of pollutants to submit to the Water Pollution Control Bureau of the Environmental Improvement Division a discharge plan, which substitutes for the permit procedures used in other states (D. Boyer, New Mexico Water Pollution Control Bureau, personal communication). The plan must demonstrate that the discharges will not cause groundwater contamination to exceed the specified standards, by stating the location of the discharge, an estimate of the concentration of water contaminants in the discharge, and the quantity of the discharge. In addition, the plan must contain a detailed description of the technological controls the discharger will use to insure compliance with the regulations. Once a discharge plan is approved, its specifications become binding commitments on the discharger and can be enforced by the agency. The discharge plan generally does not contain effluent limitations, the state having determined that the large number of hydrologic and geologic variables makes limitations impractical, at least on a uniform basis. Operators of solid-waste-disposal sites are exempt from the discharge-plan requirement. They must instead obtain a permit from the Solid Waste Section of the Environmental Improvement Division (New Mexico Health and Environment Department, 1982).

The New Mexico regulations establish procedures for obtaining modifications and variances in permits. A modification will be issued upon a showing that the discharger cannot meet the requirements of the permit, but that the requirements, in turn, are more stringent than is necessary to satisfy the water-quality standards. A variance, on the other hand, may also be issued to a discharger who is unable to meet the water-quality standards if he demonstrates to the Commission at a public hearing that it is economically or technologically infeasible to achieve the standard or that the cost of doing so far exceeds the benefits. The Commission has been reluctant to grant variances if other alternatives, such as extentions of time for compliance, are available, and it will not grant variances under any circumstances for pollutants that are dangerous to human health. These extensions are generally granted for six months, with a possibility for further extensions depending upon whether the discharger has been cooperative in its compliance efforts (D. Boyer, New Mexico Water Pollution Control Bureau, personal communication).

Monitoring requirements, such as frequency and points of measurement, are established case-by-case. The New Mexico regulations call for both self-monitoring and monitoring by the Water Pollution Control Bureau. Lack of adequate monitoring is viewed by the agency as the major flaw in its pollution-control program (M. Goad, New Mexico Water Pollution Control Bureau, personal communication). Monitoring efforts have, for the most part, been limited by cost and personnel constraints. For this reason, the Water Pollution Control Bureau sought and obtained increased funding for monitoring programs in 1981 from the state legislature.

New York

Of the states which have established groundwater-classification systems and groundwater standards, New York has one of the most comprehensive. Its Department of Environmental Conservation (DEC) has established a classification system that divides groundwater into three classes (see Chapter 11). For the highest-quality water, numerical standards, some of them derived from similar guidelines under the federal Safe Drinking Water Act, have been established for 83 organic and inorganic substances. Although the other two classifications do not have numerical standards, the regulations prohibit discharges which impair their best usage or which are "deleterious, harmful, detrimental or injurious to the public health, safety or welfare" (6 New York Codes, Rules and Regulations §§703.5, 1978).

In addition, New York is unique in that its DEC has developed uniform effluent limitations paralleling the water-quality standards. These limitations generally permit pollutant concentrations twice as great as those tolerated by the water-quality standards, apparently on the assumption that a 50% dilution will occur by the time the effluent reaches the aquifer. These effluent limitations are incorporated into permits for discharges to groundwater, issued as part of the State Pollutant Discharge Elimination system administered by DEC.

New York, like several other states, has incorporated a non-degradation policy into its water-quality statute. It is unclear, however, what practical purpose this policy serves. DEC has not required that waters of higher quality than contemplated by the water-quality standards be maintained at that higher level; it allows for degradation to the limits of the standards. Water that is of poorer quality than the standards permit cannot be further degraded and may be ordered restored to the level of the standards in cases where cleanup is feasible, but that would be required even without the non-degradation policy (M. Goroski, New York Department of Environmental Conservation, personal communication).

In some parts of New York, local governments have taken even further steps to protect groundwater quality. Nassau and Suffolk Counties, where groundwater pollution is particularly troublesome, received an EPA grant to prepare an areawide management plan for water quality under §208 of the Clean Water Act (Tripp and Jaffe, 1979). The two counties are divided into eight management zones. The plan provides for strict land-use controls for zones that may be over prime recharge areas and for zoning which specifies minimum lot size. Furthermore, Long Island has been designated a sole-source aquifer under the Safe Drinking Water Act, which means that projects with a potential for causing significant deterioration in groundwater quality could be denied federal assistance.

All monitoring and enforcement in the state is handled as part of the State Pollution Discharge Elimination System (SPDES) program. This program adheres to the provisions for self-monitoring, reporting, and hearings contained in the federal National Pollution Discharge Elimination System (NPDES) regulations. In addition, some independent surveillance and inspection is conducted. DEC, through its nine regional offices, and the Department of Health share the responsibility for administrating the program. In Region I, which includes Long Island, the locus of much of the state's groundwater contamination, the health departments of Nassau and Suffolk (U.S. EPA, 1980c) counties conduct monitoring and enforcement programs. Because of the severe pollution problems on Long Island, the monitoring efforts undertaken by these two counties have been extensive. In 1976 both counties began to analyze water from all the wells used for community water supplies. As a result of these efforts, 23 wells in Nassau County and 13 in Suffolk County were closed (CEQ, 1980).

Enforcement is handled primarily through the county health departments. If the department is unable to resolve a dispute, it will be referred to a DEC Regional Office and then to the DEC Commissioner, whose orders are subject to court review. The New York regulations also establish procedures for granting variances and modifications of permits. As yet, the New York groundwater program has encountered relatively little resistance by dischargers, but such opposition may well develop as enforcement procedures become more rigorous (M. Goroski, New York Department of Environmental Conservation, personal communication).

Virginia

Groundwater in Virginia is in plentiful supply and is generally of high quality, although high concentrations of sodium are found in the eastern part of the state (P. J. Smith, Virginia Water Control Board, personal communication). The state's Water Control Board establishes criteria in the form of a range of concentration levels for specific contaminants, and standards of quality in the interest of public health in the form of allowable concentrations of pollutants; both standards and criteria may be legally enforced. Some of the standards are derived from the federal Safe Drinking Water Act.

Virginia's groundwater-standards program is different from that of other states in that most of the standards, particularly those for naturally occurring elements, vary for the state's four geological provinces, reflecting differences in the natural quality of the water. When due to human activities, water is of a quality poorer than that specified by the standards, the state may require the discharger to attempt to clean up the aquifer (U.S. EPA, 1980c).

The state has adopted a non-degradation policy that, in theory, prohibits disposal of any waste into groundwater. The policy is not legally enforceable, however, and in reality permits for discharges into groundwater may be obtained under the NPDES program. The Water Control Board manages these permits for point sources, lagoons, and non-active-waste sites. Permits are also issued by the state Health Department for activities with ground-water-contamination potential, such as landfills and the land spreading of wastes.

Monitoring programs generally focus on specific sources of groundwater contamination, particularly landfills and waste-disposal sites. The operators of new sites of contamination are required to monitor the sites as a condition of obtaining a permit. In addition, the state manages a groundwater-quality network (T. Wagner, Virginia Water Control Board, personal communication). The Water Control Board maintains 120 wells throughout the state which monitor water quality in order to check for violations of the standards. Virginia has recently obtained increased funding from the state legislature for new groundwater-monitoring stations.

When a complaint of contamination is made, an investigator from the Pollution Response Section of the Water Control Board surveys the site of pollution and attempts to trace its source. If the violator can be found, the Pollution Response Section will provide suggestions for the prevention of further contamination. In the event that compliance cannot be obtained from a polluter, the matter will be turned over to the Enforcement Division (D. Chance, Virginia Water Control Board, personal communication).

Fourteen

Statutory and Regulatory Provisions That Have Been Proposed to Enable States to Protect and Manage Groundwater Resources

- Suggestions that have been made for the types of statutes and regulations that should be in place if a state were to be well equipped to protect its groundwater resources are summarized.
- Interstate Compacts affecting groundwater are infrequent, but those that exist are detailed.
- Suggestions made at the Interstate Conference on Water Problems on Federal-State Cooperation on Groundwater Protection are discussed, as are those outlined in a 1979 report of a U.S. Government Interagency Task Force, and those developed in the Planning Workshops to Develop Recommendations for a Groundwater Protection Strategy organized by EPA in 1980.

Implicit in any kind of legislation is a concept of the type of society the community, state, or country wishes to have and the methods that can be used to achieve it. Often legislation is enacted merely in reaction to a specific situation, without thought to how that situation may be changed. Solutions that may change the situation and reduce groundwater contamination include the encouraging of new technologies, the questioning of the siting of particular activities, and a review of the activity to determine its importance to society. It is beyond the scope of this book to recommend the level of involvement of local, state, and federal departments in such decisions. There have, however, been suggestions for the types of statutes and regulations that should be in place if a state is to be well equipped to protect its groundwater resources (Lehr et al., 1976; U.S. EPA, 1977), but these may not contain all the aspects deemed useful. The creation of a new state agency responsible for implementing such statutes and regulations, although a possibility, is not a necessity. Although the schemes would not change water-allocation laws, they would be able to control water withdrawals. Schemes proposed by Lehr et al. and by EPA recognize the need for sufficient, but not overly protective, laws, and that effective protection measures must be based on a thorough understanding of the fundamentals of groundwater. The scheme outlined by Lehr et al. (1976) is divided into two categories for statutory and regulatory provisions and may be summarized as follows:

Statutory Provisions

1. Declaration of public policy and legislative intent that the Act is designed to protect, preserve, and enhance the quality and quantity of groundwater
2. Definitions of "groundwater," "pollution," "source," "person,"
3. Powers and duties of the responsible agency
4. The ability to adopt, amend, and repeal regulations necessary to fulfill the goals of the Act
5. Recommendations and assistance to other agencies concerned with activities that could be expected to impinge on groundwater
6. Requirement of permits for operating potential sources of groundwater pollution
7. Prohibition against issuing a permit for special instances involving hazardous wastes and other threats to the quality of groundwater
8. Permit procedure which should define conditions for issue, maximum duration, conditions for denial, suspension or revocation of a permit, appeals thereof, the posting of bonds, and the administrative authorities
9. The right to enter and inspect property where violations against the Act may be occurring
10. Records accessible to the public unless it is proven that to divulge production or financial trade secrets would affect competition
11. Compliance orders issued to any person believed not in compliance with the Act, outlining the corrective action to be taken
12. Civil action of agency for temporary or permanent injunctive relief
13. Civil penalties or fines levied on any person in violation of the Act
14. Claim for damages from a person in violation of the Act
15. Criminal penalties for wilfully or negligently violating the Act,

making false statement or hindering the agency from carrying out the provisions of the Act

16. Enforcment of the Act by any citizen who wishes to undertake a civil action on his own behalf
17. Cumulative remedies
18. Severability of Provisions of the Act

Regulations Designed to Prevent Groundwater Pollution

With the authority granted under the suggested Act outlined above, the state administrator would need to formulate specific regulations to carry out the legislative intent of the Act. Existing regulations may already cover some of the suggested requirements of the Act. The following are intended as guidelines for the areas requiring regulations, but the list is not all-inclusive, although for the most part, it covers all of the sources of contamination outlined in Part I of this report.

Landfills, dumps, and excavations; holding ponds and lagoons; waste and wastewater sludges and effluents; waste piles and stockpiles; animal feedlots; fertilizers and pesticides; surface-water infiltration; septic tanks; storage and transmission facilities; accidental spills; highway salting; air pollution; drainage wells and sumps; artificial recharge; disposal wells; water-supply wells; exploration holes and abandoned wells; secondary recovery of oil and gas; mining and groundwater development—the regulation of all these activities would include installation, operation, and abandonment procedures, utilization and disposal practices, and other practices which might affect the quality or quantity of groundwater. The scheme outlined by Lehr et al. does not appear to include siting recommendations for new or expanded facilities.

The scheme outlined in the 1977 Report to Congress on Waste Disposal Practices and Their Effect upon Groundwater (U.S. EPA, 1977) also recognizes the need for reasonable rules and regulations, with a clear identification of the activities that need to be regulated. It differs from that outlined by Lehr et al. (1976) in that it suggests that aquifer uses for things other than the provision of drinking water should be defined, namely storage capacity for liquids and gases, and use for waste disposal. Because of this provision the scheme also includes the possibility of imposing charges for groundwater use and aquifer-storage uses. The suggested rules should prevent and control unwanted contamination and degradation of both groundwater and surface water, provide the necessary data to evaluate the areal extent and nature of the contamination, provide for remedial actions, and provide a regulatory framework whereby aquifers can be used for waste treatment or storage.

The primary regulatory control mechanisms outlined in the Report to Congress (U.S. EPA, 1977) are aimed at the same sources of contamination covered by the scheme proposed by Lehr et al. (1976) described on pages 284–285, and they have been divided into four categories (Table 14–1). Category I sources should require a permit for discharge or injection control. A permit would be required for Category II activities which posed an exceptional threat to groundwater, for example, the use of landfills and lagoons. Category III cases would require facility-construction standards or guidelines or manuals on use. For category IV activities, in addition to facility-construction standards, controls such as withdrawal limits and land-use restrictions would be required.

Interstate Compacts

Although interstate compacts regulating the use of surface water are common, there are very few which regulate the use of groundwater. California and Nevada have an Interstate Compact which states that groundwater can be developed provided that the use in one state does not reduce the other's allocation (Nevada Division of Water Resources, 1976; California Governor's Commission to Review California Water Rights Law, 1978). The Compact also states that groundwater collection will not draw directly from allocated surface water, and thus wells within 500 feet of a stream must be sealed to a depth of 50 feet. Any disputes which arise are settled by the California–Nevada Compact Commission (Wickersham and Canter, 1980).

The Federal Interstate Compacts for the Delaware River Basin and the Susquehanna River Basin provide the authority to monitor groundwater quality and to develop and implement plans for groundwater protection (Wickersham, 1981). The Interstate Compact for the Delaware River Basin has identified the groundwater overdraft that occurs in the Triassic Lowlands portion of the basin during dry as well as drought years. In addition, large withdrawals from the aquifers in the coastal plain have reversed the hydraulic gradient from discharge to the estuary to recharge from the estuary. The aquifers are thus exposed to degradation from sea-water intrusion and toxic spills (U.S. Water Resources Council, 1981b). In the Susquehanna River Basin, the Interstate Compact has identified problems resulting from the dewatering of limestone quarries and coal fields. The most favorable aquifers in Pennsylvania have been polluted by water from coal mines (U.S. Water Resources Council, 1981b).

Table 14–1. Classification of Sources and Causes of Groundwater Pollution Used in Determining Level and Kind of Regulatory Control

WASTES		*NON-WASTES*	
CATEGORY I	CATEGORY II	CATEGORY III	CATEGORY IV
Systems, facilities or activities designed to discharge waste or waste waters (residuals) to the land and ground waters	Systems, facilities or activities which may discharge wastes or waste waters to the land and ground waters	Systems, facilities or activities which may discharge or cause a discharge of contaminants that are not wastes to the land and ground waters	Causes of ground water pollution which are not discharges
LAND APPLICATION OF WASTE WATER—spray irrigation, infiltration-percolation basins, overland flow *SUB-SURFACE SOIL ABSORPTION SYSTEMS*—(septic systems) *WASTE DISPOSAL WELLS AND BRINE INJECTION WELLS* *DRAINAGE WELLS AND SUMPS* *RECHARGE WELLS*	*SURFACE IMPOUNDMENTS*—waste holding ponds, lagoons and pits *LANDFILLS AND OTHER EXCAVATIONS*—landfills for industrial wastes, sanitary landfills for municipal solid wastes, landfills for municipal water and waste water treatment plant sludges, other excavations (e.g., mass burial of livestock) *ANIMAL FEEDLOTS* *LEAKY SANITARY SEWER LINES* *ACID MINE DRAINAGE* *MINE SPOIL PILES AND TAILINGS*	*BURIED PRODUCT STORAGE TANKS AND PIPELINES* *STOCKPILES*—highway deicing salt stockpiles, ore stockpiles *APPLICATION OF HIGHWAY DEICING SALTS* *PRODUCT STORAGE PONDS* *AGRICULTURAL ACTIVITIES*—fertilizers and pesticides, irrigation return flows *ACCIDENTAL SPILLS*	*SALT-WATER INTRUSION*—sea water encroachment, upward coning of saline ground water *RIVER INFILTRATION* *IMPROPERLY CONSTRUCTED OR ABANDONED WELLS* *FARMING PRACTICES*—(e.g., dry land farming)

Source: U.S. EPA, 1977.

Federal-State Cooperation on Groundwater Protection

The Interstate Conference on Water Problems (ICWP) is an independent national association of state, intrastate, and interstate officials concerned with the management of water resources. It was established in 1959 and works cooperatively with the National Governors' Association, the National Conference of State Legislators, and the Council of State Governments. It also serves as an advisory group for other organizations. Its goal is to facilitate cooperation among state, intrastate, and interstate officials and agencies on the management of water and related land uses. It deals with water-resource legislation and the federal-state relationship. It is managed by a twelve-member Board of Directors and has numerous task forces. The ICWP believes that although the 1978 Presidential Memorandum concerning an effort to reform water policy recognized that the states have the primary responsibility for the management of water resources, the national effort to implement water policy does not take this into account in certain policy areas.

According to the ICWP Policy Statement for 1980–81, some effective state programs for groundwater planning and management have been hampered by federal programs that are administered through separate federal agencies with little or no coordination with state agencies. It is also stated that such federal programs have ignored the relation between water quantity and water quality. The ICWP thinks that better coordination and integration of federal groundwater programs with state efforts would assist state programs. It suggests that any federal groundwater strategy should:

- involve all agencies concerned with groundwater management, with active state participation from the start
- utilize the states' responsibility for groundwater use, management, and protection
- have general goals, with the provision of federal research and technical assistance at the request of the state
- be flexible enough to accommodate the different hydrogeological, climatic, historical, legal, and social factors associated with the various groundwater basins

Certain parts of the President's Water Policy Message of June 1978 were specifically directed to the problems of groundwater. The implementing directives were issued to the federal agencies in a Presidential Memorandum. The Secretary of the Department of the Interior was responsible for oversight and supervision and created nineteen task forces to assist in emergency implementation. Federal-state cooperation on groundwater supplies was the responsibility of one of these task forces. In its final report the United States Government Interagency Task Force

2b (1979) came to certain conclusions about federal responsibilities concerning groundwater depletion, quality protection, and the relations to instream-flow sustenance, the three areas outlined in the Presidential Message. Improved and expanded consideration of groundwater in the federal planning process and expanded mutual assistance and cooperation between federal and state agencies in the resolution of groundwater programs were recommended. Both needs could be met under existing authorities. The two needs were defined after the task force had agreed upon the following perceptions (U.S. Government Interagency Task Force, 1979):

"A. Major Federal water decisions should be based on consideration of all water resources. The groundwater resource is only weakly represented in Federal decision-making processes relating to water resources, and organizational and staffing improvements and specific additions to planning instructions are necessary first steps to upgraded planning practices and assistance programs concerning the groundwater resource.

"B. Independent planning and management of surface water and groundwater supplies should give way to integrated water management utilizing and protecting all available water sources to best advantages.

"C. Degradation of groundwater quality is a progressive loss of usable water resource, and groundwater quality considerations should be primary, integral components of water resources planning and management decisions.

"D. Wisdom, experience and expertise in the planning, development, and management of the Nation's groundwater resource, like the resource itself, are dispersed nationally, regionally, among the states and locally; and more effective collaboration, information exchange and mutual assistance are necessary steps to improved groundwater utilization and protection."

The introduction of a consideration of groundwater resources into the federal planning process can be achieved through the efficient application of existing agency authorities and responsibilities (U.S. Government Interagency Task Force, 1979). The Task Force stated that the U.S. Water Resources Council could provide adequate oversight, sponsorship, and stimulation of increased agency effort. The U.S. Water Resources Council had its budget cut in Fiscal Year 1982 from $30 million to $1.7 million, however, and the projected budget for Fiscal Year 1983 is zero. There are presently two Bills in Congress that may provide for an organization to succeed the Water Resources Council, a possible National Water Resources Board. Although the Administration had not at first thought it necessary to replace the Water Resources Council, this viewpoint seems to be changing. The estimated funding for such a Board would be in excess of $20 million. It is not known when a decision on this matter will be forthcoming (T. Maywalt, U.S. Water Resources Council, personal communication).

The Interagency Task Force recommended six measures for mutual federal and state cooperation and assistance as follows:

1. Federal agencies should actively promote joint planning with local and state agencies and regional organizations concerning groundwater resources.
2. The *Principles and Standards* published by the U.S. Water Resources Council should contain guidelines to establish cooperative planning between federal agencies and the states.
3. Federal agencies should encourage an exchange of technology and mutual staffing assistance with the states to cover the hydrogeological, legal, administrative, and economic management of groundwater.
4. Advanced training in groundwater hydrology and the planning and management of water resources should be sponsored.
5. Federal and state agencies should be encouraged to re-examine and improve the policies, laws, regulations, and management and administrative practices affecting groundwater.
6. A National Groundwater Advisory Commission should be formed. Membership would include representatives of business, industry, agriculture, science, education, and government. Such a commission, during its proposed three-year tenure, would analyze reliable information concerning groundwater in order to examine the policy and the legal and management requirements of groundwater resources and their role in land and water utilization and to elucidate an improved national groundwater policy.

In its *Planning Workshops to Develop Recommendations for a Ground Water Protection Strategy,* the Environmental Protection Agency (EPA, 1980b) outlines five possibilities for different levels of involvement of federal, state, and local governments in carrying out various aspects of a groundwater-protection strategy. They are as follows:

Option 1. The states would take primary responsibility for implementing federally developed national standards. This would include, among others, issuing permits, site inspections, and enforcement actions. In designing the program and establishing minimum standards, the federal agency would specify monitoring requirements, specific ambient standards, or technology-based standards.

Option 2. The states would prepare and submit program plans for federal approval in response to federal minimum requirements. Such requirements could be based on groundwater-quality standards or on technology-based standards. The state would define the role of local and other organizations. The federal government could provide financial and technical assistance to the states.

Option 3. The states would prepare individual program plans that were consistent with broad federal guidelines, which would be subject to federal approval mainly on procedural grounds. Such plans would be designed to meet specific state and local needs.

Option 4. State and local governments would set and enforce standards consistent with broad federal goals, and the federal government would provide technical assistance and support. This would place primary responsibility on the state and local governments, while EPA would conduct research to provide technical assistance and would see that the broad federal goals were met.

Option 5. The states would develop plans and programs, and the federal government would provide support and technical assistance only. This would give full responsibility to the states.

In assessing these options, EPA (1980b) notes that many responsibilities for groundwater protection could be assumed by federal, state, or local agencies. Some situations would indicate a national dominant interest, such as the effects of contaminated groundwater on public health and safety, and thus would be appropriately handled by a federal agency. Some tasks may need resources available only at the federal level. Some problems, however, such as contamination due to highway deicing-salts, are local in nature and cannot be dealt with at a national level. All problems should be assessed with the view to determining at which level they could be dealt with most appropriately and efficiently. The proposed groundwater strategy put forward by EPA in November 1980 is discussed fully on pages 189–202, together with the reactions to the proposal by environmentalists and industry.

References

Air/Water Pollution Report. 1982. Silver Springs, Md.: Business Publishers, Inc. 19 July.

American Petroleum Institute (API). 1975. *Annual Statistical Review.* Washington, D.C.: American Petroleum Institute. 79pp.

______ . 1980. *Underground Spill Cleanup Manual.* API Pub. 1628. Washington, D.C.: American Petroleum Institute. 34pp.

Arizona Division of Health Services. 1979. *Arizona Surface Impoundment Assessment—Ground Water Contamination Cases.* Chap. 6. Phoenix, Ariz. 47pp.

______ . 1982. Draft Framework for Arizona Groundwater Quality Protection. Phoenix, Ariz.: Bureau of Water Quality Control.

Atkinson, C. 1981. *Statement of the American Water Works Association on the EPA's Proposed Ground Water Protection Strategy.* Denver, Colo.: America's Water Works Association. 29 January.

Ballentine, R. K. 1977. Impact of Federal Legislation Other Than the Safe Drinking Water Act (SDWA) on Ground Water Protection. In *Public Policy on Ground Water Quality Protection,* ed. W. R. Kerns. pp. 102–20. Proceedings of a National Conference at Virginia Polytechnic Institute and State University, Blacksburg, Va. 13–16 April.

______ , S. R. Rezner, and C. W. Hall. 1972. *Subsurface Pollution Problems in the United States.* Washington, D.C.: U.S. EPA Office of Water Programs. Technical studies report: TS-OO-72-02. 24pp.

Banks, H. O. 1981. Management of Interstate Aquifer Systems. *Journal of Water*

Resources Planning and Management Division. Proceedings of the American Society of Civil Engineers 107(2):563–77.

Bear, J. 1972. *Dynamics of Fluids in Porous Media.* New York: American Elsevier. 764pp.

Bekure, S. 1971. An Economic Analysis of the Intertemporal Allocation of Groundwater in the Central Ogallala Formation. Ph.D. Diss., Oklahoma State University at Stillwater.

Berg, J. W., and F. Burbank. 1972. Correlations Between Carcinogenic Trace Metals in Water Supplies and Cancer Mortality. *Annals of the New York Academy of Science* 199:249–64.

Bittinger, M. W. 1981. The Ogallala Story—What Have We Learned? *Ground Water* 19(6):586–87.

Bouwer, H. 1981. Protecting the Quality of Our Groundwater: What Can We Do? *Groundwater Monitoring Review* 1(2):22–26.

Boyle, W. 1981. Control Measures—Subsurface Disposal. In *National Center for Ground Water Research (NCGWR). Proceedings of a Conference on Microbial Health Consideration of Soil Disposal of Domestic Wastewaters.* Pp. 209–26. Norman, Okla. May.

Braids, O. C. 1981a. Behavior of Contaminants in the Subsurface. In *Seminar on the Fundamentals of Ground Water Quality Protection.* Presented by Geraghty and Miller, Inc., and American Ecology Services, Inc. Cherry Hill, N.J. 5–6 October.

———. 1981b. Casing Materials for Monitoring Wells. In *Seminar on the Fundamentals of Ground Water Quality Protection.* Presented by Geraghty and Miller, Inc., and American Ecology Services, Inc. Cherry Hill, N.J. 5–6 October.

———, and N. P. Gillies. 1977. Ground Water. Literature Review of Water Pollution. *Journal of the Water Pollution Control Federation* 49(6):1302–7.

Bredehoeft, J. D., and T. Maini. 1981. Strategy for Radioactive Waste Disposal in Crystalline Rocks. *Science* 213 (17 July):293–96.

Bunch, S. E., and P. Jacobs. 1979. Health Costs Due to Environmental Hazards. *Journal of Environmental Health* 41(5):267–69.

Burge, W. D., and P. B. Marsh. 1978. Infectious Disease Hazards of Landspreading Sewage Wastes. *Journal of Environmental Quality* 7(1):1–9.

Cabelli, V. 1981. Epidemiological Approach Toward Determining Endemic Transmission of Waterborne Disease. In *National Center for Ground Water Research (NCGWR). Proceedings of a Conference on Microbial Health Considerations of Soil Disposal of Domestic Wastewaters.* Pp. 177–87. Norman, Okla. May 1981.

California Department of Water Resources. 1975. *California's Ground Water.* Bulletin 118. September. 135pp.

———. 1980. *Ground Water Basins in California: A Report to the Legislature in Response to Water Code Section 12924.* Bulletin 118–80. January. 73pp.

California Governor's Commission to Review California Water Rights Law. 1978. *Summary of Final Report.* Sacremento, Calif. December.

California State Water Resources Control Board, Surveillance and Monitoring

Section. 1981. *Assessment of Ground Water Problems and Potential Issues for Use at Program Conference.* Internal memo, 30 January.

______ , and Regional Water Quality Control Boards. 1980. *Water Quality/Water Rights: 1978–80 Report.* 48pp.

Cambridge Analytical Association. 1980. *Cost of Chemical Determinations of Water Samples.* Watertown, Mass.

Canter, L. W., R. C. Knox, R. P. Kamat. 1982. *Evaluation of Septic Tank System Effects on Ground Water Quality.* Norman, Okla.: National Center for Ground Water Research. May. 158pp.

Carter, L. J. 1983. The Radwaste Paradox. *Science.* 219(4580):33–36.

Cassidy, P. A. 1981. *Ground-Water Pollution Literature Search.* Vol. 1. Marcus Hook, Pa.: Suntech Group.

Centers for Disease Control (CDC). 1979. *Foodborne and Waterborne Disease: Annual Summary 1977.* HEW (CDC) 79-8185. 87pp.

______ . 1980. *Water Related Disease Outbreaks: Annual Summary 1978.* Department of Health and Human Services Publication no. CDC 80-8385. 37pp.

______ . 1981. *Water Related Disease Outbreaks: Annual Summary 1979.* Department of Health and Human Services Publication no. CDC 81-8385. 23pp.

Chemical Manufacturers Association (CMA). 1980. *CMA Ground Water Information Booklet.* Washington, D.C. 16pp.

Colorado Department of Health. 1973. *Criteria Used in the Review of Waste Water Treatment Facilities.* Denver, Colo.

Comstock, G. W. 1979. Water Hardness and Cardiovascular Diseases. *American Journal of Epidemiology* 110(4):375–400.

Congressional Research Service. 1980. *Resource Losses from Surface Water, Ground Water and Atmospheric Contamination: A Catalog.* Serial no. 96-9. 249pp.

Connecticut Department of Environmental Protection. 1980. *Connecticut Water Quality Standards and Criteria.* 9 September. 28pp.

Conolly, R. 1980. *Toxic Chemical Contamination of Ground Water.* Testimony given in the U.S. EPA oversight hearings, 24–25 July. 18 September.

Conservation Foundation. 1981. *Ground Water Supplies: Are They Imperiled?* Monthly letter, June 1981. 8pp.

Cooper, R., and A. Olivieri. 1981. Public Health Risk Evaluation of Wastewater Disposal Alternatives. In *National Center for Groundwater Research (NCGWR). Proceedings of a Conference on Microbial Health Considerations of Soil Disposal of Domestic Wastewaters.* Pp. 189–208. Norman, Okla. May.

Council on Environmental Quality (CEQ). 1980. *Eleventh Annual Report.* U.S. GPO. 87pp.

______ . 1981a. *Contamination of Ground Water by Toxic Organic Chemicals.* Prepared by David E. Burmaster. 85pp.

______ , and U.S. Department of State. 1981b. *Global Future: A Time to Act. Report to the President on Global Resources, Environment, and Population.* U.S. GPO 1981-336-342/8011. 209pp.

______ . 1981c. *12th Annual Report.* U.S. GPO. 291pp.
Crandall, R. W., and L. B. Lave, eds. 1981. *The Scientific Basis of Health and Safety Regulation.* Studies in the Regulation of Economic Activity. Washington, D.C.: The Brookings Institution. 309pp.
Craun, G. F. 1979. Waterborne Disease—A Status Report Emphasizing Outbreaks in Ground Water Systems. *Ground Water* 17(2):183–91.
______ , and L. J. McCabe. 1973. Review of the Causes of Waterborne Disease Outbreaks. *Journal of American Water Well Association* 65(1):74–84.
______ , L. J. McCabe, and J. M. Hughes. 1976. Waterborne Disease Outbreaks in the U.S.: 1971–74. *Journal of American Water Well Association* 68:420–24.

Davis, S. N., and R. J. M. DeWiest. 1966. *Hydrogeology.* New York: John Wiley and Sons. 463pp.
Dawson, J. W., 1979. State Groundwater Protection Programs—Inadequate. In *Proceedings of the Fourth National Groundwater Quality Symposium.* Pp. 102–8. Minneapolis, Minn. 20–22 September 1978.
Demopoulos, H. B., and E. G. Gutman. 1980. Cancer in New Jersey and Other Complex Urban/Industrial Areas. *Journal of Environmental Pathology and Toxicology* 3:219–35.
Dermer, O. C., V. S. Curtis, and F. R. Leach. 1980. *Biochemical Indicators of Subsurface Pollution.* Ann Arbor, Mich.: Ann Arbor Science. 203pp.
Deutsch M. 1963. *Ground Water Contamination and Legal Controls in Michigan.* U.S. Geological Survey Water Supply Paper 1691. 79pp.
Dolmatch, T. B., ed. 1982. *Information Please Almanac.* New York: Simon & Schuster. 958pp.
Domenico, P. A. 1972. *Concepts and Models in Ground Water Hydrology.* New York: McGraw Hill. 405pp.

Engberg, R., and R. F. Spalding. 1978. *Ground Water Quality Atlas of Nebraska. Resource Atlas no. 3.* Lincoln: University of Nebraska. 39pp.
Environment Reporter. 1982. Washington, D.C.: The Bureau of National Affairs, Inc. P. 1714, 23 April.
Environmental Defense Fund (EDF). 1981. *Comments on EPA Proposed Ground Water Protection Strategy.* Washington, D.C. January.
Everett, L. G. 1980. *Ground Water Monitoring.* Schenectady, N.Y.: General Electric Co. Technology Marketing Operation. 440pp.
Exner, M. E., and R. F. Spalding. 1979. Evolution of Contaminated Ground Water in Holt County, Nebraska. *Water Resources Research* 15(1):139–47.

Florida Department of Environmental Regulation. 1980. *Florida Surface Impoundment Assessment: Final Report.* January. 298pp.
______ . 1981a. *Hazardous Waste Inventory, June 1981.* Tallahassee, Fla. 59pp.
______ . 1981b. *Summary of Known Cases of Ground Water Contamination in Florida.* Ground Water Section. Tallahassee, Fla. September. 12 pp.
______ . 1981c. Water Quality Standards. 30 November. 11pp. In *Rules of the Department of Environmental Regulation.* Chap. 17-3.

______. 1981d. Permits. In *Rules of the Department of Environmental Regulation.* Chap. 17–4. Tallahassee, Fla. 30 November.

______. 1982a. *Hearing Draft of Proposed Groundwater Rules.* Tallahassee, Fla.

______. 1982b. *Groundwater Program Strategy.* Tallahassee, Fla.

Ford, M., R. Piskin, M. Hagele, R. Strom, and J. Dickman. 1981. *Inventory and Preliminary Assessment of Class I and Class II Injection Wells in Illinois.* State of Illinois EPA. Division of Land/Noise Pollution Control. August. 111pp.

Freeze, R. A., and J. A. Cherry. 1979. *Groundwater.* Englewood Cliffs, N.J.: Prentice-Hall. 604pp.

Frick, D., and L. Shaffer. n.d. *Assessment of the Availability, Utilization and Contamination of Water Resources in New Castle County, Delaware.* Prepared by Office of Water and Sewer Management, Department of Public Works, New Castle County, Del., for U.S. EPA Office of Solid Waste Management Programs. Newark. Contract no. WA-6-99-2061-J. 215pp.

Fuhriman, D. K., and J. R. Barton. 1971. *Ground Water Pollution in Arizona, California, Nevada and Utah.* U.S. EPA. Office of Research and Monitoring. Report no. 16060ERU. 249pp.

Gallaher, B. M., and M. S. Goad. 1981. *Water Quality Aspects of Uranium Mining and Milling in New Mexico.* Special Publication no. 10. Sante Fe: New Mexico Geological Society. Pp. 85–91.

Geraghty, J. J. 1981. Containment of a Plume of Contaminated Ground Water. In *Seminar on The Fundamentals of Ground Water Quality Protection.* Presented by Geraghty and Miller, Inc., and American Ecology Services, Inc. Cherry Hill, N.J. October.

______, D. W. Miller, F. van der Leeden, and F. L. Troise. 1973. *Water Atlas of the United States.* 3d ed. Syosset, N.Y.: Water Information Center, Inc. 122 plates.

Geraghty and Miller, Inc. 1979. *Investigations of Ground Water Contamination in South Brunswick Township, N.J.* Syosset, N.Y.: Geraghty and Miller, Inc. 49pp + 10 appendices.

Gerba, C. 1981. Virus Occurrence in Ground Water. In *National Center for Ground Water Research (NCGWR). Proceedings of a Conference on the Microbial Health Considerations of Soil Disposal of Domestic Wastewaters.* Pp. 144–57. Norman, Okla. May.

Gibb, J. P., and M. O'Hearn. 1980. *Illinois Ground Water Quality Data Summary.* Prepared by Illinois State Water Survey for the Illinois Environmental Protection Agency. Contract no. 1-47-26-84-353-00. 60pp.

Gillies, N. P., and O. C. Braids. 1980. Ground Water. *Journal of the Water Pollution Control Federation* 52(6):1528–33.

Gormly, J. R., and R. F. Spalding. 1979. Sources and Concentrations of NO_3-Nitrogen in Ground Water of the Central Platte Region, Nebraska. *Ground Water* 17(3):291–300.

Grad, F. P. 1981. *A Treatise on Environmental Law.* N.Y.: Matthew Bender.

Greenberg, M., T. Burke, J. Caruana, G. W. Page, and K. Ohlson. 1981a. Approaches and Initial Findings of a State-Sponsored Research Program on Population Exposure to Toxic Substances. *The Environmentalist* 1:53–63.

———, and G. W. Page. 1981b. Planning With Great Uncertainty: A Review and Case Study of the Safe Drinking Water Controversy. *Socio-Economic Planning Science* 15:64–74.

Hadeed, S. J. 1979. *DBCP Well Sampling Program for Yuma County, Arizona* (7 June–26 July 1979). Phoenix: Arizona Department of Health Services. 33pp.

Hagedorn, C. 1981. Transport and Fate: Bacterial Pathogens in Ground Water. In *National Center for Ground Water Research (NCGWR). Proceedings of a Conference on the Microbial Health Considerations of Soil Disposal of Domestic Wastewaters.* Pp. 84–102. Norman, Okla. May.

Hajali, P. A., and L.W. Canter. 1980. *Rehabilitation of Polluted Aquifers.* National Center for Ground Water Research Report no. NCGWR 80-12. Norman, Okla. 46pp.

Handman, E. H., and J. W. Bingham. 1980. *Effects of Selected Sources of Contamination on Ground Water Quality at Seven Sites in Connecticut.* U.S. Geological Survey and Connecticut Department of Environmental Protection. Open File Report 76-1596. Hartford. 63pp.

———, I. G. Grossman, J. W. Bingham, and J. L. Rolston. 1979. *Major Sources of Ground Water Contamination in Connecticut.* U.S. Geological Survey and Connecticut Department of Environmental Protection Open File Report 79-1069. 59pp.

Harris, R. H. 1982. Health Effects Associated with Organic Chemical Contaminants in Ground Water. In *Abstracts of Papers Presented at American Association for the Advancement of Science Meeting.* Washington, D.C. P. 335. January.

Hernandez, J. W. 1977. The Underground Injection Program Under the National Safe Drinking Water Act. In *Public Policy on Ground Water Quality Protection,* ed. W. R. Kerns. Pp. 92–101. Proceedings of a national conference at Virginia Polytechnic Institute and State University, Blacksburg, Va. 13–16 April.

High Plains Associates: Camp, Dresser & McKee, Inc., Black & Veatch, and Arthur D. Little, Inc. 1982. *Six State High Plains—Ogallala Aquifer Regional Resources Study.* March.

Hileman, B. 1982. Nuclear Waste Disposal: A Case of Benign Neglect? *Environmental Science and Technology* 16(5):271A–75A.

Hines, N. W. 1977. A Decade of Nondegradation Policy in Congress and the Courts: The Erratic Pursuit of Clean Air and Clean Water. *Iowa Law Review* 62:643–711.

Hubert, J. S., and L. W. Canter. 1980a. *Health Effects from Ground Water Usage.* Norman, Okla.: National Center for Ground Water Research (NCGWR). Report no. NCGWR 80-17. 300pp.

———, and L. W. Canter. 1980b. *Acid Rain and Ground Water Quality.* Norman, Okla.: National Center for Ground Water Research. Report no. NCGWR 80-25 (TP). 15pp.

Illinois Environmental Protection Agency. 1971. *Design Criteria Used in the Review of Waste Water Treatment Facilities.* Springfield.

Inside EPA. 1980. Washington, D.C.: Inside Washington Publishers. Pp. 7–8. 9 May.
Inside EPA. 1982. Washington, D.C.: Inside Washington Publishers. 5 February.
Inside EPA. 1982. Washington, D.C.: Inside Washington Publishers. 12 March.
Inside EPA. 1982. Washington, D.C.: Inside Washington Publishers. 9 April.
Inside EPA. 1982. Washington, D.C.: Inside Washington Publishers. 7 May.
Inside EPA. 1982. Washington, D.C.: Inside Washington Publishers. 6 August.

Jones, D. C. 1973. *An Investigation of the Nitrate Problem in Runnels County, Texas.* EPA-R2-73-267. 214pp.
Josephson, J. 1980. Safeguards for Ground Water. *Environmental Science and Technology* 14(1):38–44.
______. 1981. Ground Water Strategies. *Environmental Science and Technology* 14(9):1030–35.
Junk, G. A., R. F. Spalding, and J. J. Richard. 1980. Areal, Vertical and Temporal Differences in Ground Water Chemistry II—Organic Constituents. *Journal of Environmental Quality* 9(3):479–83.

Keeley, J. W. 1976. Ground Water Pollution Problems in the United States. In *Proceedings of a Water Research Conference, "Ground Water Quality—Measurement, Prediction and Protection."* Pp. 17–32. University of Reading, Berkshire, England. 6–8 Sept.
______. 1977. Magnitude of the Ground Water Contamination Problem. In *Public Policy on Ground Water Protection,* ed. W. R. Kerns. Pp. 2–10. Proceedings of a national conference at Virginia Polytechnic Institute and State University, Blacksburg, Va. 13–16 April.
Kerns, W. R., ed. 1977. *Public Policy on Ground Water Protection.* Proceedings of a national conference at Virginia Polytechnic Institute and State University, Blacksburg, Va. 13–16 April. 163pp.
Kim, N. K., and D. W. Stone. n.d. *Organic Chemicals and Drinking Water.* Albany: N.Y. State Department of Health. 132pp.
Kim, S. W., P. R. Johnson, R. S. Murphy. 1969. *A Ground Water Summary for Alaska.* Fairbanks: University of Alaska Institute of Water Resources. Report no. IWR-10. 30pp.
Knight, A. W., and M. A. Simmons. 1980. *Water Pollution: A Guide to Information Sources.* Detroit, Mich.: Gale Research Co. 278pp.
Knowlton, H. E., and E. J. Rucker. 1979. Land Farming Shows Promise for Refinery Waste Disposal. *The Oil and Gas Journal* 77 (May 14):108–16.
Krone, R. B., P. H. McGauhey, and H. B. Gotars. 1957. Direct Discharge of Ground Water with Sewage Effluents. *American Society of Civil Engineers. J. Sanit. Eng. Div.* 83 (SA4):1–25.
______, G. T. Orlab, and C. Hodgkinson. 1958. Movement of Coliform Bacteria Through Porous Media. *Sewage Industrial Wastes* 30:1–13.

Lance, J. C. 1981. Microbial Health Considerations of Soil Disposal of Domestic Wastewaters: Soil Considerations. In *National Center for Ground Water*

Research (NCGWR). Proceedings of a National Conference on the Microbial Health Considerations of Soil Disposal of Domestic Wastewaters. Pp. 11–23. Norman, Okla. May.

Last, J. M. 1980. *Public Health and Preventive Medicine,* ed. Maxcy-Rosenau. 11th ed. Norwalk, Conn.: Appleton-Century-Crofts.

Legrand, H. E. 1965. Patterns of Contaminated Zones of Water in the Ground. *Water Resources Research* 1:83–95.

Lehr, J. H. 1975. Ground Water Pollution—Problems and Solutions. In *Water Pollution Control in Low Density Areas,* ed. W. J. Jewell and R. Swan. Hanover, N.H.: University Press of New England. Pp. 111–20.

———. 1981. Groundwater in the Eighties. *Water and Engineering Management* 123(3):30–33.

———. 1982. How Much Ground Water Have We Really Polluted? *Ground Water Monitoring Review,* Winter, pp. 4–5.

———, and W. A. Pettyjohn. 1975. The Integrity of Ground Water. In *The Integrity of Water. Proceedings of a Symposium.* Pp. 41–57. Washington, D.C.: EPA Office of Water and Hazardous Materials. U.S. GPO stock no. 055-001-01068-1. 10–12 March.

———, W. A. Pettyjohn, M. S. Bennett, J. R. Hanson, and L. E. Sturtz. 1976. *A Manual of Laws, Regulations and Institutions for the Control of Ground Water Pollution.* Prepared for U.S. EPA, EPA-440/9-76-006. 381pp.

Lemmon, J. 1980. Drums Along the Salt. In *Proceedings of the Arizona Section of the American Water Resources Association Symposium on Water Quality Monitoring and Management.* Pp. 7–12. Tucson, Ariz. 24 October. 138pp.

Leopold, L. B. 1974, *Water: A Primer.* San Francisco: W. H. Freeman and Co. 172pp.

Lindorff, D. E., and K. Cartwright. 1977. *Ground Water Contamination: Problems and Remedial Actions.* Illinois State Geological Survey, Environmental Geology Notes no. 81. May. 58pp.

MacKichan, K. A., and Kammerer, J. C. 1961. *Estimated Use of Water in the United States, 1960.* U.S. Geological Survey Circular 456. 26pp.

Magnuson, P. 1981. *Ground Water Classification.* Syosset, N.Y.: Geraghty and Miller, Inc. 56pp.

Maine Department of Environmental Protection. 1979. Classification of Surface Waters. In *Title 38.* Chap. 3. September. 58pp.

Mapp, H. P., and V. R. Eidman. 1976. A Bioeconomic Simulation Analysis of Regulating Ground Water Irrigation. *American Journal of Agricultural Economics* 58(3):391–402.

Mason, T. J., and F. W. McKay. 1974. *U.S. Cancer Mortality by County: 1950–1969.* Washington, D.C.: U.S. Dept. of Health, Education and Welfare Publication no. (WIH) 74-615.

Massachusetts Department of Environmental Quality Engineering, Division of Water Supply. 1981. *Ground Water Strategy.* Boston.

Matthess, G. 1982. *The Properties of Ground Water.* New York: John Wiley and Sons. 406pp.

McGauhey, P. H. 1976. Man-Made Contamination Hazards. *Ground Water* 2:10–13.

Meyer, C. F., ed. 1973. *Polluting Ground Water: Some Causes, Effects, Controls and Monitoring.* U.S. EPA Environmental Monitoring Series. EPA-600/4-73-001b.

Miller, D. W. 1981a. Basic Elements of Ground Water Contamination. In *Seminar on the Fundamentals of Ground Water Quality Protection.* Presented by Geraghty and Miller, Inc., and American Ecology Services, Inc. Cherry Hill, N.J. 5–6 October.

______. 1981b. Tools for Investigating Ground Water Contamination. In *Seminar on the Fundamentals of Ground Water Quality Protection.* Presented by Geraghty and Miller, Inc., and American Ecology Services, Inc. Cherry Hill, N.J. 5–6 October.

______. 1981c. Planning On-Site Investigations. In *Seminar on the Fundamentals of Ground Water Quality Protection.* Presented by Geraghty and Miller, Inc., and American Ecology Services, Inc. Cherry Hill, N.J. 5–6 October.

______, F. A. DeLuca, and T. L. Tessier. 1974. *Ground Water Contamination in the Northeast States.* Prepared for U.S. EPA Office of Research and Development. EPA 660/2-74-056. 328pp.

Miller, J. C., P. S. Hackenberry, and F. A. DeLuca. 1977. *Ground Water Pollution Problems in the Southeastern United States.* Prepared for U.S. EPA Office of Research and Development. EPA 600/3-77-012. 361pp.

Murray, C. R., and E. B. Reeves. 1972. *Estimated Use of Water in the United States in 1970.* U.S. Geological Survey Circular no. 676. 37pp.

______. 1977. *Estimated Use of Water in the United States in 1975.* U.S. Geological Survey Circular no. 765. 39pp.

Nace, R. L., ed. 1971. *Scientific Framework of World Water Balance.* UNESCO Tech. Papers Hydrol. no. 7. 27pp.

National Academy of Sciences (NAS). 1977. *Drinking Water and Health.* Vol. 1. Washington, D.C.: National Academy Press. 939pp.

______. 1979. *The Geochemistry of Water in Relation to Cardiovascular Disease.* Washington, D.C.: National Academy Press. 98pp.

______. 1980a. *Drinking Water and Health.* Vol. 2. Washington, D.C.: National Academy Press. 393pp.

______. 1980b. *Drinking Water and Health.* Vol. 3. Washington, D.C.: National Academy Press. 415pp.

______. 1981a. *Drinking Water and Health.* Vol. 4. Washington, D.C.: National Academy Press. 226pp.

______. 1981b. *Coal Mining and Ground Water Resources in the United States.* Washington, D.C.: National Academy Press. 197pp.

______. 1981c. *The Health Effects of Nitrate, Nitrate and N-Nitroso Compounds.* Part 1. Washington, D.C.: Committee on Nitrate and Alternative Curing Agents in Food. 529pp.

National Center for Ground Water Research (NCGWR). 1981. *Microbial Health Considerations of Soil Disposal of Domestic Wastewaters. Proceedings of the Conference.* Norman, Okla. 11–12 May. 242pp.

National Governor's Association Center for Policy Research, Office of State Services. 1981. *State Integrated Toxics Management: Fact and Challenge.* National Technical Information Service (NTIS) PB. 81-24240.6. 308pp.

National Technical Information Service (NTIS). 1978. *Published Search: Ground Water Pollution Part I—General Studies. 1964–1976.* Vol. 1. 275pp.

———. 1980. *Published Search: Ground Water Pollution: General Studies.* 1977–January 1980. Vol. 2. 214pp.

Nebraska Department of Environmental Control. 1978. *Ground Water Protection Standards.* 30 October. Lincoln. 11pp.

———. 1980a. *Water Quality Report. Pursuant to Section 305(b) of the Clean Water Act.* Lincoln. 303pp.

———. 1980b. *Final Report: Nebraska Surface Impoundment Assessment.* January. Lincoln. 72pp.

———. 1981. *An Investigation of the Causes of Nitrate Contamination in the Ground Water of the Lower Big Nemaha Drainage Basin.* Ground Water Quality Protection Program. Lincoln. 8pp.

Nelson, W. R. n.d. *Evaluating the Environmental Consequences of Ground Water Contamination.* Washington, D.C.: Energy Research and Development Administration. Prepared from ERDA Contract E-(45-1)-2320. 129pp.

Neri, L. C., D. Hewitt, and G. B. Schreiber. 1974. Can Epidemiology Elucidate the Water Story? *American Journal of Epidemiology* 99(2):75–88.

Nevada Division of Water Resources. 1976. *Nevada Water Laws, Title 48.* Chap. 534. Carson City.

New Hampshire Office of State Planning. 1981. *Ground Water in New Hampshire.* April. Concord. 48pp.

New Jersey Department of Environmental Protection, Division of Water Resources. 1981a. *Ground Water Pollution Index, 1975–June 1981.* Trenton. 55pp.

———. 1981b. Ground Water Quality Standards. In *New, Revised, and Amended Rules Concerning Water Quality Standards.* Chap. 6.

New Mexico Environmental Improvement Division. 1980. *New Mexico Surface Impoundment Assessment.* February. Sante Fe. 157pp.

New Mexico Health and Environment Department. 1982. *New Mexico Water Quality Control Commission Regulations* (as amended through 29 January 1982). § 3-106(c).

New York Department of Environmental Conservation. 1978. *Ground Water Classifications, Quality Standards and/or Limitations.* Effective 1 September. 16pp.

North Carolina Environmental Management Commission. 1979. *Classifications and Water Quality Standards Applicable to the Ground Water of North Carolina.* Effective 10 June. 7pp.

Okun, D. A. 1980. Water Quality Management. In *Public Health and Preventive Medicine,* ed. Maxcy-Rosenau. 11th ed. Pp. 975–1018. Norwalk, Conn.: Appleton-Century-Crofts.

Page, G. W. 1981. Comparison of Ground Water and Surface Water for Patterns and Levels of Contamination by Toxic Substances. *Environmental Science and Technology* 15(12):1475–81.

______. In press. *Maximum Contaminant Levels for Toxic Substances in Water: A Statistical Approach.* Water Resources Bulletin.

Paige, S., C. Morgan, H. Bryson, G. Hunt, P. Roqoschewski, P. Spooner, D. Twendell, and R. Wetzel. 1980. Preliminary Design and Cost Estimates for Remedial Actions of Hazardous Waste Disposal Sites. In *Management of Uncontrolled Hazardous Waste Sites.* Proceedings of the U.S. EPA national conference. Pp. 202–7. Washington, D.C. 15–17 October.

Pennsylvania Department of Environmental Resources, Bureau of Water Quality Management. 1972. *Spray Irrigation Manual.*

Pettyjohn, W. A., ed. 1972. *Water Quality in a Stressed Environment: Readings in Environmental Hydrology.* Minneapolis, Minn.: Burgess Publishing Co. 309pp.

Piskin, R., L. Kissinger, M. Ford, S. Colantino, and J. Lesnak. 1980. *Inventory and Assessment of Surface Impoundments in Illinois.* Prepared by State of Illinois EPA Div. of Land/Noise Pollution. January. 160pp.

Pories, W. J., E. G. Mansour, and W. H. Strain. 1972. Trace Elements That Act to Inhibit Neoplastic Growth. *Annals of the New York Academy of Science* 199:265–71.

Porter, K. S. 1977. Agricultural Practices: Policy Implications. In *Public Policy on Ground Water Protection,* ed. W. R. Kerns. Pp. 47–65. Proceedings of a national conference at Virginia Polytechnic Institute and State University, Blacksburg, Va. 13–16 April.

Press, F., and R. Siever. 1978. *Earth.* San Francisco: W. H. Freeman and Co. 613pp.

Radiation Management Corporation. 1981. *Cost of Selected Chemical Determinations. Philadelphia.* 1980.

Report to the Congress of the U.S. by the Comptroller General. 1980. *Ground Water Overdrafting Must be Controlled.* CED-80-96. 12 September. 52pp.

Robertson, F. N., 1975. Hexavalent Chromium in the Ground Water in Paradise Valley, Arizona. *Ground Water* 13(6):516–27.

Rolston, J. L., I. G. Grossman, R. S. Potterton, and E. H. Handman. 1979. *Places in Connecticut Where Ground Water is Known to Have Deteriorated in Quality.* U.S. Geological Survey Miscellaneous Field Studies Map. MF-981-b.

Romero, J. C. 1972. The Movement of Bacteria and Viruses through Porous Media. In *Water Quality in a Stressed Environment, Readings in Environmental Hydrology,* ed. Wayne A. Pettyjohn. Pp. 200–223. Minneapolis, Minn.: Burgess Publishing Co.

Russell, C. S., ed. 1978. *Safe Drinking Water. Current and Future Problems.* Proceedings of a national conference held in Washington, D.C. Resources for the Future. Research Paper R-12. 641pp.

Salt Institute. 1980. *Survey of Salt, Calcium Chloride and Abrasive Use in the United States and Canada for 1978–1979.* Salt Institute RP-2-80-2M. Alexandria, Va. 57pp.

Scalf, M. R., J. W. Keeley, and C. J. LaFevers. 1973. *Ground Water Pollution in the South Central States.* Prepared for U.S. EPA. EPA-R2-73-268. 181pp.

______ , and W. J. Dunlap, 1977. *Environmental Effects of Septic Tank Systems.* Prepared for U.S. EPA. EPA-600/3-77-096.

______ , J. F. McNab, W. J. Dunlap, R. Cosby, and J. S. Fryberger. 1981. *Manual of Ground Water Quality Sampling Procedures.* Robert S. Kerr Environmental Research Laboratory, Office of Research and Development. Ada, Okla.: U.S. Environmental Protection Agency. 93pp.

Schmidt, K. D. 1972. Ground Water Contamination in the Cortaro Area, Pima County, Arizona. In *Hydrology and Water Resources in Arizona and the Southwest,* Vol. 2. Proceedings of the 1972 meetings of the Arizona Section of the American Water Resources Association and the Hydrology Section of the Arizona Academy of Science. Prescott, Ariz. 5–6 May.

______ . 1973. Ground Water Quality in the Cortaro Area Northwest of Tuscon, Arizona. *Water Resources Bulletin* 9(3):598–606.

Schneider, W. J. 1972. Hydrologic Implications of Solid Waste Disposal. In *Water Quality in a Stressed Environment: Readings in Environmental Hydrology,* ed. W. A. Pettyjohn. Pp. 130–45. Minneapolis, Minn.: Burgess Publishing Co.

Schroeder, H. A. 1969. The Water Factor. *New England Journal of Medicine.* 280: 836–83.

Shaper, A. G. 1974. Soft Water, Heart Attacks and Stroke. *Journal of the American Medical Association* 230:130–31.

Sharrett, A. R. 1979. The Role of Chemical Constituents of Drinking Water in Cardiovascular Diseases. *American Journal of Epidemiology* 110(4): 401–19.

Sills, M., J. Struzziery, and P. Silbermann. 1980. Evaluation of Remedial Treatment, Detoxification and Stabilization Alternatives. In *Management of Uncontrolled Hazardous Waste Sites.* Pp. 192–201. U.S. EPA National Conference. Washington, D.C.

Skogerboe, G. V., W. R. Walker, D. J. Meyer, and R. S. Bennett. 1973. *Selected Irrigation Return Flow Quality Abstracts, 1970–71.* EPA-R2-73-271. 285pp.

Sobsey, M. 1981. Transport and Fate of Viruses in Soil. Pages 103–125 in *National Center for Ground Water Research (NCGWR). Proceedings of the Conference on Microbial Health Considerations of Soil Disposal of Domestic Wastewaters.* Norman, Okla. May.

South Carolina Department of Health and Environmental Control. 1980. *Inventory of Ground Water Contamination Cases in South Carolina.* March. 58pp.

______ . 1981. *Inventory of Known Ground Water Contamination Cases and Generalized Delineation of Five Ground Water Recharge Areas in South Carolina.* Draft. November. 122pp.

Spalding, R. F., J. R. Gormly, B. H. Curtiss, and M. E. Exner. 1978a. Nonpoint Nitrate Contamination of Ground Water in Merrick County, Nebraska. *Ground Water* 16(2):86–95.

______ , G. A. Junk, and J. J. Richard. 1978b. Pesticides in Ground Water Beneath Irrigated Farmland in Nebraska. *Pesticides Monitoring Journal* 14(2):70–73.

______ , M. E. Exner, J. J. Sullivan, and P. A. Lyon. 1979. Chemical Seepage from a Tail Water Recovery Pit to Adjacent Ground Water. *Journal of Environmental Quality* 8(3):374–83.

______ , and M. E. Exner. 1980. Areal, Vertical and Temporal Differences in

Ground Water Chemistry. Part I: Inorganic Constituents. *Journal of Environmental Quality* 9(3):466–79.

Stengel, R. 1982. Ebbing of the Ogallala. *Time,* 10 May.

Texas Department of Water Resources. 1979. *Ground Water Availability in Texas: Estimates and Projections through 2030.* September. 77pp.

Thomas, H. E., and D. A. Phoenix. 1976. *Summary Appraisals of the Nation's Ground Water Resources—California Region.* U.S. Geological Survey Professional Paper 813-E. 51pp.

Thompson, D. R. 1977. Surface and Subsurface Mining: Policy Implications. In *Public Policy on Ground Water Quality Protection,* ed. W. R. Kerns. Pp. 22–29. Proceeding of a national conference at Virginia Polytechnic Institute and State University, Blacksburg, Va. 13–16 April.

Tinlin, R., ed. 1976. *Monitoring Ground Water Quality: Illustrative Examples.* Santa Barbara, Calif.: General Electric Co./TEMPO. EPA-600/4-76-036. 81pp.

Todd, D. K. 1959. *Ground Water Hydrology.* New York: John Wiley and Sons. 336pp.

Toups, J. M. 1974. *Water Quality and Other Aspects of Ground Water Recharge in Southern California.* Paper presented at the annual conference of the American Water Well Association, 15 May.

Tourbier, J. 1977. Convivial Technology as a Local Approach to Ground Water Protection: The Christina River Basin Experience. In *Public Policy Ground Water Quality Protection,* ed. W. R. Kerns. Pp. 130–42. Proceedings of a national conference at Virginia Polytechnic Institute and State University, Blacksburg, Va. 13–16 April.

Tripp, J. T. B., and A. B. Jaffe. 1979. Preventing Ground Water Pollution: Towards a Coordinated Strategy to Protect Critical Recharge Zones. *Harvard Environmental Law Review* 3(1):1–47.

Tucker, R. K. 1981. *Ground Water Quality in New Jersey: An Investigation of Toxic Contaminants.* New Jersey Dept. of Environmental Protection, Office of Cancer and Toxic Substances Research. 60pp.

UNESCO. 1980. *Aquifer Contamination and Protection.* International Hydrological Programme. Project 8.3 of the Studies and Reports in Hydrology 30. Paris. 440pp.

United States Congressional Research Service. 1980. *Resource Losses from Surface Water, Ground Water and Atmospheric Contamination: A Catalog.* Report prepared for the U.S. Senate Committee on Environment and Public Works. 246pp.

United States Department of Commerce. 1974. *Statistical Abstract of the United States, 1974.* Social and Economic Statistics Administration, Bureau of the Census. 1028pp.

______. 1977. *Transport Statistics in the United States for the year ended 31 December 1976.* Part 6: Pipelines. Prepared by the Bureau of Accounts, Interstate Commerce Commission. U.S. GPO Stock No. 026-000-01101-9. 29pp.

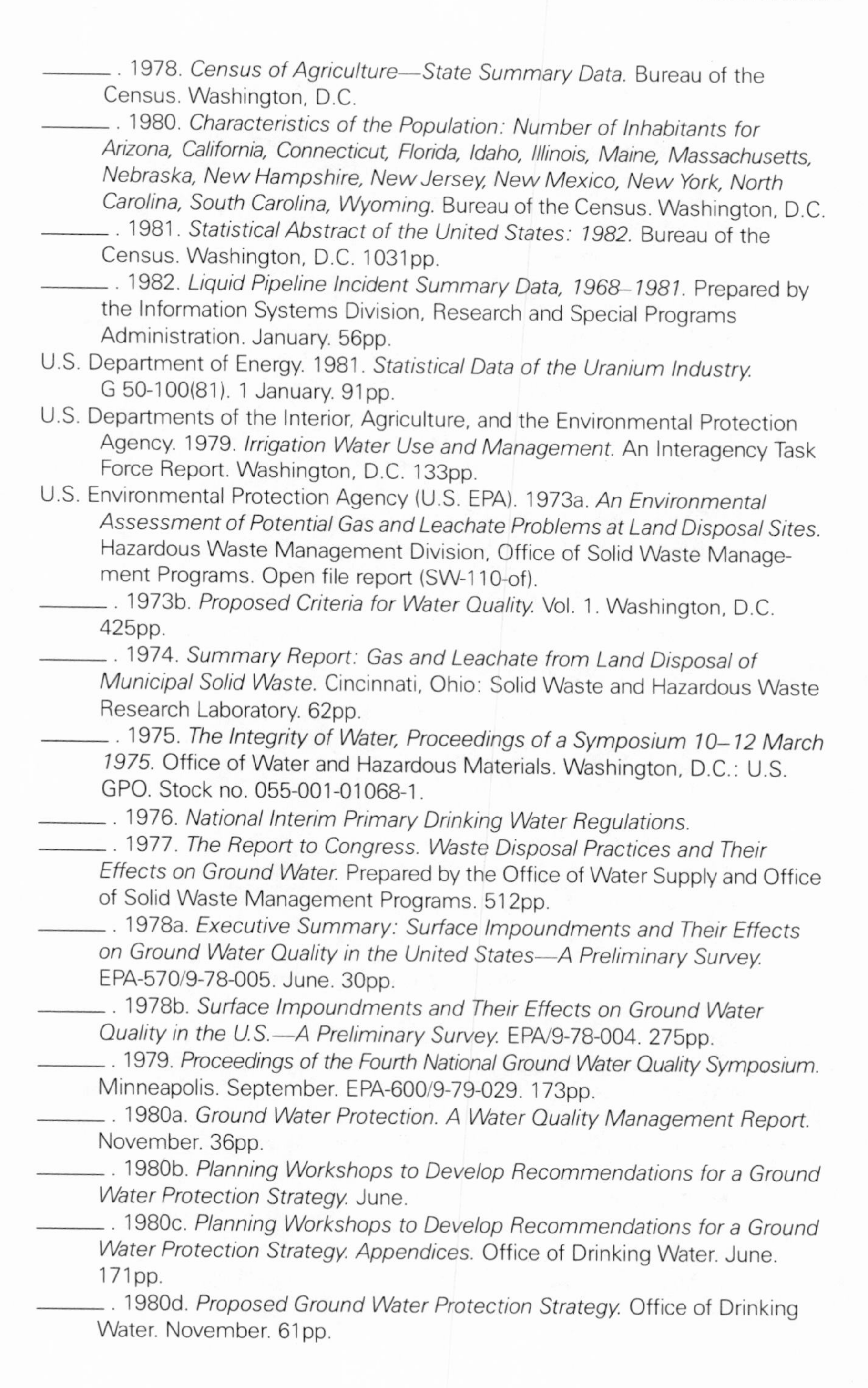

———. 1978. *Census of Agriculture—State Summary Data.* Bureau of the Census. Washington, D.C.

———. 1980. *Characteristics of the Population: Number of Inhabitants for Arizona, California, Connecticut, Florida, Idaho, Illinois, Maine, Massachusetts, Nebraska, New Hampshire, New Jersey, New Mexico, New York, North Carolina, South Carolina, Wyoming.* Bureau of the Census. Washington, D.C.

———. 1981. *Statistical Abstract of the United States: 1982.* Bureau of the Census. Washington, D.C. 1031pp.

———. 1982. *Liquid Pipeline Incident Summary Data, 1968–1981.* Prepared by the Information Systems Division, Research and Special Programs Administration. January. 56pp.

U.S. Department of Energy. 1981. *Statistical Data of the Uranium Industry.* G 50-100(81). 1 January. 91pp.

U.S. Departments of the Interior, Agriculture, and the Environmental Protection Agency. 1979. *Irrigation Water Use and Management.* An Interagency Task Force Report. Washington, D.C. 133pp.

U.S. Environmental Protection Agency (U.S. EPA). 1973a. *An Environmental Assessment of Potential Gas and Leachate Problems at Land Disposal Sites.* Hazardous Waste Management Division, Office of Solid Waste Management Programs. Open file report (SW-110-of).

———. 1973b. *Proposed Criteria for Water Quality.* Vol. 1. Washington, D.C. 425pp.

———. 1974. *Summary Report: Gas and Leachate from Land Disposal of Municipal Solid Waste.* Cincinnati, Ohio: Solid Waste and Hazardous Waste Research Laboratory. 62pp.

———. 1975. *The Integrity of Water, Proceedings of a Symposium 10–12 March 1975.* Office of Water and Hazardous Materials. Washington, D.C.: U.S. GPO. Stock no. 055-001-01068-1.

———. 1976. *National Interim Primary Drinking Water Regulations.*

———. 1977. *The Report to Congress. Waste Disposal Practices and Their Effects on Ground Water.* Prepared by the Office of Water Supply and Office of Solid Waste Management Programs. 512pp.

———. 1978a. *Executive Summary: Surface Impoundments and Their Effects on Ground Water Quality in the United States—A Preliminary Survey.* EPA-570/9-78-005. June. 30pp.

———. 1978b. *Surface Impoundments and Their Effects on Ground Water Quality in the U.S.—A Preliminary Survey.* EPA/9-78-004. 275pp.

———. 1979. *Proceedings of the Fourth National Ground Water Quality Symposium.* Minneapolis. September. EPA-600/9-79-029. 173pp.

———. 1980a. *Ground Water Protection. A Water Quality Management Report.* November. 36pp.

———. 1980b. *Planning Workshops to Develop Recommendations for a Ground Water Protection Strategy.* June.

———. 1980c. *Planning Workshops to Develop Recommendations for a Ground Water Protection Strategy. Appendices.* Office of Drinking Water. June. 171pp.

———. 1980d. *Proposed Ground Water Protection Strategy.* Office of Drinking Water. November. 61pp.

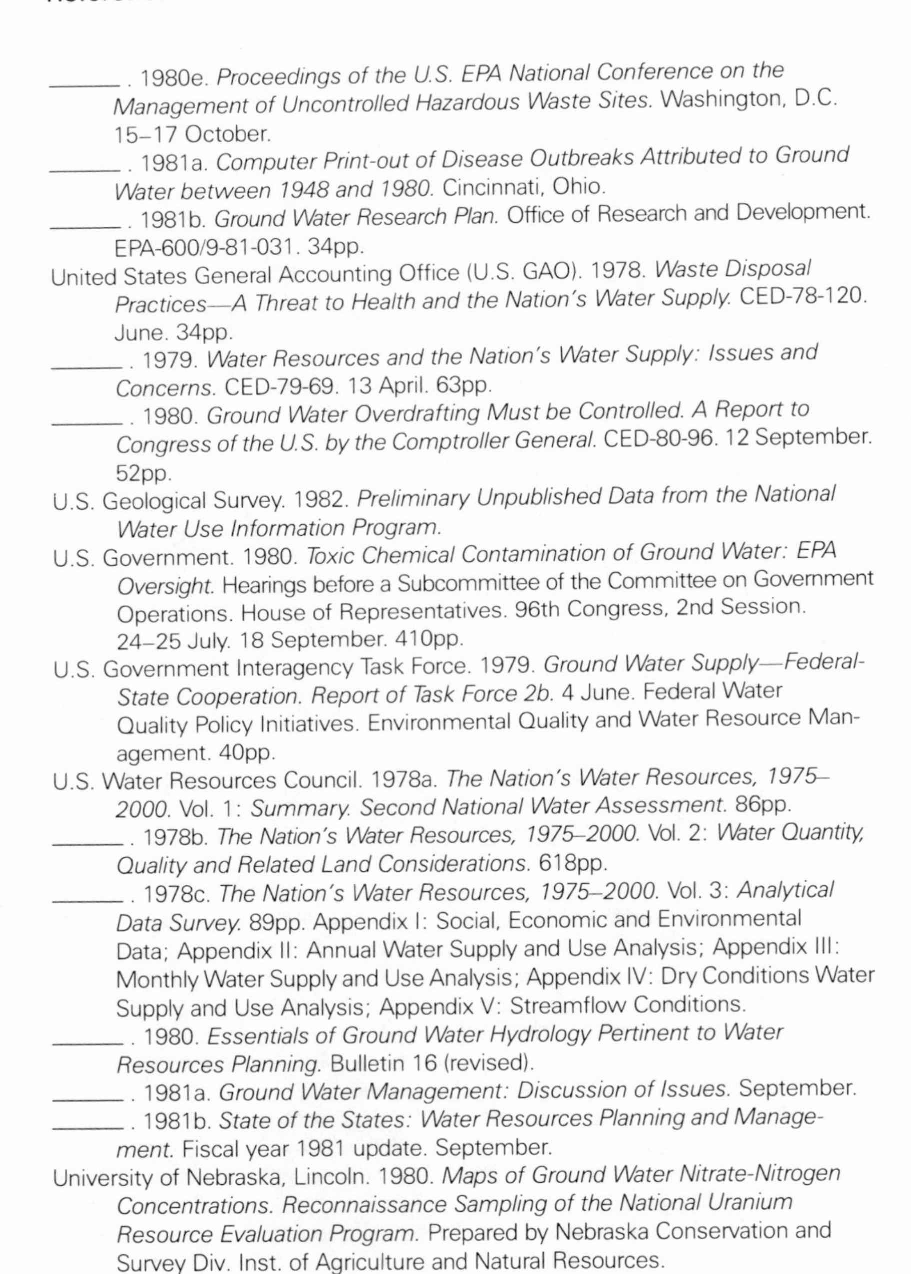

______. 1980e. *Proceedings of the U.S. EPA National Conference on the Management of Uncontrolled Hazardous Waste Sites.* Washington, D.C. 15–17 October.

______. 1981a. *Computer Print-out of Disease Outbreaks Attributed to Ground Water between 1948 and 1980.* Cincinnati, Ohio.

______. 1981b. *Ground Water Research Plan.* Office of Research and Development. EPA-600/9-81-031. 34pp.

United States General Accounting Office (U.S. GAO). 1978. *Waste Disposal Practices—A Threat to Health and the Nation's Water Supply.* CED-78-120. June. 34pp.

______. 1979. *Water Resources and the Nation's Water Supply: Issues and Concerns.* CED-79-69. 13 April. 63pp.

______. 1980. *Ground Water Overdrafting Must be Controlled. A Report to Congress of the U.S. by the Comptroller General.* CED-80-96. 12 September. 52pp.

U.S. Geological Survey. 1982. *Preliminary Unpublished Data from the National Water Use Information Program.*

U.S. Government. 1980. *Toxic Chemical Contamination of Ground Water: EPA Oversight.* Hearings before a Subcommittee of the Committee on Government Operations. House of Representatives. 96th Congress, 2nd Session. 24–25 July. 18 September. 410pp.

U.S. Government Interagency Task Force. 1979. *Ground Water Supply—Federal-State Cooperation. Report of Task Force 2b.* 4 June. Federal Water Quality Policy Initiatives. Environmental Quality and Water Resource Management. 40pp.

U.S. Water Resources Council. 1978a. *The Nation's Water Resources, 1975–2000.* Vol. 1: *Summary. Second National Water Assessment.* 86pp.

______. 1978b. *The Nation's Water Resources, 1975–2000.* Vol. 2: *Water Quantity, Quality and Related Land Considerations.* 618pp.

______. 1978c. *The Nation's Water Resources, 1975–2000.* Vol. 3: *Analytical Data Survey.* 89pp. Appendix I: Social, Economic and Environmental Data; Appendix II: Annual Water Supply and Use Analysis; Appendix III: Monthly Water Supply and Use Analysis; Appendix IV: Dry Conditions Water Supply and Use Analysis; Appendix V: Streamflow Conditions.

______. 1980. *Essentials of Ground Water Hydrology Pertinent to Water Resources Planning.* Bulletin 16 (revised).

______. 1981a. *Ground Water Management: Discussion of Issues.* September.

______. 1981b. *State of the States: Water Resources Planning and Management.* Fiscal year 1981 update. September.

University of Nebraska, Lincoln. 1980. *Maps of Ground Water Nitrate-Nitrogen Concentrations. Reconnaissance Sampling of the National Uranium Resource Evaluation Program.* Prepared by Nebraska Conservation and Survey Div. Inst. of Agriculture and Natural Resources.

van der Leeden, F., L. A. Cerrillo, and D. A. Miller. 1975. *Ground Water Problems in the Northwestern United States.* Prepared for U.S. EPA, Office of Research and Development. EPA-660/3-75-018. 361pp.

Van Everdingen, R. O., and R. A. Freeze. 1971. *Subsurface Disposal of Waste in Canada.* Inland Waters Branch Tech. Report. Dept. of Environment, Canada.

Walker, W. H., 1969. Illinois Ground Water Pollution. *Journal of the American Water Well Association* 61(1):31–40.

Warner, D. L., and D. H. Orcutt. 1973. Industrial Waste Water Injection Wells in the United States—Status of Use and Regulation. In *Underground Waste Management and Artificial Recharge,* ed. J. Braunstein. Amer. Association Petrol. Geol., U.S. Geol. Surv. International Association of Hydrologic Science 2.

Warren, J., H. Mapp, D. Ray, D. Kletke, and C. Wang. 1982. Economics of Declining Water Supply in the Ogallala Aquifer. *Ground Water* 20(1):73–79.

Weimar, R. A. 1980. Prevent Ground Water Contamination Before it's Too Late. *Water and Wastes Engineering,* February. Pp. 30–33, 63.

Wendt, C. W., A. B. Onken, O. C. Wilke, and R. D. Lacewell. 1976. *Effects of Irrigation Methods on Ground Water Pollution by Nitrates and Other Solutes.* EPA-600/2-76-291. December. 331pp.

Wickersham, G. 1981. A Preliminary Survey of State Ground Water Laws. *Ground Water* 19(3):321–27.

———, and L. W. Canter. 1980. *Summary of State Ground Water Laws.* National Center for Ground Water Research Report no. NCGWR 80-19. Norman, Okla. 50pp.

Wilkins, J. R., N. A. Reiches, and C. W. Kruse. 1979. Organic Chemical Contaminants in Drinking Water and Cancer. *American Journal of Epidemiology* 110(4):420–48.

Winograd, I. J. 1981. Radioactive Waste Disposal in Thick Unsaturated Zones. *Science* 212(4502):1457–63.

Wolman, A. In press. Public Health Effects of Contaminated Groundwater. In *Proceedings of a NSF and the Environmental Assessment Council Workshop on Groundwater Contamination in the United States.* 14–15 March. Washington, D.C.: National Science Foundation.

World Health Organization. 1979. *Human Viruses in Water, Wastewater and Soil.* World Health Organization Technical Report Series 639. Geneva. 50pp.

Wyoming Department of Environmental Quality, Water Quality Division. 1980. Quality Standards for Wyoming Ground Waters. *Water Quality Rules and Regulation,* chap. 8. 9 April. 13pp.

Index

Index

Index

Index

Index